ATADOS A UNA ESTRELLA

Celis, Claudia
    Atados a una estrella / Claudia Celis – 3a ed. – México : Ediciones SM, 2016
    133 p. ; 21 x 13 cm. – (Gran angular ; 12)

    ISBN : 978-607-24-2248-3

    1. Literatura mexicana. 2. Novela juvenil. 3. Niños – Síndrome de Down.
    I. t. II. Ser.

    Dewey 863 C45 2003

© Claudia Celis
Diseño de portada: Magali Gallegos Vázquez

Primera edición, 2002
Tercera edición, 2016
D. R. © SM de Ediciones, S. A. de C. V., 2002
Magdalena 211, colonia del Valle,
03100, Ciudad de México.
Tel.: (55) 1087 8400
Para conocer SM, su fondo editorial y sus servicios: www.ediciones-sm.com.mx

ISBN 978-607-24-2248-3
ISBN 978-968-779-177-7 de la colección Gran Angular

Miembro de la Cámara Nacional de la Industria Editorial Mexicana
Registro número 2830

Impreso en México / *Printed in Mexico*

ATADOS A UNA ESTRELLA

CLAUDIA CELIS

1

Sí NOS vamos a casar, eso es seguro; lo que todavía no sabemos es cuándo, ni dónde vamos a vivir. Es que a Roberto le ofrecen un trabajo muy bueno en Michoacán, mucho mejor que el que tiene en el periódico donde trabajan mi mamá y él. Aquí, Roberto es reportero; allá, sería subgerente. El sueldo y las prestaciones son bastante mejores, pero no sabemos qué hacer. Es que tendríamos que alejarnos de Lucero, y eso es lo que no nos gusta. Roberto y yo estamos muy acostumbrados a ella, y ella a nosotros. Aunque el plan sería venir lo más seguido posible y llevárnosla con frecuencia, pero ya no sería lo mismo; Michoacán no está a la vuelta de la esquina. Allá, también me ofrecen un trabajo más o menos bueno; digo más o menos, porque no me gusta mucho, aunque pagan bien. Es en una compañía muy importante, pero a mí me interesa la psicología clínica, no la laboral.

Lo de casarnos en abril depende también de Lucero; es que todavía está un poco delicada. Total, estamos hechos bolas... Cuando le dijimos a Lucero que nos íbamos a casar y que tal vez nos fuéramos a vivir a Michoacán, casi se me rompe el corazón. Oí ruidos en el comedor: un lento, pero firme teclear en la máquina de escribir de mi mamá; me extrañó, porque mi mamá no estaba. Me asomé y la vi dándole a las teclas con todas sus fuerzas.

Me acerqué. Tenía sobre la mesa una tarjeta que me había mandado Roberto y estaba copiando de ahí, según ella, las letras de mi nombre.

—A... /... e... /... i... t... a —decía en voz alta a cada letra que ponía, aunque en realidad escribía cualquier otra.

—¿Qué haces? —le pregunté.

Ella saltó del susto.

—*¡Olita lejo* tu *tajeta* en su *luga!* ¡No voy a *quesescomponel* la máquina! ¡Lo *toy haceno* con *quidado!* ¡No te vas a *enojá contigo, Alelita!* —me contestó con su voz ronca, a punto de llorar.

Me dio mucha ternura y también me sentí culpable porque sé que a veces me desespero y la regaño. Le acaricié el pelo y le dije que no me estaba enojando, que solo quería saber qué estaba haciendo.

—*Toy paticando* —me dijo, y siguió, con sus manitas regordetas y sus dedos cortos, imprimiendo las supuestas letras de mi nombre en el papel que había metido todo chueco en la máquina.

—¿Y qué es lo que practicas? —le pregunté.

—¿No sabes *leí?* —replicó, sin dejar de escribir y de decir las letras al hacerlo: *A... /... e... /... i... t... a.*

—¿Y para qué estás escribiendo mi nombre? —insistí.

—No *toy esquibiendo* tu *nombe* —respondió molesta—, *toy paticando,* ya te lo *lije.* —Se limpió la nariz con el pañuelo que mi mamá le pone siempre, prendido con un seguro, en la ropa, a la altura del pecho.

Mi paciencia se estaba acabando.

—¿Y qué es lo que practicas?

—¡Ay, *pes* tu *nombe!* —me respondió y siguió escribiendo, acercándose exageradamente al teclado de la máquina para poder ver las letras, ya que, en cuanto puede, se quita los lentes porque no le gustan.

Guardé la calma y, con mucha paciencia, le volví a preguntar:

—¿Y para qué practicas mi nombre?

Como si fuera algo obvio y no le cupiera en la cabeza que yo no adivinara el motivo de su práctica, me dijo:

—*Ayyy, pes pada esquibilte cuano te vayas a tu chuacán.*

Mi corazón se encogió.

—Todavía no es seguro que Roberto y yo nos vayamos a Michoacán, chiquita —le dije.

—*¿Pedo qué tal si sí? Yo tengo que patical para equibilte cando etés en tu chuacán.*

Lucero nunca ha aceptado que Michoacán se llame así. Toda una tarde me la pasé corrigiéndola:

—Michoacán, Lucero.

—*Tu chuacán.*

—Michoacán.

—*Tu chuacán.*

—¡Que digas Michoacán! —le dije desesperada.

—*¡Mida, Alelita* —replicó enojada, limpiándose la nariz y la boca con su pañuelito—, yo no tengo *nigún chuacán* y tú y mi mamita chula me dicen que nunca diga *mentidas,* así que no voy a *decil* que ese *chuacán* es mío! —me miró tristemente y agregó—: ese *chuacán e* tuyo y de *Lobelto.*

—Y, si nos vamos para allá, también va a ser tuyo, chiquita —le dije.

—*¡Ay, Alelital ¿Cómo qués?* Mío es *Méchico;* mi *maesta dice que yo vivo en Méchico, no en Chuacán. Mida, hata me señó a canta: Mechicanos a gito e gueda... e casedo apestáy ebidó... y tetembe su centos la teda... a sonodo jujuy de cañón* —y dijo muy satisfecha—: *Es elino ¿ves que sí lo sé?*

—¡Qué bien te lo sabes!, ¿eh? Te felicito. Pero allá también podrías cantar el Himno Nacional, porque Michoacán es parte de México —le dije.

—No, Alelita, no... —respondió muy seria—, *e* que tú no sabes; *Méchico e Méchico y Chuacán e Chuacán.*

—Entonces, ¿en Michoacán cuál himno cantarías?

—*Pes niguno...* —Me miró con tristeza—. *E que en tu quela no te señan nada..., pedo yo te voy seña. Mida, Alelita, Méchico e Méchico y Chuacán e Chuacán... a vé, lepite: Méchico
e Méchico y Chuacán e Chuacán.*

—Michoacán también es México —traté de explicarle—:
Es un estado que...

Ella me interrumpió:

*No, no, Alelita... a vé, lepite: Méchico e Méchico y Chua-
cán e Chuacán.*

—México es México y Michoacán es Michoacán —repetí.

Sabía que no quitaría el dedo del renglón; cuando a Lucero se le mete una idea en la cabeza, por nada en el mundo
puedes hacer que la modifique.

—*Beño, Alelita* —me dijo— ya no me *quites tempo, voy
a seguí paticando: A... l... e... l.. i... t... a...* —siguió escribiendo—, *y tolavía me fata paticá Lobelto* —me advirtió.

2

DESDE chicas, yo me desesperaba con Lucero. Es que es muy terca. Además, a veces me hacía sufrir porque es la persona más indiscreta que conozco y nos hacía pasar, a mi mamá y a mí, cada vergüenza... Ahora, que va a cumplir dieciocho años, todavía lo hace.

Me acuerdo del día de la zapatería, ella tenía como seis años:

—¡*Quedo* esos!... ¡Y esos! —Frente a la zapatería señalaba los zapatos.

Yo sabía que ningunos le quedarían. No podría dar paso con ellos. Lucero solo usa sus "tanques", como llamamos a sus zapatos ortopédicos, porque con sus pies planos y sus deditos desproporcionados, cualquier otro tipo de zapato le molesta.

Y aunque la compra sería inútil, porque ni siquiera a mí me servirían ya que ella calza bastante más chico que yo, estaba segura de que mi mamá se los compraría. Mi mamá le daba, y le sigue dando, gusto en todo.

—¡*Quedo* esos, mamita chula..., y esos y esos! ¿Sí, chulita?

Mi mamá abrió su bolsa, revisó el monedero y entramos a la zapatería.

En aquel tiempo, yo le tenía muchos celos a Lucero. Me caía mal. Se puede decir que casi la aborrecía. Para mí, ella solo era una niña demasiado consentida. Era la hermanita fea, moquienta, babeante y deforme que me hacía sentir avergonzada delante de mis amigos y de toda la gente.

—¿Me *pedo ponel* esos, y esos, y esos, y *tambán* esos? —gritó con su voz ronca y gangosa, señalando, a lo loco, los zapatos.

—Claro que sí, chiquita, todos los que quieras —le respondió mi mamá con cariño.

—¿Yo también me puedo probar unos? —le pregunté algo cortada. La inseguridad me dominaba cuando pretendía competir con Lucero.

—Espera, Adelita, vamos a ver... Después de que Lucero escoja los suyos, a ver si nos alcanza para los tuyos.

La respuesta no me sorprendió. Enfurruñada, me senté a contemplar cómo mi mamá complacía a su hijita.

¡Cuántas veces había deseado despertar y verme transformada! No anhelaba ser rubia de ojos azules, no quería convertirme en princesa o en estrella de cine, no quería ser Miss Universo ni Marilyn Monroe; no. Yo deseaba ser una niña Down, como Lucero.

Muchas veces, cuando ella dormía, cogía sus lentes y me los ponía; me paraba frente al espejo, mirando con dificultad a través de los cristales con demasiado aumento; me jalaba los ojos con los dedos para rasgarlos; abría un poco la boca y sacaba tantito la lengua. Quería tener la cara de Lucero. Me jorobaba un poco y sacaba el estómago. Quería tener el cuerpo de Lucero. Enchuecaba los pies y caminaba torpemente, para verme como Lucero, para ser como ella... ¡Para que mi mamá me quisiera como a Lucero! Cada par de zapatos que se probaba, le provocaba una emoción exagerada. Trastabillando caminaba hasta el espejo y se quedaba embobada, contemplando sus pies, adornados con zapatos de moños y de cintas de colores.

De pronto, se quedó atenta a otra imagen. Observó, con curiosidad, la figura del espejo y después a la dueña de los pies que ahí se reflejaban.

—Mamita ¿veda que esos *capatos* no son *pada* viejitas?
—dijo, sin quitar la vista de la señora que estaba a su lado probándose unos zapatos altísimos.

La señora la miró con sorpresa, y la sorpresa se fue transformando en enojo.

Mi mamá saltó del sillón como impulsada por un resorte, llegó a donde estaba Lucero y le dijo en voz baja:

—No hagas comentarios de la gente, chiquita.

—¿*Pol* qué no, mamita chula? —le preguntó en voz alta y luego se respondió ella misma—: ¿*Polque* se enoja la vieja? —dijo, mirando a la señora.

"¡Trágame tierra!", pensé.

Y esperé (debo confesar que con gusto) el regaño que mi mamá le iba a dar.

Pero no la regañó. A Lucero nunca la regañaba.

La expresión de enojo de la señora cambió cuando se fijó bien en Lucero y la miró con ternura.

—No se preocupe —le dijo a mi mamá y se empezó a alejar haciendo equilibrio sobre sus tacones.

—Así caminan las mojigangas, ¿*vedá*, mamita? —todavía alcanzó a decir Lucero antes de que la señora estuviera lo suficientemente lejos para no oírla.

A Lucero le impresionaban, y le impresionan hasta la fecha, las mojigangas que desfilan por las calles en las fiestas de fin de año en Querétaro. Varias veces, cuando hemos estado en casa de mi abuelita Adela para esas fechas, las hemos visto. Son señores que se disfrazan y caminan sobre zancos, aparentado ser enormes títeres.

Después de probarse no sé cuántos zapatos, Lucero dijo:

—¡*Quedo* mis "tanques", mamita! *Mejol cómpale capatos* a *Alelita polque* a ella sí le quedan y no se le *apachudan* sus dedos.

—¡Yo no quiero nada! —dije resentida.

¡No podía aceptar que mi mamá me comprara zapatos solo porque su hijita no había querido ninguno para ella!

11

En ese tiempo yo no entendía por qué mi mamá se pasaba horas contemplando a Lucero, mientras dormía. Por qué todas las noches se acostaba con ella, abrazándola y acariciándole el pelo, casi siempre llorando en silencio. Por qué se enojaba con mi papá y pasaba todo el tiempo llevando a su niña a terapias y más terapias, como si mi papá y yo no existiéramos. Por qué cuando alguna de sus amigas hablaba de sus hijos, de la edad de Lucero, a ella se le llenaban los ojos de lágrimas y se ponía tan triste; por qué cuando veía correr y jugar a cualquier niño, ella lo miraba con coraje, se puede decir que con envidia; parecía que ningún niño le caía bien... A veces sentía que yo tampoco.

—¿Puedo invitar a comer a Karina? —le preguntaba yo. Karina era una amiga de la primaria con la que me llevaba bien. Era una de las pocas que no me preguntaba nada de mi hermana... Porque cómo me chocaban las otras niñas:

—¿Qué tu hermanita es mongolita?

—¿Tu hermanita puede comer como toda la gente?

—¿Qué tu hermanita nació loquita?

—Oye, ¿tu hermanita hace pipí y popó normal, o le tienen que poner sonda? Porque fíjate que al niño de mi vecina, que también es retrasado, se la tienen que poner porque...

Yo me daba la vuelta y las dejaba con la palabra en la boca, odiaba que se metieran con Lucero. Pensaba que ese era solo problema mío y de nadie más... ¡Y qué problema! Mi mamá me respondía, invariablemente, que no podía invitar a Karina.

—Tenemos que llevar a Lucero a su terapia.

¡Lucero! ¡Lucero! ¡Siempre era lo mismo! Llegar de la escuela, comer y acompañar a mi mamá a las terapias, pasarme ahí más de una hora, aburrida, y regresar a la casa a hacer la tarea y a ver a mi mamá hacerle los ejercicios a Lucero.

Todo, todo era Lucero. Lo peor fue cuando la maestra de mi hermana quiso que yo también aprendiera a hacerle los ejercicios. Me negué rotundamente. Ya nada más faltaba que yo también me dedicara solo a ella, como mi mamá.

3

CUANDO Lucero nació, yo iba a cumplir seis años. Casi seis años de haber sido la niña de mis papás, la consentida, la única, el centro de toda su atención y el ombligo del mundo. De pronto, todo cambió. Y cambió desde varios meses antes de su llegada. Desde el día en que mi mamá llegó con el resultado de esos análisis que decían positivo, todo en mi casa empezó a girar alrededor de ese gran acontecimiento.

Mi cuarto de juegos, donde tenía mi colección de *barbies,* mis muñecos de peluche y el tocacintas y los casetes que mi papá me había regalado de cumpleaños, cambió por completo: encajes por acá, telas de animalitos por allá, cortinas y tapices nuevos, muñecos de peluche, moisés de tira bordada, cuna dorada, bañera de color frambuesa, lámparas de colores pastel, y me prohibieron entrar. Todas mis cosas y yo nos amontonamos en mi recámara.

Cuando lograba colarme a mi antiguo cuarto de juegos, el murmullo de palabras: *no toques, no tientes, no ensucies, no entres, salte de ahí,* me perseguía.

Mi mamá ya no platicaba conmigo, mi papá ya no me llevaba a tomar helados ni poníamos los casetes de *rock* para enseñarme a bailar.

Todas las noches, antes de dormir, me ponía a llorar un rato, pero nadie se daba cuenta. A veces despertaba con los ojos hinchados.

—¿Qué te pasó, Adelita? ¿Por qué lloraste? ¡Ven, chiquita, todos te queremos mucho!

Eso quería que me hubieran preguntado, pero nadie lo hacía.

Mis papás, mis abuelitos y mi tía Rosario (hermana de mi mamá) solo hablaban de dietas y ejercicios para mi mamá y de nombres para el futuro bebé.

—Saluda a tu hermanito. —Mi mamá me cogía la mano, me hacía ponerla sobre su estómago abultado, esperaba un movimiento y me abrazaba feliz.

Pero yo no compartía esa felicidad. Lo que en realidad deseaba era que mi mamá me dijera que se había equivocado, que no estaba embarazada y que estaba engordando solo porque quería ser gorda.

Me volví más callada y enojona que antes. Solo platicaba con mi primo Andrés, aunque, a veces, más me valía no haberlo hecho:

—Cuando nazca el bebé ya no me van a querer —me quejaba con él.

—Sí —me decía—, a los bebés siempre los quieren más que a los grandes. Te va a pasar lo que a Julio, el de mi salón: desde que nació su hermanita ya no lo quieren y lo regañan por todo.

—¿Y crees que cuando nazca el bebé ya no me van a querer nada?

—Tampoco exageres —me decía—; a Julio todavía lo quieren, aunque muy poco. Fíjate, el otro día no fue su mamá por él a la escuela y la maestra se lo tuvo que llevar a su casa y creo que hasta en la noche fue su papá por él.

Yo me imaginaba que a partir de que naciera el bebé yo ya no iba a importarles. Quizá algún día nadie me recogería en la escuela y tendría que ponerme a trabajar vestida de payaso en los semáforos o lavando parabrisas. Me llenaba de terror.

Me pasaba horas mirándome en el espejo.

"¿Qué pasa? —me preguntaba—. ¿Ya no soy bonita? ¿Me volví fea? ¿Soy una niña mala?"

Me peinaba con mucho cuidado y me lavaba muy bien las manos, los dientes y la cara, para que todos me vieran bonita, para que me hicieran caso, para que me quisieran.

Nadie me miraba. Solo hablaban del bebé que mi mamá tenía dentro.

Busqué la compañía de mi abuelita Esperanza, pero no resultó. Ella se la pasaba tejiendo y haciéndole ropita a su futuro nieto. A mí ya no me cosía nada, y eso que ella siempre hacía mi ropa y también la de mis muñecas. Mi abuelito Jorge sí me hacía caso, pero como él siempre estaba tan ocupado, por más que quería, no podía estar mucho tiempo conmigo.

Además, yo no me atrevía a decirle a nadie lo que sentía.

Pensaba que todos me tomarían por una niña mala y envidiosa; solo hablaba con mi primo Andrés, pero él, como ya dije antes, no me daba muchas esperanzas.

Mi único consuelo era hablar con mi abuelita Adela. Le hablaba a escondidas, porque, como era larga distancia, mis papás no me dejaban. Ella, tan buena que es, venía siempre que podía.

—Mi muchachita —me decía—, es normal que ahorita todos estén al pendiente de tu mami y del bebé que va a tener, ¿no ves que las mamás que están esperando y los bebés que están en su pancita necesitan muchos cuidados?

—¿Y yo ya no necesito cuidados porque ya soy grande? —le preguntaba.

—No es eso, mi niña, tú también necesitas cuidados porque, aunque ya eres grandecita, todavía necesitas de los mayores, pero como eres tan lista y tan buena niña, tú también puedes ayudar a tu mami y a tu papi y comprenderlos, no enojarte con ellos porque ahora ya no pueden estar tanto contigo como antes —me sentaba en sus piernas y me decía—: Vas a ver, Adelita, cuando nazca tu hermanito tú lo vas a cuidar... Va a ser como tu muñequito y, cuando crezca un poco, vas a jugar con él y a divertirte mucho.

Las palabras de mi abuelita Adela me tranquilizaban un poco, además, como siempre que venía ella me hacía mucho caso, pues yo me sentía mejor. Desgraciadamente, ella solo podía venir los fines de semana y tenía que volver a Querétaro el domingo, porque en ese tiempo tenía una agencia de viajes y la tenía que atender.

Cuando mi abuelita Adela regresaba a su casa, yo me quedaba sola otra vez.

4

LUCERO fue un bebé muy deseado, muy esperado. Recuerdo perfectamente el día que nació.

Era sábado y, como todos los sábados, mis abuelitos Esperanza y Jorge (los papás de mi mamá) habían llegado desde temprano a mi casa, y mi abuelita Adela (mamá de mi papá) había llegado desde el jueves de Querétaro a esperar el nacimiento.

Los dolores habían despertado a mi mamá pero no dijo nada hasta las dos, cuando nos acabábamos de sentar a comer.

—Ya es hora —dijo, poniéndose las manos atrás, en la cintura y haciendo un gesto de dolor.

Mi papá se levantó muy asustado y tiró el salero de un manotazo.

Fue como si hubiera recibido una descarga eléctrica. El salero se rompió y la sal se regó por el piso.

—¡No! —gritó mi abuelita Esperanza. En cuclillas se puso a recoger, desesperada, puñitos de sal, y los empezó a aventar hacia atrás, por encima de sus hombros.

—¡Es de mala suerte! ¡Es de mala suerte! —repetía.

Mi papá la miró enojado. A veces las supersticiones de mi abuelita le caían en gracia, pero, en esos momentos...

Mi mamá le habló por teléfono a mi tía Rosario y le dijo que se fuera yendo al hospital.

En el hospital, había una cafetería que Andrés y yo, acompañados unas veces por mi abuelita Adela y otras, por mi abuelito Jorge, visitamos infinidad de veces.

Lucero nació a las ocho de la noche.

Una enfermera fue a avisamos que había sido niña y que en un momento más, en cuanto la llevaran al cunero, nos llamarían para que pudiéramos verla. Pasó mucho tiempo y nadie nos llamaba. El doctor se presentó en la sala de espera y le pidió a mi papá que lo acompañara. Se metieron a un cuarto que estaba al final del pasillo. Antes de que mi papá volviera, Andrés, mis abuelitos y yo alcanzamos a ir a la cafetería tres veces más.

Mi papá regresó, se sentó de golpe en uno de los sillones y, tapándose la cara, comenzó a llorar. Yo sentí tremendo miedo. Pensé que algo muy malo le había pasado a mi mamá.

—¿Qué ocurre? —le preguntó mi abuelito, temblando de arriba abajo.

Mi papá no podía contestar. Tenía las quijadas trabadas. Los músculos de su cara, hechos nudo, se le notaban a través de la piel.

—Alfredo, hijo —dijo mi abuelita Adela—, ¿algo está mal? Mi papá no respondió, se levantó y salió de la sala de espera y luego del hospital.

Mi abuelita Esperanza, exagerada como es, empezó a llamar a gritos al doctor y se fue caminando de prisa por el pasillo. Entró, sin llamar, al cuarto donde mi papá había estado hablando con él. Se tardó un buen rato.

Regresó con una expresión muy rara, como si estuviera sonámbula.

—La niña nació mal —murmuró y se dejó caer en el mismo sillón que antes ocupara mi papá.

Mi papá regresó en ese momento y mi abuelita Esperanza lo miró con reproche.

—¡La sal! —le dijo con dureza.

Mi papá le echó ojos de pistola.

—¡No diga tonterías, es increíble que sea usted tan ignorante y crea en esas estúpidas supersticiones! —gritó.

Fue la primera vez y, hasta la fecha, la única que mi papá le ha hablado así a mi abuelita.

Todos nos quedamos en silencio.

Andrés se me acercó y empezamos a platicar en voz baja:

—¿Cómo habrá nacido? —me dijo—. Yo sé de algunos niños que nacen con dos cabezas o con cola de cochino.

—¿De veras? —le pregunté horrorizada.

—O con una torta de sangre en vez de cabeza y tres brazos y cuatro piernas.

—A lo mejor tiene cuernos —le dije temblando.

—O patas de cabra y barba de chivo —me dijo.

Mi miedo era terrible. En la escuela había oído hablar del nacimiento de los hermanitos de mis compañeros, y lo único que comentaban era si había sido niño o niña. Nadie hablaba de problemas.

—¡Quiero ver a mi mamá! —fue lo único que se me ocurrió decir.

Me la imaginaba horrorizada, cargando algo así como una gran tarántula, un gran alacrán, o una enorme víbora de dos cabezas. Así me la imaginaba, porque era lo peor que en ese tiempo yo me podía imaginar.

—Ven, Adelita, al ratito vamos con tu mami. —Me abrazó mi tía Rosario; era la única que parecía darse cuenta de que yo también estaba ahí y de lo que estaba sintiendo.

—Tía —le dije, temblando sin control—, quiero ver a mi mamá... Quiero irme con mi papá y con mi mamá a la casa. Si esa niña no sirve, que la tiren a la basura.

—No digas eso, chiquita —me dijo—, es tu hermanita —yo creo que vio en mis ojos el miedo y agregó—: No te preocupes, mi amor, vas a ver que todo va a salir bien. —Me abrazó y, recostada en sus piernas, me dormí.

5

Ese DÍA, ya muy tarde, salimos todos del hospital sin que yo hubiera podido ver a mi mamá y mucho menos a la niña.

En mi cama no podía dormir y me pasé a la cama de mi papá.

—¿Por qué nació mal mi hermanita, papá? —le pregunté abrazándolo.

—No sé —me respondió malhumorado, sin corresponder a mi abrazo.

—¿Qué tiene? ¿Cómo está? —le dije, esperando que su respuesta me consolara e hiciera desaparecer el miedo y la angustia que me estaban asfixiando, pero no fue así; solo me dijo:

—Cállate y duérmete.

Me hice bolita y traté de dormir, pero solo pensaba en monstruos y espantos. Al fin, el llanto callado me hizo dormir. Al otro día llegaron a la casa mi tía Rosario y Andrés para quedarse hasta que mi mamá pudiera regresar.

A la semana, mi mamá llegó a la casa con la niña. Con mi nueva hermanita. Con Lucero. Las vecinas de la privada ya no hicieron la fiesta de bienvenida que iban a hacer. Ninguna fue a conocer a la niña, solo la señora Rocío, que vive a la vuelta, pero mi mamá no quiso que la viera. Oí que le dijo a mi tía Rosario que solo era por una curiosidad morbosa por lo que la quería ver. Entonces yo no entendía esas palabras, pero sabía que era algo malo de parte de la señora Rocío. Lucero no estaba tan mal. Al menos a mí no me lo parecía. Tenía los ojos hinchados y apenas los podía abrir, parecían dos rendijas; su cabeza era grande y aplastada por detrás; su cuello, muy corto y ancho; su nariz, muy chata, y por su boca, rara y pequeña, se asomaba la punta de su lengüita rosa, como los gatitos de la Algodona (una gata que tuvo mi primo Andrés) que habían nacido muertos. Lo que más extraño se veía en ella era que la piel de su cara estaba muy flojita, parecía que traía puesta una máscara de hule.

Ni de broma imaginaba que la piel flojita era lo de menos. Lucero tenía mil problemas más. Muchas malformaciones en su físico y en sus órganos internos, pero eso ya lo supe muchos años después.

Yo estaba feliz de que mi mamá hubiera regresado a casa. La había extrañado demasiado. Pensé que todo sería como antes, pero no.

Pasaron el moisés de Lucero al cuarto de mi mamá y ella se la pasaba ahí, encerrada con la niña. Había oído que batallaba mucho para darle de comer porque Lucero no podía succionar. Yo pensaba que solo era capricho de esa niña para retener a mi mamá a su lado, porque la quería nada más para ella. Creía que era una gran arpía que había venido a hacerme sufrir y quitarme el amor de mi mamá. Yo busqué consuelo en mi papá, pero no encontré nada en él; al contrario: parecía rechazarme y evitaba mi presencia.

"¿Qué pasa? —me preguntaba desconsolada—. ¿Mi papá ya no me quiere?"

6

Mi tía Rosario por fin regresó a su casa, pero solo iba a dormir. Ella había ocupado por completo el lugar de mi mamá: llegaba desde temprano para darme de desayunar y llevarme a la escuela junto con mi primo Andrés, se iba a trabajar, iba por nosotros, preparaba la comida, atendía a mi papá y hacía todo el trabajo de mi mamá. Era muy cariñosa conmigo, pero, no sé por qué, yo no podía corresponderle... Lo que yo quería era a mi mamá.

Mi papá cada vez se comportaba más extraño. Casi no estaba en la casa, y, cuando estaba, se enojaba por todo y se ponía a discutir con mi tía, hablando siempre de lo mismo:

—¡Esto no tenía por qué pasarnos, Rosario! Laura es muy joven y los dos estamos sanos y sin ningún problema.

—También en las parejas jóvenes puede ocurrir —le decía mi tía.

—¿Quién tuvo la culpa, Rosario? ¿Quién?

—Nadie es culpable, Alfredo; son cosas que pasan...

—¿Y por qué a nosotros?... ¡Esto es una injusticia, una pesadilla!... —Y se ponía de muy mal genio y a veces hasta lloraba.

Yo sentía que la sangre me hervía. Le tenía mucho rencor a esa niña. Ella me había quitado a mi mamá y la culpaba también del genio horrible de mi papá, de su tristeza y de que, además, lo peor de todo, él me hubiera dejado de querer.

Mi papá para nada iba a ver a Lucero. Dormía en el sofá de la sala y no le dirigía la palabra a mi mamá. Yo no entendía qué estaba pasando, pero sabía que todo eso lo había provocado Lucero. Por las noches, en vez de rezar la oración que mi abuelita Adela me había enseñado: "Niñito Jesús, que estás en el Copón, echa un brinquito y ven a mi corazón", yo decía: "Niñito Jesús, que estás en el Copón, echa un brinquito y llévate a Lucerito". Rezaba con todo fervor y cada mañana amanecía con la esperanza de que el Niñito Jesús me hubiera hecho caso y que esa niña ya no estuviera en mi casa, que hubiera desaparecido. Pero no, ella no desaparecía y cada vez necesitaba más cuidados y atenciones de mi mamá.

Mi papá empezó a beber. Llegaba a la casa dando tumbos y diciendo disparates. Yo, al principio, no entendía nada; nunca lo había visto así. Después, me empezó a dar miedo. Eran gritos sin razón, groserías, golpes en los muebles; aventaba los vasos y los trastes y, de repente, lloraba. Era un llanto de coraje, de impotencia y, luego, de mucha, mucha tristeza.

Mi mamá a veces lo trataba de calmar y otras, lo regañaba; pero como nada daba resultado, lo que hacía ella era encerrarse con Lucero en su recámara, hacerse la sorda y dejarme a mí sola con mi papá... ¡A mí me daba pavor!

Una noche, estando yo ya acostada, lo oí entrar hablando solo. Hablaba fuerte y con voz de enojo. Me hice bolita en mi cama y me tapé con las cobijas hasta la cabeza. Entró a mi cuarto y me dijo:

—¡En esta casa no hay nadie que me atienda! ¡Levántate, Adela, dame una copa!

A mí nunca me había dicho "Adela" y yo pensé: "¿Una copa? ¿Cómo se hacen las copas?". Empecé a temblar, cerré fuertemente los ojos y traté de hacerme la dormida. Seguramente él notó mi temblor y me destapó, quitándome las cobijas de un tirón.

—¿Hasta tú me vas a ignorar? —gritó—. ¡Levántate a atender a tu padre!

Yo sentí que una humedad caliente me envolvía, luego se iba enfriando, hasta casi congelarme. Me había hecho pipí. Comencé a llorar. Él fue hasta mi pequeña cajonera y le dio un golpe con el puño cerrado. Rompió la tapa del mueble y yo sentí que a mí me había roto el corazón.

En eso, entró mi mamá.

—¡Alfredo! —gritó. Lo hizo de una manera para mí desconocida. Nunca había visto esa seriedad, se puede decir severidad, en la cara y en la voz de mi mamá—. ¡No te permito estas majaderías, y menos con Adelita! —luego, su voz cambió; con un tono ronco, tranquilo, pero firme, le dijo—: Hazme el favor de retirarte de aquí... del cuarto de la niña, y de la casa.

Mi papá se quedó quieto, sorprendido, como paralizado. Luego, se acercó a ella, amenazante. Yo vi eso y me llené de terror. Sin poderme contener, grité:

—¡Vete de aquí, papá! ¡Vete, vete, vete!

Él me miró sin dar crédito a lo que había oído, bajó los brazos en actitud de derrota y salió.

Mi mamá me abrazó y yo a ella, muy fuerte, con toda el alma. Era la primera vez que me abrazaba desde que nació Lucero.

—Ven, hijita, vamos a bañarte.

Me levantó de la cama cuando se dio cuenta de que estaba toda mojada. Mientras yo me bañaba, ella volteó el colchón y puso sábanas y cobijas limpias en mi cama. Cuando salí del baño, me dijo:

—¿Te quieres acostar conmigo?

Yo sentí que el corazón se me salía por la boca.

—¡Sí! —le respondí.

Creía que ella se iba a acostar en mi cama, pero cuando vi a dónde me invitaba a dormir, a su cuarto, con Lucero, le dije que mejor me quedaba ahí.

Ella me arropó, me dio un beso, las buenas noches, me persignó y se fue.

Yo no pude dormir. Recordaba el terrible episodio con mi papá, veía mi cajonera rota y solo podía pensar en su puño pegándole con coraje.

Pensaba que tal vez si yo hubiera estado ahí, a mí me habría roto la cabeza. Me imaginaba a mi mamá abrazando a su niña, arrullándola y durmiéndose, muy tranquila, con ella.

—¡Papito, papito! —lloraba en silencio. Pensaba que él ya no estaba en la casa y no sabía si iba a regresar. Estaba muy confundida. Por un lado, él me daba miedo, pero, por otro, me dolía que se hubiera ido. También recapacité mucho en que tal vez lo mejor sería que yo me fuera con mi papá. Total, si mi mamá ya no quería a nadie más que a Lucero, pues no tenía caso que yo siguiera en la casa. Sin embargo, la nueva personalidad de mi papá no me gustaba nada, así es que estaba hecha un lío. ¡Qué infeliz me sentí esa noche!

7

SIN MI papá, en la casa todo era más tranquilo, pero yo lo extrañaba. A pesar de que, aun estando él, yo de todos modos estaba sola, siempre tenía la esperanza de que él volviera a ser el mismo de antes, de que volviera a llevarme a la nevería y ponernos a bailar aquí en la casa con nuestros discos de *rock*.

"¿Ya se acabó todo con él? —me preguntaba—. ¿Ya no va a volver nunca?", me atormentaba pensando.

Mi tía Rosario era la única que hablaba con mi mamá; las dos se encerraban en el cuarto con Lucero y hablaban y hablaban sin parar. Mi primo Andrés y yo nos íbamos a mi cuarto y, aunque yo procuraba no hablar con él, porque cuando lo hacía, me dejaba con el ánimo por los suelos, lo tenía que hacer, ya que era mi única compañía:

—¿Verdad que mi papá pronto va a regresar y ya no va tomar vino? —le preguntaba, esperanzada en que su respuesta coincidiera con mi anhelo.

—¡Ay, cómo crees, Adelita!, tu papá ya no va a regresar y ya para siempre va a seguir tomando vino. ¿Que no conoces a los borrachos? Y, además, ¿para qué quieres que regrese? Yo tengo un amigo que tiene un papá borracho y él está muy contento cuando no está porque, cuando está, le pega a su mamá y a veces hasta a él.

Mi corazón se hacía polvo. Me imaginaba a mi papá como un ogro, pegándonos sin parar a mi mamá y a mí.

—Pero tal vez si regresa y le digo que lo quiero mucho y que ya no tome vino, él me haga caso.

—¡Ay, Adelita!..., se ve que no tienes nada de experiencia con los borrachos.

—¿Y tú sí? —le preguntaba sabiendo de antemano que él tampoco la tenía, pero él me respondía:

—Claro que yo sí. He visto muchas películas de borrachos y ellos nunca le hacen caso a nadie, y menos a sus hijas, y no dejan de emborracharse nunca y cada vez toman más y más vino.

—¿A poco tu mamá te deja ver esas películas?

—Bueno... No... pero cuando voy a casa de mis amigos, las veo.

Y me dejaba totalmente desmoralizada. Por eso, con él, instintivamente, yo no quería cruzar palabra.

En cuanto llegaba yo le sugería que nos fuéramos a mi recámara a jugar. Jugábamos con mis *barbies* y sus muñecos extraterrestres y, aunque él era muy pesado para jugar, yo lo prefería. Mi abuelita Adela le hablaba muy seguido por teléfono a mi mamá, pero ella la evitaba. Siempre me decía que le dijera que estaba muy ocupada con Lucero o que estaba en el baño. Yo no podía decirle mentiras a mi abuelita:

—Yo creo que no quiere hablar contigo, abuelita, porque me dijo que te dijera que está en el baño, pero no es cierto.

—No te preocupes, mi amor —me respondía—, solo dile que la mando saludar y que la quiero mucho.

Mi papá se había ido a Querétaro a vivir con ella y yo creo que mi mamá pensaba que siendo ella su mamá quería abogar por él; por eso no le contestaba el teléfono.

Mi abuelita Esperanza, cada vez que venía, atormentaba a mi mamá:

—No seas tonta, Laura, tu marido es tu marido y, sea como sea, es un respeto en tu casa. ¿Vas a estar como tu hermana Rosario? ¡Lo que yo he sufrido con esa muchacha! ¡De lo que la gente hablara de ella!

—Mamá, lo que diga la gente es lo que menos me importa. Por favor, deja que yo resuelva mi vida a mi modo.

—Me estás diciendo que no me meta, ¿verdad? Pues, bueno, allá tú, pero recuerda que el tiempo me dará la razón.

—Sí, mamá —le respondía, desalentada—, gracias por tus consejos. Ahora tengo muchas cosas que hacer.

—Sí, ya me voy, no tienes que decírmelo.

Y se iba molesta.

Mi abuelito Jorge sólo venía a decirle a mi mamá que contaba con él para todo y que qué se le ofrecía.

—Nada, papacito, solo que de repente vengas a alegrarme el día con tu presencia —le respondía mi mamá.

—Adelita ha de extrañar a Alfredo, voy a venir cuantas veces pueda para llevármela al parque a tomar un heladito, ¿te parece bien?

—Gracias, papito —le decía mi mamá y lo abrazaba muy fuerte.

Cuando una vez mi mamá contestó el teléfono y era mi abuelita Adela, y no le quedó más remedio que hablar con ella, estuvieron platicando mucho rato y, cuando colgó, la vi mucho más tranquila. Luego, oí que le dijo a mi tía Rosario que su suegra era una santa; que le había dado a entender que estaba de su parte, que le había dicho que mi papá estaba cometiendo un grave error, y también que si necesitaba dinero le avisara. Mi mamá le había dicho que no, que no se preocupara, que mi abuelito Jorge la estaba ayudando.

De todos modos, muy seguido llegaban cartas de mi abuelita Adela y siempre traían un billetito dentro.

Un día, llegó a la casa sin avisar y le dijo a mi mamá que estaba preocupada por mi papá, porque se veía muy deprimido. Que le habían hablado de su trabajo y le habían dado casi un ultimátum para que se presentara.

—Sé que se debe de sentir muy mal —le dijo mi mamá—, porque Alfredo nunca ha sido irresponsable. Pero esto de la niña lo ha sacado completamente de quicio. Parece que es algo más fuerte que él.

—Vas a ver, hija —le dijo mi abuelita—, Alfredo va a recapacitar... Y si no, de todos modos te pido que no me alejes de ustedes; yo te quiero como si fueras mi hija y a mis niñas ¡ni se diga!

—Gracias, siempre he contado con usted —le dijo mi mamá y se abrazaron muy fuerte.

Yo la abracé de las piernas y le dije:

—Abuelita: cuando crezca voy a ser como tú.

Y, bueno, no lo he logrado, pero lo intento, lo intento...

8

A LOS pocos días de aquello, mi papá empezó a hablarnos todos los días por teléfono; de repente le llegaban flores a mi mamá de su parte, y a mí, regalitos. Luego, por fin vino a la casa. Trajo tremenda despensa y llegó en un plan muy cariñoso. Estábamos los tres en la sala y me dijo que si los dejaba solos. Yo me fui de ahí pero me quedé lo bastante cerca como para oír de lo que hablaban e intervenir por si me necesitaba mi mamá. ¡Qué cosa horrible era tenerle miedo a mi papá!

—Laura, perdóname —le dijo—, no sé qué me pasó. Yo creo que todo esto ha sido muy fuerte para mí, creo que me ha afectado demasiado..., pero he recapacitado y sé que no puedo vivir sin ustedes.

Yo me sentí feliz. ¡Por fin mi papi volvía a ser el mismo!

—Mira, Alfredo —le dijo mi mamá—, no se trata nada más de lo que tú sientas; yo estoy mucho más tranquila sin ti y no quiero que regreses a la casa.

"¡Mamá, qué estás diciendo! —pensé yo—. ¡Cómo le dices esas cosas a papá! ¡Yo sí lo necesito! ¡Yo sí lo quiero en la casa!"

—Desde que nació Lucero no he sentido ningún apoyo en ti —continuó mi mamá—; al contrario, te has comportado de la manera más ruin y egoísta que se puede comportar un compañero... un esposo... un padre. Cuando nació Adelita, no había hombre más feliz y más orgulloso que tú, y, ahora que mi pequeñita ha tenido la desgracia de haber nacido con un problema, del que ella menos que nadie es culpable, tú te has transformado, has mostrado tal falta de humanismo que asusta... Tú no quieres a Lucero... No la sientes tu hija... —Se soltó llorando—. No me abraces, vete, por favor.

—Pero, Laura...

—¡Vete, Alfredo! ¡No quiero volver a verte! —le dijo en un tono muy feo.

Mi papá se levantó del sillón y, sin decir nada, salió de la casa. Me acuerdo que yo me dirigí a mi recámara a esperar a que mi mamá fuera a explicarme qué había pasado y a consolarme. Pero no fue. La esperé mucho tiempo. Me quedé dormida, vestida, sobre la cama.

9

YO ME refugiaba en mis muñecas, en mi primo Andrés y en mi abuelito Jorge, aunque él trabajaba mucho y casi no podía venir. También le hablaba a mi abuelita Adela casi a diario y, claro, cuando llegaba el recibo del teléfono, mi mamá me ponía como lazo de cochino, pero no me importaba.

Un día vino mi abuelito Jorge a la casa. Me trajo un divertido juego de química y a Lucero una cobijita hermosa, color de rosa, que parecía de espuma. Mi mamá lo recibió con gusto, pero él pareció asustarse al verla.

—Laura —le dijo—, estás muy desmejorada, ¿cuánto has adelgazado, hija?

—No sé, siempre he sido delgada —respondió mi mamá poniéndose tensa y agresiva.

—No te molestes, hija —le dijo con toda calma—, ya sé que siempre has sido delgadita, pero yo creo que no te estás cuidando bien, que necesitas distraerte un poco, ¿por qué no llevamos a las niñas a dar una vuelta al parque y nos tomamos un heladito o un refresquito?

—¡Sí, abuelito, vamos! —contesté de inmediato, entusiasmada.

—Si quieres llévate a Adelita —le dijo mi mamá—, a Lucero no la puedo sacar.

—¿Por qué no, hija?, el día está precioso y a ella le sentaría muy bien airearse y asolearse tantito.

Mi mamá, sin poderse contener, se puso a llorar.

—Mira, Laura, tienes que relajarte, hija... No tienes que pensar que a Lucerito no la puedes sacar a la calle porque no es una bebita como otras muchas. Piensa que Dios te la mandó así, porque en ella Él te mandó un angelito. Debes tomarlo con más alegría, Laura... Lucero es una niña preciosa y todos la queremos.

Mi mamá abrazó a mi abuelito y, llorando aún, le dijo:

—Sí, papi, ella es preciosa; yo la quiero mucho..., pero me duele, papá, me duele...

Cuando se tranquilizó, aceptó la invitación de mi abuelito, arregló a Lucero como muñeca y, sin fijarse siquiera si yo estaba bien peinada, nos fuimos al parque. Nos sentamos en una banquita, mi abuelito nos compró un helado, y luego jugó conmigo con una pelota que llevábamos; mi mamá se quedó en la banquita con Lucero. Estábamos de lo más contentos, cuando sin decir agua va, se levantó y nos dijo:

—¡Vámonos!

Empezó a caminar de prisa hacia la casa. Mi abuelito y yo nos miramos sorprendidos y la seguimos.

Cuando llegamos, mi mamá, antes de encerrarse en su recámara con Lucero, le dijo a mi abuelito:

—¡No soporto que toda la gente vea a mi niña como bicho raro!

Mi abuelito estuvo conmigo toda la tarde, enseñándome a usar el juego de química. Antes de irse, le habló a mi tía Rosario y ella y Andrés se quedaron en la casa hasta que me dormí.

10

MI PAPÁ llegó una tarde, con muchos regalos para Lucero. "¡Nada más esto me faltaba! —pensé yo—. Ahora hasta mi papá se va a poner de parte de esa niña..."

¡Increíble! Mi mamá lo recibió con gusto. Estuvieron platicando. Mi papá le dijo que ya había vuelto al trabajo, que ya no estaba bebiendo y que comprendía que todo lo que había hecho había sido terrible, luego, la abrazó y le dijo que la amaba igual que cuando eran novios. Se besaron y yo sentí mi corazón brincar de alegría.

Mi felicidad no duró mucho. Los dos se fueron a la recámara de mi mamá y estuvieron todo el tiempo con Lucero. Mi papá la cargó por primera vez en tres meses y le dijo muchas palabras de cariño. A mí casi no me hizo caso, solo cuando se fue me dijo:

—Nos vemos mañana, mi amor. —Y me abrazó.

Al día siguiente, cuando regresé de la escuela, mi mamá me dijo que mi papá iba a regresar a la casa. Yo brinqué de gusto. Por la tarde él llegó con una maletita deportiva con alguna ropa nueva, ya que cuando se fue de la casa no se llevó nada suyo.

Los primeros días estuvo muy bien con mi mamá, pero, no sé por qué, se volvieron a distanciar. Él volvió a estar de mal humor y a veces triste. La única diferencia era que ya no se dormía en la sala y que tampoco tomaba vino.

Conmigo fue cariñoso unos días, pero después volvió a lo mismo: parecía no darse cuenta de mi presencia. Volví a culpar a Lucero de todo lo que pasaba.

Cuando mi mamá se metía al baño, que eran los únicos momentos que dejaba a Lucero sola, yo iba hasta su moisés y le decía:

—¿Por qué no te alivias, niña? ¿Siempre vas a estar enferma para que mi mamá te consienta y mi papá esté triste? Eres muy mala, ¿sabes?, y además muy fea.

Me daban ganas de golpearla, pero me contenía. Me imaginaba a mi mamá azotándome sin compasión si algo malo le pasaba a su niña.

Aquello que le decía a Lucero de que era fea no era cierto; era una bebita rara, pero no fea. Además, pensaba yo que, aunque en verdad fuera fea, mi mamá de todos modos la querría más que a mí.

11

MI PAPÁ empezó a hacer todo lo posible por internar a Lucero en una institución para niños con síndrome de Down.

—No estoy hablando por mí ni por ti, Laura —le dijo a mi mamá—, esto es lo que le conviene a ella. La podremos ir a visitar cuando queramos y traerla a casa todos los fines de semana. Dejemos de ser egoístas y apoyémosla. En esa institución le van a dar las atenciones que necesita y la van a ayudar a desarrollarse como es debido. Ponte a pensar en lo que el doctor nos ha dicho acerca de su salud. Ella necesita estar en donde, si se presenta una emergencia, pueda tener una pronta ayuda. Si se nos pone malita aquí ¿qué vamos a hacer, Laura? Piénsalo.

Estas palabras convencieron a mi mamá. La institución tenía fama de que ahí atendían a los niños muy bien, aunque era carísima.

Yo me puse feliz. Pensé que si dejaban a Lucero en ese lugar, seguramente al principio iríamos a verla todos los días, luego, cada fin de semana, después, cada quince días o cada mes, y, al final, nos olvidaríamos de ella. Todo volvería a ser como antes. Un lunes, mis papás la llevaron. Pero la cosa no era como mi papá había dicho: "La podremos visitar cuando queramos y traerla a casa todos los fines de semana"; no. La podríamos ir a visitar los fines de semana, pero nada más.

En cuanto Lucero ya no estuvo en la casa, todo cambió. Mi papá volvió a ser el de antes: cariñoso, animado y contento.

Por aquellos días llegaba con flores para mi mamá y con regalitos para mí. Volvimos a ir a la nevería y a bailar *rock*... ¡Yo no me cambiaba por nadie, estaba feliz! Pero mi mamá no sentía lo mismo. Siempre estaba preocupada y nerviosa. No se despegaba del teléfono. A cada rato se comunicaba a la institución para saber de Lucero. No hablaba más que de Lucero. La extrañaba cada minuto. El fin de semana que fuimos a visitarla, mi mamá cogió a su niña y salió con ella de la institución. Mi papá tuvo que arreglar en la administración todo lo necesario para que la dieran de alta.

Finalmente Lucero estaba de nuevo en la casa, y el mal humor de mi papá, mi soledad y mi angustia, también.

12

UNA NOCHE, Lucero se puso mal. Los gritos de mi mamá me despertaron:

—¡Háblale al doctor Del Valle, Alfredo! ¡La niña está morada, casi no puede respirar!

Salí de mi cuarto medio dormida. Vi a mi papá en el teléfono.

—Que en un momento el doctor se va a comunicar para acá —le dijo a mi mamá—, tranquilízate. —Y colgó el aparato.

Pasaron unos minutos y el doctor no llamaba. Lucero cada vez estaba peor.

—¡Vuelve a llamarlo, por favor! —le suplicó mi mamá, desesperada.

Mi papá fue al teléfono y marcó. Me di cuenta de que lo hacía manteniéndolo sin línea.

—Papá —le dije—, si aprietas ese botón el teléfono no sirve.

Me hizo señas para que no dijera nada. Mi mamá, con su niña en los brazos, parecía morir de angustia. Me dio lástima.

—Le voy a decir a mi mamá —lo amenacé.

—¡No, Adelita! —me dijo y marcó el teléfono.

El doctor Del Valle es el pediatra que, hasta la fecha, atiende a Lucero. Esa noche él se hizo cargo de todo, al poco tiempo de haberlo llamado llegó una ambulancia.

Cuando mis papás llegaron con la niña, el doctor ya estaba en el hospital. La internaron. Mi tía Rosario había ido por mí y nos fuimos a su casa. Mi tía decidió que yo durmiera con Andrés en su recámara. Antes de acostamos, me preguntó:

—¿Ya te vas a quedar a vivir aquí?

—¿Por qué me lo preguntas? ¿Tú quieres que me quede?

Estaba llena de esperanzas de que dijera que sí.

—Pues, francamente, no —me contestó.

—¿Por qué? ¿Tú tampoco me quieres ya? —le dije con tristeza.

—¡Ay, Adelita, cómo no te voy a querer, si eres mi prima favorita!... Bueno, aunque eres casi la única, porque Lucero está muy chiquita...

—¿Entonces por qué?

—Pues porque mi cama es muy chica, y con lo gorda que estás...

"¿Gorda?", me sorprendí. Yo nunca había pensado que era gorda.

Desde ese día tenía un problema más en mi vida.

Ese día Lucero se había puesto mal porque tiene problemas con su corazón. El doctor Del Valle les dijo a mis papás que muchos niños Down los tienen; que debían seguir el tratamiento al pie de la letra y evitar enfriamientos, ya que una gripe podía ser fatal para Lucero.

Ya en la casa, los cuidados de mi mamá para Lucero se duplicaron y el abandono hacia mí, también. Además, con lo que me había dicho Andrés yo me sentía peor que antes, aunque, cada vez que me veía en el espejo, no notaba esa gordura de la que hablaba mi primo.

De todos modos, dejé de comer. Yo no quería ser gorda como mi abuelita Esperanza, sino delgada como mi mamá, mi tía Rosario y mi abuelita Adela.

La única que se dio cuenta de mi falta de apetito y de que estaba bastante desmejorada, fue mi abuelita Adela, y eso que solo venía los fines de semana.

—¿Por qué no quieres comer, hijita? —me preguntó.

—Porque no tengo hambre —le respondí, tratando de poner fin a la plática.

—Pero si te hice tus tortillitas de harina y tu chorizo, que tanto te gustan...

A mí se me iban los ojos con las tortillitas y con el chorizo, pero quería adelgazar.

—A ver, mi vida, dime la verdad —me dijo—, ¿estás triste? ¿Tienes algún problema?

—Pues... —No me atrevía a decirle el motivo verdadero por el que no quería comer, a pesar de que me moría de hambre.

—Dime qué te pasa, chiquita... ¿Ya no me tienes confianza, o no te gusta la comidita que te hago?

Yo ni de chiste quería que mi abuelita pensara nada de eso, así que decidí decirle la verdad:

—Es que estoy muy gorda.

—¿Qué? —se asombró—. ¿Gorda tú?

—Sí, abuelita, tengo que adelgazar.

—Pero si eres una varita de nardo. ¿Quién te dijo que estás gorda?

—Andrés —le confesé.

—¡Ay, ese niño! —exclamó—. No le hagas caso, chiquita, tu primo muchas veces nada más habla por hablar... A ver, espérame tantito. —Y fue a la recámara de mis papás.

Regresó con la cinta métrica y me midió el pecho, la cintura y la cadera.

—¡Perfecto! —dijo—. ¡Tienes las medidas perfectas! ¡Como las de Miss Universo!

Yo le creí y me sentí soñada. Mi abuelita nunca mentía.

Todavía recuerdo que esos taquitos de chorizo que me comí aquel día, me supieron a gloria.

13

UNA TARDE que hacía muchísimo frío mi papá entró a la recámara, cargó a Lucero y, destapándola, la asomó a la ventana. Mi mamá se estaba bañando.

—No hagas eso, papá —le dije, horrorizada, pues aunque Lucero me caía mal, no era para tanto.

Él me miró con complicidad y me pidió silencio; luego, le quitó a Lucero toda la ropita y extendió los brazos exponiéndola totalmente a la tarde helada. Él se empezó a reír con una sonora risa ronca y malvada. Yo temblé.

—¡Papá! ¡Por favor no, papá! —le pedí con energía.

Pero él no me escuchaba, estaba como poseído por algún espíritu maligno. Vi el cuerpecito de Lucero temblando sin control, y luego, quieto.

—¡No! —grité.

Y caminando con muchos trabajos, porque sentía mi cuerpo paralizado del susto, fui al baño a avisarle a mi mamá. Abrí la puerta, ella se estaba secando.

—¿Por qué no tocas? Sabes que no debes entrar al baño sin tocar —me dijo molesta.

—¡Ven, mamá! ¡Ven, mamá! —fue todo lo que pude decir.

—¡Salte de aquí, Adelita, deja que termine de bañarme en paz!—me ordenó.

—¡Ven, mamá! —repetí.

Estaba yo tan asustada que no podía coordinar las ideas para explicarle lo que estaba sucediendo en la recámara.

Ella se envolvió en la toalla y me quiso sacar del baño, pero yo le apreté fuertemente la mano y la jalé, llevándola hacia donde estaba mi papá, aún riéndose roncamente, con el cuerpecito de Lucero expuesto al frío.

Mi mamá miró aquello y cayó al suelo de rodillas.

—¡Mi niña! ¡Mi niña! —se lamentaba y tapándose la cara empezó a llorar sin control.

Yo fui a donde estaba mi papá y, sacando fuerzas de no sé dónde, le quité a Lucero de los brazos. Él se quedó mirándome con una mirada rara, como perdida y vacía, y también se puso a llorar. Lucero estaba morada, no respiraba ni se movía. La estreché fuertemente entre mis brazos para darle calor, pero me daba la sensación de estar abrazando un hielo.

Miré a mi alrededor y vi a mis papás abrazados, llorando muy tristemente. Yo me senté en la cama con mi hermanita en los brazos y ella se derritió. De pronto, sobre mis piernas, sOlo había un charco de agua.

—¡Lucero! ¡Lucero!

Mis propios gritos me despertaron. Estaba empapada en sudor y temblaba sin control. Miré mis brazos y mis piernas para ver si estaban mojados y volteé para todos lados, todavía medio dormida, sin poder distinguir si había sido sueño o realidad aquella monstruosa escena. Todo estaba tranquilo, yo estaba en mi recámara y la casa, en silencio.

De todos modos, de puntitas, sin hacer ruido, fui a la cuna de Lucero, acaricié su cuerpecito caliente y comprobé que estuviera bien arropada.

14

POR ESO no me explico cómo fue posible que, aun después de aquella horrible pesadilla, yo misma aprovechaba cualquier momento en que mi mamá dejaba sola a Lucero, para torturarla. Unas veces, le tapaba la boca y la nariz hasta que se amorataba; otras, le apretaba con fuerza un brazo o una piernita hasta que en su carita aparecía aquel gesto de dolor que me causaba tanta satisfacción. Quería que gritara, que llorara.

Pero Lucero no lloraba ni gritaba. Yo no sabía que no podía hacerlo porque sus músculos eran muy débiles y le costaba mucho trabajo sacar la voz. Únicamente me miraba con sorpresa. Incrédula. Me castigaba pareciendo disculparme, dándome a entender que comprendía que todas esas barbaridades yo no las podía haber hecho a propósito... y luego me sonreía. ¡Qué mal me hacía sentir! De momento me arrepentía, pero el arrepentimiento pronto quedaba en el olvido y volvía a aprovechar las ausencias de mi mamá para repetir aquellas crueldades. Deseaba que Lucero no hubiera nacido, que desapareciera, que la pudiéramos poner en una bolsa de plástico (como a los gatitos muertos de la Algodona) y enterrarla debajo del olivo del parque (como a ellos). Deseaba que mi papá volviera a estar contento, que mi mamá me quisiera, que todo fuera como antes de su llegada. La culpaba de todo lo malo que me estaba pasando.

15

CADA vez me refugiaba más en mis muñecas. En la escuela no hablaba casi con nadie, y con mi primo Andrés, como ya dije, no me gustaba platicar cuando iba a mi casa, o yo a la de él, porque en vez de animarme me hacía sentir peor.

—Andrés —le dije un día—, ¿tú crees que las hermanitas enfermas vivan mucho tiempo?

—¡Ay, Adelita! —me contestó—, viven más que nadie. Fíjate que un amigo me contó que hay un viejo que tiene ciento ochenta años y de chiquito estaba enfermo, como tu hermanita.

—¿Ciento ochenta años? —le pregunté asombrada.

—O ciento noventa —me dijo y me asombré más todavía.

—¿Y ahora ese viejo ya no está enfermo? —le pregunté.

—Claro que no, las personas solo están enfermas cuando son chiquitas, como Lucero.

—¿Entonces Lucero cuando sea grande se va a curar y va a vivir ciento ochenta años?

—¡Ciento noventa! —me corrigió.

"¡En la torre!", pensé, además de que tendríamos Lucero para rato, también se iba a aliviar. Me la imaginaba sin esa cara tan chata, sin esos ojitos bizcos, sin esa cabeza tan aplastada y sin babear ni moquear.

—Entonces Lucero ya va a estar muy bonita y mi mamá todavía la va a querer más —le dije.

—Pues sí —me respondió—, imagínate, si ahorita la quiere más que a ti, pues cómo la va a querer entonces...

Por eso no me gustaba platicar con Andrés. En cuanto llegaba a mi casa o yo iba a la de él, inmediatamente lo invitaba a jugar; prefería aguantar sus tosquedades.

16

ENTRE terapias, enfermedades y el gran amor de mi mamá, Lucero crecía. Al igual que mi soledad. Todo giraba alrededor de Lucero.

Su tiempo era primordial; el mío no importaba. Cualquier adelanto en ella era toda una proeza; en cambio, mis buenas calificaciones y mis esfuerzos no contaban. Empecé a bajar en la escuela, a desobedecer y a portarme mal y, como por arte de magia, mi mamá volvió a fijarse en mí. Pasaba tardes enteras sermoneándome y revisando mis tareas... ¡El tiempo de las terapias y los ejercicios de Lucero al fin era mío!

Pero no por mucho tiempo.

—Si necesita castigarla, castíguela. Si reprueba, que repita el año. No puedo pasarme las tardes supervisando y corrigiendo algo que ella hace mal porque quiere. Adela tiene toda la capacidad del mundo para hacer las cosas bien, directora, ella no tiene ningún impedimento. El tiempo lo necesito para Lucero.

¡Adela! ¡Me había dicho *Adela!*

Yo estaba agazapada afuera de la dirección de la primaria, oyendo esa plática. El ánimo se me fue hasta el suelo. Comprendí que mis tardes acompañada de mi mamá, aunque fuera regañándome, se habían acabado.

Lejos de mejorar, mi conducta empeoró. Ya no era a propósito que yo me portara mal o que no hiciera bien las cosas; sencillamente así me salían y no estaba en mí remediarlo.

Los adelantos en Lucero eran asombrosos: su motricidad había mejorado muchísimo y su mente funcionaba casi como la de cualquier otro niño de su edad, ya que el síndrome, en ella, afecta principalmente su sistema muscular. Lucero tiene un retraso mental leve, y, aunque a veces razona como una niña pequeña, otras, nos sorprende. Además, tiene una memoria buenísima y un sentido de la crítica excepcional.

Sus adelantos se podían comparar con mis atrasos. Yo iba cada vez peor.

Esto duró hasta que una noche que mi papá no estaba, me despertó un llanto y escuché una conversación:

—Cálmate, Laura, todo se va a arreglar.

La voz era de mi tía Rosario; el llanto, de mi mamá.

—Es que no sé qué hacer... No sé cómo hacerles entender a Alfredo y a Adelita que necesito que me ayuden con Lucero; que es nuestro deber sacarla adelante y hacerla feliz... ¡Lucero nos necesita tanto! —le dijo mi mamá—. Ella es un ser indefenso. Como un día me dijo mi papá: es un ángel que Dios me mandó... ¡Ellos no comprenden cuánto me necesita!

—Mira, Laura —le dijo mi tía con seriedad—, yo te comprendo y te admiro, porque ¡cómo has luchado y trabajado por la salud y el bienestar de Lucero! Hay madres que nunca aceptan a los hijos cuando tienen este tipo de problemas; se bloquean y fingen que todo está bien, que no pasa nada; entonces, los tienen en el abandono y, casi puedo asegurar, preferirían verlos muertos. Hay otras que, simplemente, los abandonan, como la mamá de Roland y, otras más, creo que la mayoría, que se avergüenzan de ellos, que los encierran en su casa, sin atenderlos como es debido, y no les importa su desarrollo, los tratan peor que a animalitos y hasta los maltratan y hacen cosas para provocar que ellos se enfermen, a ver si así se deshacen del problema. También hay quienes los encierran en alguna institución; y digo encierran, porque no es que los lleven a donde ellos estarían bien y recibirían las terapias y el trato adecuados, sino a horribles lugares para enfermos mentales, donde los pobrecitos, la mayoría de las veces, terminan enloqueciendo. Pienso que a Lucero le tocó la suerte de haber tenido una madre como tú, tan dedicada, tan amorosa, pero ¿te has puesto a pensar en que Adelita y Alfredo también te necesitan?

Mi mamá se quedó callada un largo momento y luego respondió:

—¡Adelita no tiene ningún problema! ¡Ella es una niña sana, normal, inteligente y bonita! ¡Y Alfredo es un adulto que ha triunfado en la vida! —le respondió mi mamá, agresiva.

—¿Y por eso no te necesitan?

Mi mamá guardó silencio. Yo estaba ansiosa por conocer su respuesta.

—No puedes decir que soy una mala esposa o una madre descuidada con Adelita —dijo a la defensiva—, ella lo tiene todo: una buena escuela, ropa bonita... ¡Se le da todo lo que se puede!

—¿La has visto imitar a Lucero frente al espejo? —le preguntó mi tía Rosario.

Me sentí desenmascarada. Creí que nadie me había visto hacer eso.

—¡Cómo! —exclamó mi mamá—. ¿La imita? ¿Le hace burla?

—-No me has entendido, Laura —le explicó pacientemente—, Adelita imita a Lucero porque quisiera ser como ella, porque le tiene envidia.

—¡Eso no es posible! —gritó mi mamá—. ¿Cómo una niña como Adelita va a envidiar a alguien como la pobrecita de mi Lucero? —Empezó a llorar de nuevo—. ¿Qué le podría envidiar?

—A ti —respondió simplemente mi tía.

—¡Pero si yo no la descuido! ¡Yo estoy siempre pendiente de sus cosas, de lo que necesita! Yo... —se interrumpió—. ¿De veras imita a Lucero?

—¿Te lo diría si no fuera cierto?

—¡Ay, Rosario! —dijo mi mamá—. ¡Pobrecita de mi Adelita! ¡Pobrecita! —repetía angustiada—. ¡Qué tonta he sido! ¿Cómo no me había dado cuenta? ¿Qué debo hacer para que ella sepa lo mucho que la quiero, lo mucho que me importa? ¡Tú sabes cómo la quiero, Rosario! ¡Mi princesa.... mi niña bonita.... mi amor...!

Del resto de la conversación ya no me acuerdo, creo que me quedé dormida. Lo que necesitaba oír ya lo había oído. *Mi princesa..., mi niña bonita..., mi amor.*

Esas palabras se quedaron grabadas en mi mente como una canción, como un arrullo.

Esa noche me soñé en brazos de mi mamá, como hacía años no pasaba. La soñé besándome cariñosa y diciéndome una y otra vez que me quería mucho.

17

A PARTIR de aquella noche las cosas cambiaron. Entre mi mamá y yo nació un sentimiento de amor y de unión increíble. No puedo asegurar si fue ella la que cambió de actitud o fui yo. La unión y el amor entre mi mamá y yo incluyeron a Lucero. Yo me tranquilicé. Sabía que quería a Lucero, pero que también me quería a mí. Eso era lo más importante en mi vida.

Al acercarme a Lucero empecé a conocerla. Me dio trabajo al principio, porque ella me rechazaba, no confiaba en mí. Claro, después de todas las groserías que le hacía y los malos tratos que le daba cuando mi mamá no me veía, no era para menos.

Poco a poco me fue queriendo y yo a ella muchísimo.

—¿Ya ves? —me dijo un día Andrés—. Tú que te preocupabas tanto porque creías que tu mamá quería más a Lucero que a ti... ¿No te dije muchas veces que no era cierto, que las quería igual?

—¡Sí, cómo no! —le respondí con coraje.

—¿No te aconsejé varias veces que te acercaras a Lucero, que ella es bien, pero bien simpática?

—Ajá —le dije enojada—. ¿Y qué más?

Me daba ansias que Andrés fuera así: decía una cosa y luego te aseguraba que había dicho lo contrario; pero lo decía en serio, parecía creérselo él mismo.

Lo que sí es verdad, es que Lucero es de lo más simpática; no creo que muchos puedan presumir de tener una hermanita como la mía: así de chistosa y ocurrente.

—Enseguida les traen a Lucero —nos dijo la directora una de las veces que acompañé a mi mamá a recogerla a su escuela—. Si gustan, pasen a esperarla aquí —nos invitó—, ya le fueron a avisar a su maestra.

Entramos a la dirección. Las paredes estaban adornadas con fotografías amplificadas de los alumnos. Todos idénticos. Parecían de esas tiras de muñecos de papel recortado que nos enseñaban a hacer en la escuela. Sentí mucha tristeza.

"Niños en serie", pensé. Me consoló un poco recordar que en esa escuela les enseñan a los niños a valerse por sí mismos y a ser independientes, hasta cierto punto, claro, porque, en general, siempre necesitan del apoyo de su familia para estar bien y contentos. Por ejemplo, ahí le enseñaron a Lucero a comer sola, a usar cubiertos y servilleta; a ir al baño (bueno, a veces no alcanza a llegar, pero lo intenta); a vestirse sola (lo único que no puede hacer es abrocharse los botones cuando van en la espalda, pero mi mamá siempre le compra ropa que los tenga por delante); a ponerse los zapatos (que sean de hebilla, porque agujetas no puede amarrar); más o menos a peinarse, a bañarse, a estar pendiente de limpiarse la nariz, que le escurre casi constantemente, y la boca, porque babea un poco; también le han enseñado los colores, a iluminar, a cantar y bailar, a nadar, a ayudar, en lo que pueda, al quehacer de la casa, y hasta a hablar porque cuando era bebita solo emitía sonidos raros. Ahora, aunque no puede pronunciar bien las palabras, habla bastante bien y tiene un lenguaje extenso. La escuela pertenece al DIF y es buenísima, tiene unas profesoras excelentes.

—¡Mamita chula! ¡*Alelita!* —se escuchó una alegre, ronca y gangosa voz en la puerta.

Mi hermana Lucero, bajita y regordeta, corría con torpeza hacia nosotras, detrás de ella venía su maestra. Lucero llegó y nos abrazó tan efusivamente, que mi mamá y yo estuvimos a punto de perder el equilibrio.

—¡Ten cuidado Lucero, las vas a tirar! —le advirtió la directora.

—¡No *mice* pipí! —exclamó Lucero sin soltarnos del apretado abrazo—. Lo que pasa *e* que sudé mucho, ¿*vedá maesta*?

La maestra sonrió y le entregó a mi mamá una bolsa de plástico con la ropa mojada.

—¿Vedá que *tambén* por la colita se suda, mamita chula? —le preguntó, limpiándose la nariz y la boca con su pañuelito.

Mi mamá sonrió y le dijo con cariño:

—¿Y qué sudaste, chiquita? ¿Pipí?

—¡Sí, mamita, sudé pipí! —y ahogándose de risa, con esa risa gruesa y desafinada que tiene, agregó—: ¡Sudé pipí!... ¡Pipí!... ¡Ay, mamita linda, tú sí *edes* bien *chitosa*! ¿*Vedá, Alelita*, que mamita chula *e* bien *chitosa*?

La maestra se acercó a mi mamá y le dijo en voz baja:

—Tiene que reforzar en su casa el uso de los cubiertos. Hoy no los quiso usar durante el almuerzo.

Lucero se acercó a la maestra y, mirándola fijamente, dijo:

—Mamita, ¿*vedá* que *tambén* las *mujedes tenen* bigotes? Se hizo un silencio.

Como mi mamá no le contestaba, me preguntó:

—¿*Vedá, Alelita*, que sí hay *mujedes* con bigotes? —Yo permanecí callada y tuve que hacer un esfuerzo para no reír.

—*Pedo* no le hace, *maesta* —dijo Lucero al advertir que mi mamá y yo nos habíamos quedado sin habla—, ¡de todos modos *edes* muy guapa! —le dio un beso tronado y agregó—: ¡Bigotona!

Mientras yo me atragantaba por la risa, mi mamá se disculpó diciendo que no le hicieran caso, que Lucero era tan exagerada como indiscreta.

Las maestras le dijeron que no se preocupara y se despidieron amables.

En la puerta, Lucero volteó a ver a mi mamá y le reclamó en voz muy alta:

—¿*Pol* qué me echas esos ojos, mamita? —luego me miró a mí—: ¿*Vedá Alelita* que no le dije a la *didetoda* que *e* más *golda* que una ballena? ¿Vedá que no le dije que *teñe* ojos de sapo?

—-No, chiquita —le respondí—, no le dijiste nada de eso.

Mi mamá no pudo decir nada, solo se puso roja, tomó a Lucero de la mano y nos salimos.

Sin poderme contener, me fui riendo por todo el pasillo de la entrada; Lucero se contagió. Seguramente se oían nuestras carcajadas hasta la dirección.

Mi mamá nos iba regañando, aunque, de repente, también soltaba una que otra risita.

18

El LAZO de amor que existe entre nosotras tres, no incluía a mi papá. A él le dio mucho trabajo acercarse a Lucero. Al principio, cuando era chiquita, él era quien ponía barreras, después, era ella. A la hora de la comida, que era cuando estábamos los cuatro juntos, mi mamá o yo le preguntábamos:

—¿Qué hiciste hoy, Lucero?

—Nada —nos contestaba invariablemente.

Después, hacía un aparte, como en el teatro, y decía:

—Hice muchas cosas, *pedo odita* que se vaya ya sabes *quén* —aquí miraba a mi papá—, te *patico.*

Y no volvía a abrir la boca hasta que él se hubiera ido.

Y no se diga cuando mi papá nos reclamaba algo a mi mamá o a mí. Lucero llegaba corriendo de donde estuviera, nos tapaba los oídos y nos decía:

—¡No oigas al *degañón!* —Y empezaba a hacer boruca o a gritar a todo pulmón, para acallar la voz de mi papá.

Un día, que estábamos comiendo toda la familia reunida, aprovechando un silencio, Lucero, mirando fijamente a mi papá, le dijo a mi primo Andrés:

—¡Qué *beno* que tú no *tenes* papá!

—¡Lucero, no digas eso! —intervino mi mamá.

—¿*Pol* qué no, mamita? *Andes* no *teñe* enojones en su casa, *polque* mi tía *Dosadio* no e nada, *pedo* nada enojona y no *teñe* un esposo *impudente* como el tuyo.

—No digas eso de tu papá —le dijo Andrés.

—¿*Tenes* miedo de que te *legañe*? —y prosiguió, a modo de consuelo—. No tengas *medo,* él no te va a *leganal...* Él *quede* a todos, menos a mí.

—¿Por qué dices que no te quiero, Lucero? —le preguntó mi papá.

Ella no respondió y siguió comiendo.

—Chiquita —le dijo mi mamá—, tu papá te está hablando, contéstale.

— *Mejol contétale* tú, chulita, yo no le *quedo habal* —dijo resuelta.

Mi papá le dijo:

—Lucero, vete a tu cuarto, vas a estar castigada por contestarme así.

—¿Yo? —le dijo extrañada—. Si yo no te *conteté, ¿*no *oítes* que le dije a mi chulita que te *contetara* ella?

—¡Vete a tu cuarto! —le ordenó mi papá.

Lucero se levantó de la mesa, se puso a gatas y se fue a su recámara haciendo:

—¡Mau! ¡Mau!

Cada vez que mi papá la regañaba, ella, o cantaba, o hacía como gato o como perro, o hacía como que no lo oía y platicaba de cualquier cosa que se le ocurriera, ignorándolo. Nosotros, no podíamos evitarlo y nos reíamos, porque Lucero en verdad es graciosa. Mi papá se trababa del coraje y casi siempre terminaba yéndose a su recámara y no salía de ahí en varias horas.

"¿Cómo es posible que a mi papá no le den risa las ocurrencias de Lucero? —me preguntaba—. ¿Por qué lo toma tan en serio? ¿Por qué no le encuentra la gracia? ¡Pobre de mi papá, él se lo pierde!", siempre pensaba.

19

SÓLO mi primo Andrés no se reía cuando pasaba algún incidente como ese. Él quería mucho a mi papá y a veces me decía que le hubiera gustado tener un papá como el mío.

Siempre habíamos creído que el papá de mi primo Andrés se había muerto. Eso era lo que su mamá le había dicho.

Andrés a veces me decía:

—Me gustaría tener un papá como el tuyo; que me llevara a pasear en bicicleta y que me enseñara a manejar su coche.

—El mío ni me lleva a pasear en bicicleta, ni me enseña a manejar (y, en verdad, quien me enseñó a manejar fue Roberto).

—Bueno, es que tú eres mujer, pero si fueras hombre...

—¿Y a ti por qué no te lleva a pasear ni te enseña a manejar si eres hombre?

—Pero yo no soy su hijo. No es lo mismo.

—No, primo —le dije—, lo que pasa es que mi papá no piensa en nadie más que en él.

—Pues a mí me gustaría que tu papá fuera mi papá.

Mucho tiempo después, cuando yo iba en primero de prepa y Andrés en tercero, nos enteramos, por una carta que encontramos, que su papá no había muerto y que vivía en Baja California, solo que su mamá y él nunca se casaron. Este descubrimiento fue algo muy fuerte para Andrés.

Se sintió decepcionado de mi tía Rosario. No comprendía cómo ella le había podido mentir. Estaba triste, desmoralizado y confundido. Mi tía, que siempre había estado tan cerca de él, notó su cambio y se preocupó. Habló conmigo:

—Adelita, tú que conoces tanto a tu primo, a ti que te cuenta todas sus cosas, dime qué le pasa, por qué está triste y callado.

—No sé, tía; a mí no me ha dicho nada.

No me atreví a decirle lo que habíamos descubierto. Me daba pena de que se enterara que habíamos registrado sus cajones, buscando no sé qué, y que habíamos encontrado esa carta. Yo hablé con Andrés y le platiqué lo que mi tía me había dicho. Le sugerí que hablara con ella.

—No —me dijo mi primo—, no vale la pena. Si ella no me quiso decir la verdad, por algo será. Además, a mí no me importa saber nada. Para mí todo sigue igual.

Era mentira. Todo en la vida de mi primo había cambiado.

Empezó a decir que quería ser biólogo marino y que quería estudiar en Baja California. Yo sabía que su interés por irse a Baja California era por conocer a su papá, pero él no lo admitía.

Mi tía Rosario, yo no sé cómo, empezó a sospechar lo de la carta.

—Adelita —me dijo—, quiero que me digas la verdad; ¿tú sabes si Andrés leyó una carta que tenía en mi cajonera?

—Yo no sé nada, tía —le respondí sintiéndome de lo más mal por mentirle, pero no me atreví a decirle la verdad.

Hablé seriamente con Andrés y le dije que hablara con su mamá, que le dijera que había encontrado esa carta y que sabía lo de su papá. Que su mamá era la persona más buena del mundo y no se merecía estar así de preocupada por él sin saber qué le pasaba. Después de mucho, al fin lo convencí.

Mi tía se portó con él de lo más linda y le platicó cómo habían sido las cosas entre ella y su papá (que también se llama Andrés): se enamoraron muy jóvenes. De pronto, los papás de él decidieron irse a vivir a Baja California y se fueron muy apresuradamente. Ella se dio cuenta de que estaba embarazada y tuvo muchos problemas con su mamá, o sea mi abuelita Esperanza, pero mi abuelito Jorge la apoyó siempre, y también la apoyó cuando ella tomó la decisión de no decirle nada al papá de mi primo, quien se enteró de todo hasta mucho tiempo después de que Andrés había nacido. Para esto, él ya había hecho su vida allá y antes de que supiera que tenía un hijo, se había casado. Mi tía Rosario le dijo que si quería conocer a su papá no había problema, que ella iba a arreglar todo. Fue entonces cuando le cayó el veinte de que si mi primo quería irse a estudiar allá, era, precisamente, por querer conocerlo.

—Mi mamá cree que quiero irme a *estudiar* a Baja California sólo por mi papá —me dijo Andrés.

—¿Y no es por eso? —le pregunté.

—Bueno, también —admitió—, pero sí quiero estudiar esa carrera.

Y se fue.

Yo creo que también tenía vocación, porque sacó mención honorífica en su examen profesional y siempre que viene nos platica muy emocionado de su carrera.

De su papá dice que es muy buena persona y, aunque no lo ve muy seguido, se lleva bien con él y con su esposa. Dice Andrés que ella es lo más amable del mundo, pero que es bastante mayor que su papá y, curiosamente, no tienen hijos.

20

ENTRE Lucero y Andrés siempre ha habido un cariño y una comunicación muy especial.

Cuando Lucero ya estaba grandecita, como de tres años, él contribuyó mucho a que aprendiera a hablar, ya que todos entendíamos lo que quería, según los sonidos o las señas que hiciera, y se lo dábamos; Andrés no.

—Hasta que no digas "paleta", te la voy a dar —le decía. Lucero se desesperaba, se enojaba, se emberrinchaba y, a veces, hasta le pegaba o lo mordía, pero él no desistía—. Y si te portas grosera, menos te voy a dar nada —la reprendía.

Mi mamá quería intervenir, pero mi tía Rosario la convencía de que no lo hiciera.

—Es por el bien de Lucero, Laura, déjalos, ellos se quieren mucho y vas a ver cómo la táctica de Andrés va a dar buen resultado.

—Paleta... Paleta... —le repetía Andrés muchísimas veces, con una paciencia admirable, hasta que ella decía:

—*Peta.*

—¡Bien, chiquita, muy bien! —le aplaudía y le daba la paleta.

Lucero, se pasaba todo ese día repitiendo:

—*Peta... Peta... Peta....*

Y así, poco a poco, Lucero, con la persistencia de Andrés, fue aprendiendo muchas palabras.

Cuando Lucero veía un perro, decía:

—*Pedo.*

—¡No, no, no! —le decía Andrés—. ¡Eso se oye muy mal! Y, como sabía que ella no podía pronunciar la erre, la hacía repetir:

—Pelo... Pelo... Pelo...

Hasta que lo logró.

—¡*Mila pelo*! —decía Lucero cuando veía uno.

—Bueno, así no está tan peor —nos decía Andrés—, porque eso de *pedo*...

Lo que, por más intentos que hizo, no logró, es que Lucero también dijera *pelo* cuando quería decir *pero,* ahí sí dice *pedo.*

—Bueno —dijo Andrés—, es que ella es tan inteligente, que ve la necesidad de diferenciar una cosa de la otra. Cuando creció más Lucero, ellos platicaban de la vida, de la naturaleza, de las estrellas. Ahora, cada vez que Andrés viene de Baja California, continúan sus pláticas, como si no las hubieran interrumpido por tanto tiempo; como por ejemplo, la de hace algunos días:

—¿*Pada* qué nací yo, *Andés?*

—Para hacer muchas cosas, chiquita.

—¿Muchas cosas? Si yo no sé *hacel* muchas cosas.

—Claro que sabes hacer muchas cosas —le dijo mi primo acariciándole la cara.

—¿Como qué sé *hacel* yo? —preguntó Lucero, extrañada de que Andrés pensara que ella sabía hacer algo.

—¿Pues a ti qué te gusta hacer?

—¿A mí? —se quedó pensativa—. Pues *comel...*, *jugal...*, *etal* con mi mamita chula..., con *Alelita...* , *cantal...*

—Pues para eso naciste.

—¿*Pada cantal?*

—Sí, para cantar.

—¿*Pada cantal* los diez *pelitos?* —preguntó con su voz ronca, algo agitada.

—Sí, para cantar los diez perritos —le dijo Andrés, lleno de ternura.

—¡Ay, qué *beno* que sí me la sé! ¿*vedá*? —dijo entusiasmada—. Si no, ¿*pada* qué *hubiela* nacido yo?

—Y naciste para que todos te queramos, te consintamos, te demos besitos, ¡y te hagamos esto! —Y le hizo cosquillas. Lucero se retorcía y se moría de risa.

Sus reflexiones también tienen que ver con los sentimientos:

—¿*Pol* qué a veces me levanto y me dan ganas de *caminal* muy despacito y *milo* el pasto y no se ve tan *velde,* y veo las *foles decolodidas?* —le preguntó Lucero, muy pensativa.

—¿Y sientes que el tiempo pasa muy lento y no tienes ganas de reír ni de cantar?

—Ajá.

—Pues es que estás triste, chiquita.

—¿Y *pol* qué tengo que *estal tiste?* A mí no me *guta estal tiste* —le dijo negando con la cabeza efusivamente.

—Mira, Lucero, a veces tienes que estar triste para poder saber cuándo estás contenta.

—¡Ahhh! —dijo ella, meditando y luego agregó—: ¿Y *cando* estoy contenta me dan ganas de *leíl* mucho y de *guitale* a *Alelita pol* la ventana "¡*Alelita* ya te vi!", *cando legesa le* la calle?

—Sí.

—¿Y *tambén* me dan ganas *le lecilte* a ti que te *quelo* mucho y de *dalte* muchos besos?

—Sí —le dijo Andrés riendo, mirándola con ternura.

Y Lucero se le prendió del cuello y lo besó una y otra vez, y luego lo abrazó tan fuerte que lo hizo toser.

—¡*Mila* cómo *toy* contenta! ¡*Mílame, Andés*! —le dijo Lucero mientras casi lo ahorcaba.

También se pasan horas en la ventana del cuarto de Lucero contemplando las estrellas.

—¿Sabías que la Osa *Mayol* es mamá de la Osa *Menol?* —le dijo Lucero, que conoce a la perfección esas constelaciones.

—¿Ah, sí? No sabía —le respondió Andrés.

—Sí, *mílalas* —las señaló con el dedo—, *pol* eso *siempe* la "osita" está junto a la "osota" y se coge de su mano.

—¿Sí?

—Sí, como mi mamita chula y yo. ¿Y sabes que la "osita" *teñe* en la *ota* mano una *estellita* chiquita *polque* es su sonaja?

—¡No me digas! —dijo Andrés sorprendido—. ¿Y quién te lo dijo?

—*Naide*. Yo lo soñé.

—¿Sueñas con las estrellas? —le preguntó Andrés, conmovido.

—¡Sí! —le dijo Lucero—. Y *tambén* sueño con la luna, con pasteles, con *cocholates*... —se quedó pensativa un momento y le dijo:— Me *guta soñal* con *cocholates polque* ahí sí *pedo comel* muchos y no me hacen daño.

—¿Las pasitas te hacen daño? —le preguntó Andrés.

—¡No, te lo *julo* que las pasitas no me hacen daño! ¡De *velas* que las pasitas no me hacen daño y *pedo comel* muchas! —le dijo ansiosa, mirándole las manos. Entonces Andrés sacó una bolsita de papel de la bolsa de su pantalón y se la dio. Lucero la abrió y empezó a brincar de gusto.

—¡Pasitas, pasitas, me *gutan*, me *gutanl.* —Cogió un puño y se lo echó a la boca.

También se pasan tardes enteras mirando los libros de astronomía que tiene Lucero. Ella le explica cada una de las ilustraciones y le pide a Andrés que repase en voz alta lo que mi mamá y yo le hemos leído tantas veces. Ella se sabe de memoria varios párrafos y todas las explicaciones que vienen debajo de las fotos; eso se lo enseñó mi tía Rosario. Es muy chistoso, porque lo dice de corrido y con mucha seriedad:

—*Venus: el segundo de los platenas que gavitan en tono al Sol. Júpitel: el platena mayol de nuesto Sintema Solá. Tiela: platena peteneciente al sintema solá cabitado por el hombe...*

Y así, iba "leyendo" cada una de las explicaciones de las fotografías, señalando con el dedo las palabras.

—Y tú en cuál planeta vives? —le preguntó Andrés.

—¿Yo? *Pus* en Venus —respondió, como si fuera algo obvio.

—¿No vives en la Tierra?

—No, vivo en Venus —insistió.

—Mira, chiquita, vives en la Tierra pero tu planeta consentido es Venus, ¿sí?

—Bueno, si tú *queles...* —dijo conforme—, *pedo* yo todas las noches me voy volando a Venus.

Y dio por terminada la plática.

21

Mı TÍA Rosario nunca se ha querido casar, aunque ha tenido muchos pretendientes. Ella se dedica solo a su escuela y a sus pláticas sobre superación personal.

Mi tía es educadora y tiene un kínder. Las pláticas las empezó a dar a los papás de sus alumnos, quienes la recomendaron en las empresas donde ellos trabajan y ahora las da a nivel profesional y le va muy bien.

Fue por esas pláticas que mi mamá decidió volver a trabajar. Ella es periodista y siempre había trabajado, hasta que nació Lucero. Después de que ella nació, había sido tanta su aflicción, su depresión y su horrible sensación de culpa, que dejó el trabajo, sus cosas personales y todo lo suyo para dedicarse en cuerpo y alma a su hijita enferma. Mi mamá había perdido por completo su autoestima. No tenía ilusión por nada, ya no se arreglaba; le daba lo mismo verse fea que bonita. Envejeció como diez años, y nada, nada le importaba.

Por tanta insistencia de mi tía Rosario, ella aceptó ir a sus pláticas. Después de mucho tiempo, porque no fue rápido el cambio, mi mamá se convenció de que ella no era responsable de que Lucero hubiera nacido con problemas y de que ayudándose a sí misma y superándose profesional y personalmente era la única forma de ofrecer algo positivo y de poder ayudar a Lucero y a los demás.

Por desgracia mi papá nunca ha querido asistir a las pláticas de mi tía Rosario. Yo creo que realmente le servirían mucho. Aunque ahora ya está mucho mejor, todavía a veces se deprime. Lo bueno es que ya ha quedado atrás esa amargura que guardaba en su corazón y que lo había convertido en una persona triste y solitaria; por ejemplo, mi mamá le decía:

—Va a haber una cena en el periódico, ¿me quieres acompañar?

Él, invariablemente, le decía que no.

—Papá, me van a entregar el diploma de media carrera, ¿vas conmigo?

—Que te acompañe tu mamá.

—Vamos a hacer un día de campo, ¿vamos, Alfredo? —lo invitaba mi abuelito Jorge.

—No, va a haber fútbol.

Ni siquiera cuando presenté mi examen profesional quiso ir conmigo. Se me hizo increíble.

Nunca quería participar en nada ni tenía ninguna ilusión.

Pobre de mi papá, me daba lástima.

22

A VECES a mi papá le daba por hacerse el muy alegre y optimista; entonces era cariñoso con Lucero, pero ella no se acercaba a él, lo miraba con desconfianza.

En una ocasión, mi papá llegó con una gran caja envuelta para regalo.

—Te traje un regalito —le dijo a Lucero.

—¿A mí? —se asombró ella.

—Sí, hijita —dijo mi papá.

—*Epélate, olita* llamo a *Alelita* —respondió Lucero, apurada—. *Quén* sabe qué te pasó —lo miró fijamente—. ¿Alguien te picó los ojos? ¿No ves bien?

—¿Pero por qué me dices eso, nena? —se extrañó mi papá.

—*Polque* tú *pensas* que yo soy tu hijita —le dijo ella—, y no has *vito* que soy *Lucedo... ¡olita* llamo a *Alelita!* —y se alejó de prisa gritando ronco, ronco: —¡Alelita! ¡Alelita! ¡Papá te *tajo* un *legalo...!*

Por más que tratamos de convencerla de que el león con melena de listones de colores era para ella, no pudimos.

—Ay, ¿cómo *qués* que papá me va a *tael* a mí *legalo, Alelita?* ¿No ves que yo soy *Lucedo? Eto* te lo *tajo* a ti —me dijo sin querer tocar el juguete.

—Lucero, este león es tuyo —le dije—, mi papá te lo trajo porque él te quiere mucho.

—¡Ay, cómo *qués*, Alelita! —me dijo—. A mí, papá no me *quede*, mi mamita chula sí. —Se limpió la nariz con su pañuelito, dejó el león en mis manos y a mi papá consternado.

Si mi papá trataba de hablar con ella, ella se hacía la sorda o se ponía a hacer como gato o como perro. No dejaba que se le acercara.

A veces, Lucero quería jugar con el león.

—¿Me *pestas* tu *lon, Alelita?* —me decía—. No te *pocupes* —agregaba—, antes de que llegue papá te lo *legueso pada* que no te *legañe polque* me lo *pestate.*

A Lucero se le había quedado muy grabado cuando le presté el reloj que mi papá me regaló cuando cumplí quince años.

—¡Adelita! —me dijo enojado—. ¿Cómo se te ocurre prestarle tu reloj a esta niña que no tiene idea de lo que cuestan las cosas ni sabe cuidar nada? ¡Si algo le pasa, a quien voy a castigar es a ti!

Lucero vino corriendo:

—¡Quítame tu *leló, Alelita!* ¡No *quedo* que el *degañón* te *catigue* cuando se me *lompa, polque* yo soy muy tonta y *le segulo* se me va a *lompel!*

La pobrecita temblaba de angustia.

—Tú no eres tonta y sí puedes cuidar las cosas —le dije—. Quédate con el reloj, te lo regalo.

—¡Cómo *qués!* —respondió sorprendida—. ¿No ves que papá *quede* que tú tengas todo y yo nada? —comenzó a llorar—. ¡*Polfavol*, quítamelo!... ¡*Polfavol!*

—¿Por qué lloras, chiquita? —intervino mi mamá que al oírla llegó en seguida.

Le expliqué lo que había pasado y abrazándola con ternura, le dijo:

—Mira, chiquita, el reloj es de Adelita y si quiere te lo puede regalar.

—¡No, mamita chula, que no me lo *legale!* ¡*Pol favol* no me *lo legales, Alelita!* —me pidió desesperada.

—Está bien —le dije—, te lo presto.

—Bueno —aceptó.

Caminó unos pasos, regresó, y me dijo:

—Aquí *etá* tu *lelo, gacias pol pestámelo.* —Y extendió el brazo para que se lo quitara.

El león con melena de listones de colores le encantaba y a veces se pasaba largo rato contemplándolo sobre mi cama, pero no lo tocaba.

—Péiname como él —me pedía.

Pero como Lucero tiene tan poquito pelo era imposible alborotárselo. Entonces, mi mamá le compró una peluca afro y la pintamos de colores; cuando quería parecerse al león, se la ponía.

Esa peluca le duró años. A Lucero le encantaba ponérsela a Roberto.

23

HACE cinco años, cuando yo tenía dieciocho y Lucero doce, conocí a Roberto. Él tenía veintiocho años y, sin embargo, ya era calvo.

Roberto acababa de entrar al periódico donde mi mamá trabaja y vino a la casa a recoger unos papeles. Me encantó su sonrisa y no me disgustó nada cuando se quitó la boina y noté su falta de pelo. Yo también le gusté desde ese día. Ni Lucero ni mi papá lo conocieron en ese momento, porque mi papá no estaba y Lucero estaba haciendo no sé qué en su recámara.

A los pocos días, mi mamá nos dijo:

—Roberto, el muchacho del periódico que vino por los papeles el otro día, va a venir a cenar porque necesitamos hablar sobre un artículo.

—¿Y es fuerza que hablen aquí? —preguntó mi papá, disgustado.

—Bueno —dijo mi mamá—, si te molesta podríamos vernos en algún restaurante.

Él recapacitó un momento y dijo:

—No, discúlpame, está bien que lo hayas citado aquí. —Y se fue a su recámara.

Quién sabe qué cara tendría yo, porque en cuanto se fue mi papá, mi mamá me comentó:

—Roberto es un muchacho muy lindo, pero te lleva muchos años.

—¿Por qué me dices eso? —pregunté a la defensiva—. A mí no me interesa si tiene muchos o pocos años.

—Pues mira lo que son las cosas —me dijo—, él me ha preguntado mucho por ti.

—¿De veras, mamá? ¿En serio? —le dije, sin poder esconder mi emoción.

—De veras —me dijo.

—¡No puedo creerlo! —grité—. ¡Le gusto!

—¿Cómo no le vas a gustar si eres preciosa? —me dijo con cariño—. Pero no vayas tan rápido, Adelita —me pidió—, él ya está en edad casadera y tú todavía estás muy chica.

Quedamos de acuerdo en que no aceleraría las cosas de ningún modo y lo iba a conocer bien antes de tomar cualquier decisión.

Entró Lucero a la sala y nos preguntó:

—¿*Quén etá* en edad *casadeda*? ¿Qué es *casadeda*?

—Nadie, nadie —respondió mi mamá.

—¿Cómo que nadie? —dijo Lucero enojada—. ¿Ese *Lobelto* que va a *venil* está en edad *casadeda*?... ¿Qué es *casadeda*?

Uno de los hábitos de Lucero es ponerse a oír detrás de las puertas.

—¿Qué es *casadeda*? —repitió.

Sabíamos que la terquedad de Lucero no dejaría que su pregunta se quedara sin respuesta.

—*Edad casadera* quiere decir que ya tienes suficientes años para poderte casar —le dije.

—¿Yo? —se sorprendió—, ¡Ay, cómo *qués, Alelita!* ¡Si yo apenas tengo doce!

Le tuve que explicar perfectamente que no me refería a ella sino a cualquier persona. Tuve que poner miles de ejemplos, hasta que entendió y se quedó conforme. Toda la tarde me la pasé arreglando la casa. La limpié de arriba abajo, puse flores por todas partes y mi mamá le dijo a Lucero que se estuviera calladita, que solo hablara si Roberto le preguntaba algo.

—*Chilín chin chin* —le dijo.

Es una forma que usan entre ellas para dar a entender que mantendrán la boca cerrada. Con mímica hacen como si se cerraran la boca con un cierre.

—Acuérdate, chiquita, *chirrín chin chin* —repitió mi mamá cuando sonó el timbre.

Lucero se cerró el cierre, cruzó los brazos y puso una cara muy seria.

Roberto traía puesta una boina. Siempre usa boina. Se la quitó para saludarnos y la mirada de Lucero quedó fija en su lisa y brillante cabeza. Mi mamá la miró con angustia.

Roberto le preguntó a Lucero que cómo se llamaba.

—Me llamo *Lucedo* —le dijo—, como las *estellas, polque* a las *estellas també* les puedes *decil lucedos…;* y fíjate que hay una que se llama Venus y es mi amiga *polque* en la noche se asoma *pol* mi ventana y me cuida y me dice que no sea tonta y que no tenga *medo* cuando mi mamita *paga* la luz, y también me dice que no sea *foja,* que me levante cuando *senta* ganas de *hacel* pipí y… —se topó con la mirada de mi mamá, se limpió la nariz con su pañuelito y dijo rápidamente—: Él me *peguntó,* mamita, tú me *dijites* que *habala* solo si él me *peguntaba…* Y antes di que me *toy coteniendo* y no le he dicho nada de…

Y empezó a hacer señas con los ojos hacia la cabeza de Roberto.

—De… —Nuevamente las señas.

—¿De qué, Lucero? ¿De mi cabeza? —le preguntó Roberto, divertido.

—¡Sí! —exclamó feliz; pero su carita de contento cambió cuando mi papá entró a la sala—. *Mejol* luego *paticamos* —le dijo en voz baja—, ¡*chilín chin chin!* —Se puso el cierre.

Roberto nos contó de cuando era chico y de las cosas que hacía en Veracruz, donde él nació. Mi papá, que también es de allá, estuvo animadísimo platicando con él y los dos quedaron de acuerdo en cuánto extrañaban el malecón, las noches azules de Veracruz, La Parroquia, la vegetación divina, las palmeras y el mar.

Cuando terminamos de cenar, mi papá se despidió amable y se fue a su recámara. Mi mamá le ofreció café a Roberto y yo fui a la cocina para ayudarle.

—¿Tu mamá te lavaba la cabeza con jabón del *pelo agadecido?* —Mi mamá y yo oímos a Lucero y casi tiramos las tazas—. *Polque* fíjate que mi abuelito *Jolge,* que *tambén etá* pelón, me ha *paticado* que su mamá... —nos vio en la puerta de la cocina y le dijo rápidamente—: *Depés* te acabo de *contal.* —Y se tapó la boca con su pañuelito.

Durante un buen rato, Lucero permaneció así. Cuando Roberto le preguntaba algo, ella solo contestaba sí o no moviendo la cabeza, sin destaparse la boca, pero no quitaba la vista de su cabeza.

—Déjela salir de dudas sobre mi falta de pelo, ¿sí, Laurita? —le pidió Roberto a mi mamá—. En verdad a mí no me molesta.

—No, Roberto —le respondió mi mamá—, Lucero tiene que aprender a no ser indiscreta y a respetar a las personas.

—Pero si no es falta de respeto —le dijo Roberto sonriendo—, ¿qué tiene de malo que tenga curiosidad por saber por qué soy calvo? Eso es muy natural en los niños y a mí en verdad no me molesta.

—Ay, Roberto... —dijo mi mamá, afligida.

—Por favor, Laurita, déjela —insistió él.

—Bueno, está bien —aceptó mi mamá—, pregúntale a Roberto lo que quieras, chiquita.

—¡Ay, mamita chula, tú sí *edes* bien buena! —gritó eufórica Lucero—. *Alelita* —me dijo—, ¿no me vas a *leganal depués* si le digo al *señol* que se *palece* a los *malcianos* que vimos en la *pilícula* del *oto* día ¿te *acueldas?*... Los que *dijites* que tenían la cabeza como bola de *billá;* y al *ladón* de la *ota pilícula,* el que *taía* una media en la cabeza...

—Nadie te va a regañar —se adelantó a contestar Roberto—, pregúntame lo que quieras y no me digas señor, dime Roberto —le pidió.

—Pues sí, *Lobelto* —le dijo eufórica—, fíjate que mi abuelito *Jolge* dice que su mamá le lavaba la cabeza con jabón del *pelo agadecido* y que *pol* eso se quedó pelón, ¿a ti *también?*

—No sólo eso —admitió Roberto, divertido—, también mi mamá me lavaba con jabón del gato esponjado.

—¡Ay, *pobecito!* ¡Con *lazón!* —Se lanzó a sus brazos y le empezó a acariciar la cabeza con ternura. Después, sin decir nada, fue a su recámara y regresó enseguida. Traía en la mano su peluca afro—. *Tenes fío* —le dijo y se la puso. Roberto se *la dejó puesta hasta que se fue. Se veía de lo más chistoso.*

24

A MI mamá y a mí se nos hizo raro ver a mi papá tan animado platicando con Roberto. Él, por lo general, es callado y parece que siempre está enojado. Yo creo que se portó así porque como extraña tanto a Andrés desde que se fue a Baja California y, además, como Roberto y él son paisanos... A veces Roberto traía su guitarra y nos poníamos a cantar (todavía de vez en cuando lo hacemos). Mi papá y él siempre cantaban juntos "Veracruz". Mi papá canta muy bien. Le gustan las canciones de Álvaro Carrillo, de Agustín Lara, de María Griver y otras muy antiguas que no sé de quién son; Roberto lo acompañaba con la guitarra y algunas también las cantaba con él. Lucero los oía muy atenta y, cuando ya habían cantado bastante, le preguntaba a Roberto:

—¿Papá ya *telminó de cantal?*

Roberto miraba a mi papá y él le decía que sí con la mirada.

—Ya, Lucero, ¿tú quieres cantar alguna?

Invariablemente Lucero volvía a ver a mi papá y decía:

—*Al latito.*

Mi papá entendía que estaba esperando a que él se fuera; entonces, se levantaba y se despedía. Ahí era donde Lucero se daba vuelo. Cantaba, con su voz ronca y desafinada: "La patita", "Los diez perritos", "La negrita Cucurumbé," "El negrito Sandía" y todas las canciones de Cri Cri que se sabía y otras que le enseñaban en la escuela.

Roberto la acompañaba en la guitarra y le hacía ritmos y todo. Lucero hasta bailaba.

Lucero conoce muy bien el toquido de Roberto. Cuando lo oye deja de hacer lo que esté haciendo y corre, tropezándose, para ir a abrirle; lo saluda dándole un beso muy apretado y, antes, cuando tenía su peluca, iba por ella y, en cuanto Roberto se sentaba, se la ponía. Roberto también se ha encariñado con ella. De hecho, ella fue la que empezó la plática el día que Roberto me pidió que me casara con él:

—¿Tú no *tenes* hijos? —le preguntó.

—No, todavía no.

—¿Y cuando tengas hijos los vas a *quelel?*

—Claro, los voy a querer mucho.

—¿Y ya no me vas a *quelel* a mí? —preguntó preocupada.

—¡Claro que te voy a querer! —le contestó él—. ¿No ves que tú vas a ser mi cuñadita? —Me volteó a ver. Yo sentí que me puse como jitomate.

—¿*Cuñalita* es igual que hijita? —le preguntó Lucero.

—Bueno, no es igual, pero podría parecerse —dijo Roberto.

—¡Ay, qué bueno! —respondió Lucero—. *Polque* yo necesito un papá que me *quela* y tú sí me *queles.*

—Lucero, mi papá sí te quiere —le dije.

—¿Papá? —me preguntó extrañada—. ¡Ay, cómo *que!,* si él no *quele* a ninguna niña fea, solo *quele munchachas* bonitas como tú.

—Tú no eres fea, Lucerito, eres muy bonita —le dijo Roberto.

—¿Yo? —le dijo sorprendida—. ¡*Calo* que soy fea! —reflexionó un momento y luego dijo—: Papá *pensa* que soy fea.

—Es que él no ve bien —le dijo Roberto—, ¿no te has dado cuenta de que está bien cegatón?

—Cegatón... cegatón —repitió Lucero divertida—, sí, ¿*vedá? Etá* bien cegatón... ¡Cegatón, cegatón!

Se empezó a reír sin parar. Cuando terminó de reír, se limpió la nariz y la boca, y le preguntó:

—¿Y *cantos* hijos vas a *tenel?*

—Depende de cuántos quiera tener Adelita —dijo Roberto.

—¿Van a *sel* de los dos? —preguntó sorprendida.

Yo me quedé fría y le hice señas para que se callara.

—¿No me *queles decil cántos* hijos van a *tenel Lobelto* y tú? —me preguntó.

—Es que primero tengo que decirle algo a Adelita —le dijo Roberto—. Déjanos solos tantito.

—¿Olita que los deje solos van *a tenel* un hijo? —nos preguntó intrigada.

—No —contestó Roberto aguantándose la risa—, primero nos vamos a casar, si es que Adelita quiere.

Yo sentí que el corazón se me iba a salir. Las manos me empezaron a sudar.

—¡Ay! ¡*Calo* que va a *quelel!* —dijo Lucero—. Si ella todo el día *haba* de ti y le dice a mi mamita chula que *eles* bien lindo y que te *quele* mucho y...

—¡Lucero! ¡Hazme el favor de callarte! —grité.

Se quedó muda y empezó a hacer pucheros. Le dolía mucho que me enojara con ella. Me arrepentí por haberle gritado.

—Perdóname, no quise hablarte así —la abracé—, es que hay cosas que no debes decir...

—Mira, Lucerito —intervino Roberto—, Adelita y yo sabemos que los dos nos gustamos y nos queremos, pero eso nos lo tenemos que decir cuando estemos solos...

—Díganlo, yo no veo ni oigo —dijo Lucero al tiempo que se tapaba los oídos y cerraba los ojos.

—¿Por qué no vas un ratito a tu recámara y luego regresas? —le pidió Roberto.

Ella recapacitó tantito y aceptó.

—*Pedo* solo un *tatito,* ¿eh? —nos advirtió.

Todavía antes de salir de la sala nos dijo:

—¡Pedo no vayan a *tenel un hijo antes de que legese!*

Roberto se quitó la peluca, me pidió que me casara con él y yo le dije que sí.

25

ROBERTO siempre ha querido mucho a mi hermana, siempre ha participado en las cosas importantes para ella, sobre todo porque se ha dado cuenta de que desde que no está Andrés, ella se le ha acercado tratando de hallar en él a ese hermano mayor y cariñoso que mi primo siempre ha sido para ella. Cuando cumplió trece años, Roberto, mi mamá y yo la llevamos a comprar un vestido. Entramos a una tienda muy bonita y escogimos varios. La encargada del probador creía que eran para mí y nos trató muy bien, pero cuando se dio cuenta de que eran para mi hermana, cambió por completo.

—La niña no puede probarse la ropa —dijo.

Las facciones de mi mamá se transformaron y, temblándole la voz, le preguntó:

—¿Por qué no?

—Porque... —vaciló un momento—, porque la puede ensuciar.

Yo sentí como si me jalaran de los cabellos.

—¿Cómo que la puede ensuciar? ¿De qué la va a ensuciar? —le dije a gritos.

—¡Si yo me baño *dialio!* —replicó Lucero con su voz ronca. Se limpió la nariz con su pañuelito, se acercó a la señorita y la olfateó—. ¡Yo no *olo* feo! —exclamó—. ¡Mira, mamita, *ólela! ¡Ólela, Lobelto! ¡Ólela, Alelita!* —En rápido movimiento levantó el brazo de la empleada.

Apenas pudimos contener la risa. La empleada, muy enojada, le arrebató su brazo y guardó en un entrepaño del mostrador los vestidos que habíamos escogido.

—¡Desde luego que mi hija se va a probar esa ropa! —vociferó mi mamá al tiempo que los recuperaba. La empleada trató de quitárselos y se inició un violento forcejeo. El jefe de piso llegó a poner orden.

—¡Yo le voy a mi mamita chula! ¿Y tú? —le dijo Lucero al señor. Él la miró con simpatía.

Roberto le explicó al jefe de piso la situación. Él nos pidió disculpas y regañó a la empleada. Lucero estaba muy atenta de sus palabras. Cuando terminó el regaño, le dijo al señor:

—Te *fató* decile que se bañe.

El señor rio de buena gana y nos aseguró que Lucero se podía probar todo lo que había en la tienda.

Mi mamá y yo, como si nos hubiéramos puesto de acuerdo, cogimos montones de ropa y entramos con Lucero al probador. Salimos con toda la ropa revuelta, la dejamos sobre el mostrador y le informamos a la empleada que no llevaríamos nada. Ella, bufaba de coraje.

—Acomódela bien o llamamos al jefe de piso —le dijo Roberto y nos fuimos.

En otra tienda, encontramos para Lucero el vestido azul, lleno de volantes y encajes que tanto quería.

—¿Le vas a *pegal estellas*, mamita chula? —le dijo Lucero en el camino a la casa.

—Sí, chiquita —le respondió mi mamá.

—¿Y *colazoncitos lojos*?

—Sí, mi amor.

Luego, Lucero se quedó pensativa y dijo:

—*Cocholates* no, ¿*vedá*?

—No, chiquita, chocolates no —le dijo mi mamá riendo.

Los invitados para la fiesta eran, como todos los años, los compañeros y excompañeros de la escuela de Lucero, ya que ella, en realidad, no tiene amigos. Se puede decir que ni siquiera sus compañeros de escuela lo son, ya que ninguno actúa por voluntad propia y son muy dependientes de sus familiares (como Lucero de nosotros).

Es una forma de vivir muy especial la de las familias donde hay un hijo con síndrome de Down. La mayoría de las veces son familias que se aíslan. No sé si es porque interiormente uno se avergüence del niño enfermo, o si (como quiero pensar que es nuestro caso) este requiera tanto de nuestra atención que no nos da espacio para convivir normalmente con otras personas.

En realidad, yo tampoco he tenido amigos. Claro, no me he aislado por completo porque he tratado con mis compañeros de escuela; pero, por ejemplo, ellos nunca venían a mi casa a comer, a estudiar o a quedarse a dormir, como en la casa de otros. Más bien siempre era yo la que iba, pero solo un rato porque tenía el pendiente de Lucero. A veces mi mamá tenía que regresar en la tarde a su oficina y yo me hacía cargo de recogerla en su escuela y de cuidarla, porque no podemos dejarla sola en la casa; y con mi papá, sola, ella no se queda ni de chiste.

En la privada, Lucero siempre sale con mi mamá o conmigo. De más chica tuvo muchas malas experiencias con los niños vecinos: cuando la llevábamos a los juegos del parque, que está en el centro de la privada, en cuanto Lucero se subía a uno, todos los demás niños se alejaban lentamente y la veían con curiosidad y no faltaban las risitas de burla o las expresiones de rechazo y hasta de miedo. Es que Lucero tiene un aspecto muy poco agradable. Tiene en los ojos un estrabismo muy pronunciado y aparenta un retraso mental que en realidad no tiene. Hasta ahora puede dominar un poco los músculos de su cara y ya no mantiene la boca tan abierta como antes.

—¡Mamá, que esa niña tonta no se suba al columpio!

—Tú no, niña.

—¡Mírala, no puede subirse a la resbaladilla! ¡Lero, lero!

—Tú no puedes, ¡quítate!

Eran algunos de los comentarios de los niños en el parque. Mi mamá y yo siempre la teníamos que defender, pero los niños no entendían. Los niños son crueles porque no se dan cuenta de cuánto daño pueden hacer a otros niños. Y más a alguien tan indefenso y sensible como Lucero.

Cuando la llevábamos ahí, yo no la soltaba de la mano y me subía al columpio con ella, a pesar de lo grandecita que ya estaba. Solo así los niños no se atrevían a decirle nada. Pero llegaba el momento en que ella se desesperaba y quería hacer las cosas sola o ir a donde estaban los demás niños para jugar con ellos, y era ahí donde empezaban las dificultades.

Siempre que regresábamos del parque, mi mamá se veía triste y tardaba un buen rato para reanimarse. Y, la verdad, yo también.

27

VOLVIENDO a lo de la fiesta de los trece años de Lucero, estaban ya por llegar sus compañeros de escuela. Roberto y Andrés, que había venido de Baja California para estar con Lucero ese día, le habían llevado serpentinas, globos, silbatos, gorritos y espantasuegras; pero los silbatos y los globos los habíamos tenido que guardar, porque los sonidos estridentes y las explosiones, a Lucero y a todos sus compañeros, les dan mucho miedo. Mi mamá le había comprado un pastel enorme y una piñata plateada.

—De estrella, como tú —le dijo mi mamá.

Lucero y mi mamá se pasan horas contemplando las estrellas durante las noches claras.

—Esa es mi amiga, ¿*vedá,* mamita? —dice Lucero señalando a Venus.

—Sí, chiquita —le responde mi mamá.

—Y esa, esa y esa tambén, ¿*vedá?* —señala otras estrellas.

—Sí, chiquita.

Una noche, después de repetir su juego, Lucero le dijo:

—Y la Luna con su cada de conejo es mi *abelita Espedanza,* ¿*vedá?*

—¿Por qué dices que tu abuelita Esperanza es la Luna?

—*Polque* la Luna se ve muy bonita con su *cada* de conejo, *pedo mi abelita* se ve muy fea.

—¿No quieres a tu abuelita? —le preguntó mi mamá.

—*Pes...* casi no —respondió—; a mi *abelito Jolge,* sí —agregó rápidamente.

La verdad, sentí algo de tristeza por mi abuelita, pero pensé que cada quien tiene lo que se merece. Con Andrés y conmigo siempre ha sido muy cariñosa, en cambio con Lucero...

Mi mamá puso la piñata en el cuarto de Lucero, junto a la ventana.

—¿Sabes qué voy a *soñá* hoy, mamita chula? —le preguntó Lucero.

—¿Qué cosa, chiquita?

—Que mi piñata es Venus y que *pol* fin me hizo caso y que se metió *pol* la ventana y que me va a *despetal* en las noches *pada* que ya no me haga pipí en la cama.

—Sí, chiquita, ella te va a despertar para que le avises a tu hermana o a mí cuando quieras hacer pipí.

—¡A *Alelita*, mamita chula! —exclamó Lucero apurada—. A ti no *polque se pede depeltal* ya sabes.

Aquella vez mi papá no se había quedado en la fiesta de Lucero. En principio, cuando supo que los invitados solo serían los compañeros de clases de Lucero, le dijo a mi mamá que lo deprimía mucho ver juntos a tantos niños enfermos.

—Son los únicos amigos de la niña —le recordó ella.

—Ya lo sé —dijo él—, ¿y tú crees que no me duele saber que mi hija solo puede alternar con retrasados mentales?

—No los ofendas, Alfredo, esos niños no tienen la culpa de haber nacido con problemas.

—Ya sé que ellos no son culpables —se empezó a alterar—, seguramente el culpable soy yo, ¿no es así? Seguramente tú me culpas por el retraso de Lucero y por tener que soportar que cada cumpleaños de ella, esta casa se llene de...

—Alfredo, por favor... —le dijo mi mamá dándose cuenta de que Lucero estaba oyendo detrás de la puerta entreabierta de su recámara.

Mis papás se fueron a su recámara y yo creo que mi mamá lo convenció de que fuera amable con Lucero y sus amigos, porque cuando empezaron a llegar los recibió muy atento. Apenas habían llegado dos o tres cuando Lucero le dijo a mi papá:

—A ti no te envito a mi festa.

—¿Cómo? —preguntó él, desconcertado.

—¡Que se vaya, mamita chula. A él no lo envito! —le dijo a mi mamá.

La cara de mi papá se encendió y, sin decir nada, salió de la casa.

Yo no me explico por qué mi papá, por más que trataba, porque yo veía que sí trataba, no podía comportarse de otra forma con Lucero; por qué no podía aceptarla como era y, sobre todo, por qué no gozaba con sus ocurrencias en vez de deprimirse y amargarse la vida.

28

GRITOS despavoridos. Niños corriendo. Un portazo. Mi abuelita Esperanza con la cabeza abierta.

—¡Mamá! —le dijo mi mamá, asustada.

—¡Esa niña está loca! —gritó mi abuelita, deteniendo con la mano la sangre que salía por la herida de su frente.

—¿Qué pasó? —preguntó mi mamá y salimos corriendo al patio.

—La niña se puso nerviosa —respondió mi abuelito Jorge.

Los compañeros de Lucero estaban asustadísimos, abrazados a sus mamás y a sus papás.

Lucero sostenía, amenazante, el palo forrado de papel azul con el que iban a pegarle a la piñata.

—¡*Quelen lompel mi estella*, mamita chula! —gritó mi hermana, fuera de sí, con la carita llena de mocos.

Mi mamá llegó hasta ella, la limpió y la abrazó para tranquilizarla.

—Ya habíamos platicado acerca lo que es una piñata, chiquita —le dijo—, ¿te acuerdas que dijimos que es sOlo una estrella de papel y que los niños iban a pegarle para sacar los dulces que tiene adentro?

—¡No *quelo* que le peguen ni que le saquen los *duces*! —gritó vehemente—. ¡*Quelo* que se vayan todos! ¡Váyanse! ¡Váyanse! —repetía obstinada—. ¡Menos tú! —le dijo a mi abuelito Jorge—, ¡y tú, y tú! —les dijo a Roberto y a Andrés.

Mi mamá se disculpó con los papás de los niños invitados y les pidió que esperaran tantito a que Lucero se calmara. Ellos, todos, se portaron muy amables y comprensivos, ¿y cómo no, si cuántas veces habrían vivido en carne propia lo que ahí estaba sucediendo, o cosas parecidas?

Mi mamá y Lucero permanecieron abrazadas en medio del patio. Yo estaba muy asustada. Roberto y Andrés me abrazaron para tranquilizarme.

—¿Qué pasó, papá? —le preguntó mi mamá a mi abuelito Jorge.

—No quería que rompieran su piñata —respondió él—; tu mamá trató de quitarle el palo y ella le dio en la cabeza.

Mi abuelita salió al patio con un parche en la frente. Lucero, apenas la vio escondió la cara en el pecho de mi mamá y repitió con su voz aún más ronca:

—¡Que se vaya!... ¡Que se vaya!...

—Cálmate, chiquita... Ya se va —la tranquilizó mi mamá.

—¡No deberías consentirle estas cosas! —replicó mi abuelita, muy molesta—. Yo creo que, a pesar de todo, se la puede educar.

—¡Cállate, Esperanza! —exigió mi abuelito; se acercó a mi mamá y a mi hermana y les acarició el pelo. Después, nos dio un beso a Andrés y a mí y se despidió de Roberto. Tomó a mi abuelita del brazo y salieron.

Los papás de los compañeros de Lucero, uno a uno, le fueron diciendo a mi mamá que muchas gracias por todo pero que mejor se iban, ya que su hijo o su hija se había alterado un poco.

Mi mamá les dijo que esperaran un momento, que ahorita que se tranquilizaran los niños podría continuar la fiesta.

Todos los niños y niñas estaban abrazados a las piernas de su mamá o su papá, mirándolos asustados. Sólo Roland, que siempre me ha caído muy bien, porque es muy chistoso, se acercó a Lucero y le dijo:

—¡Qué *beno* que le *dites* a la vieja! Me *hubielas pesiado* el palo *pala dale* yo *tambén*.

—¡Roland —le dijo su papá—, no digas tonterías! —luego miró a mi mamá y le dijo—: Discúlpelo, señora, este niño es muy atrevido.

—No tenga cuidado, no hay problema —respondió mi mamá sonriendo—, además ya conocemos a Roland, ¿verdad? —Y miró al niño.

—Sí —dijo Roland—, y yo *tambén* te *conoco* y *conoco* a *Lucedo*. Si *Lucedo* e mi novia.

Lucero hizo tremenda cara de sorpresa y le dijo:

—¡Ay, cómo *qués*! ¿Te imaginas, tú así y yo así? ¡*Pobecitos* de nuestos hijos!

—¡No, *mida yo, mida yo*! —replicó Roland, haciendo fuerza con un brazo para enseñarle el músculo.

Esos comentarios nos hicieron reír a todos, hasta mi mamá y el papá de Roland se rieron, aunque un momento después, su mirada se entristeció.

Roland era hijo único. Su mamá era actriz, dicen que guapísima. Cuando Roland nació y se dieron cuenta del problema del chiquito, ella se fue para Estados Unidos, dejó la carrera y, dicen que se dio a la mala vida. El caso es que nunca han vuelto a saber de ella. El papá de Roland, un hombre muy guapo, director de una empresa, se hizo cargo del niño, lo lleva a sus terapias, lo estimula bastante, y ha conseguido que lo admitan en una escuela de pintura para niños normales, ya que él tiene mucho talento y hasta ha vendido cuadros. A mí me admira su caso, porque siendo el papá una persona tan ocupada siempre se da tiempo para las cosas de su hijo.

Lucero seguía abrazada a mi mamá, con el corazón agitado.

—¿Quieres jugar con tus amigos? —le preguntó mi mamá.

—No, que se vayan —dijo Lucero escondiendo la cara en el pecho de mi mamá.

Roberto, Andrés y yo los acompañamos a la salida y le dimos a cada niño la bolsa de dulces y el juguete que habíamos preparado para ellos. Los niños se fueron felices y los papás nada ofendidos.

Como que son situaciones que a ellos no les extrañan.

Roland cogió una bolsa más de dulces y miró a Roberto con complicidad, Roberto le guiñó un ojo y Roland, sonriente, chocó ruidosamente su mano con la de él.

—¡No eres nada tontito!, ¿eh? —le dijo Andrés.

El papá le pasó el brazo por los hombros y se despidió de nosotros sonriendo y moviendo la cabeza, como diciendo: "es tremendo".

Contemplamos, con tristeza, la casa adornada.

—¡Vamos a partir el pastel! —dijo Roberto.

—¡Sí! —respondió Lucero—. *Pedo* antes vamos a lleva a Venus a su *lugá*, ¿sí, *Andés*?

—¿Le sacamos los dulces? —le preguntó mi mamá.

—No —le dijo Lucero—. *Polque cando* yo esté *tiste* ella me va a *dal* un *duce*.

Andrés soltó del lazo la piñata y Lucero y él la llevaron a su lugar: en el cuarto de Lucero, bajo la ventana.

29

¡CÓMO no iba a ser así Lucero con mi abuelita Esperanza! Ella no la trataba bien y siempre la hacía menos.

Por ejemplo, ese día de su cumpleaños, mi abuelita le llevó de regalo una insignificante bolsita con chocolates.

—¡Ay, *abelita*! ¿*Pada* qué me *tajistes cocholates*? ¿No sabes que yo no *pedo comel cocholates*? ¿No sabes que me hacen *laño*? —le dijo Lucero visiblemente desilusionada—. Además, *siquiela felan* de los que me *gutan*, *pes* me los comía *anque fela* a econdidas. ¿*Vedá,* mamita chula, que a veces yo me como los *cocholates,* esos *licos* que nos *tai Lobelto* y *lego tú me legañas polque* me *enfemo*? En cambio *etos mugues... Polque mida,* mamita chula, qué *mugues cocholatitos me tajo...*

—Ya, chiquita —intervino mi mamá, entre apenada y sonriente—. Lo que pasa, mamá —le dijo a mi abuelita—, es que Lucero no puede comer chocolates.

—Sí —replicó, disgustada, mi abuelita—, ya esta niña se encargó de decirme todo acerca de los chocolates y, sobre todo, de estos que le traje.

—No te ofendas, mami —dijo mi mamá—, ya sabes cómo es Lucero de exagerada.

—De mal educada, querrás decir. Total —continuó, enojada—, con esta niña nunca quedo bien. —dejó en la mesa los chocolates y se fue para la cocina. Mi mamá la siguió.

—Le hubieras hecho algo de ropa, mamá.

—¡No, mijita! ¿Ropa a Lucero? Mira, a Adelita sí le puedo hacer cosas porque cualquier color le queda bien y luce mucho con todo —respondió mi abuelita sin fijarse que mi hermanita y yo estábamos en la puerta de la cocina; y mi abuelito Jorge, en la del patio—, en cambio Lucero necesita cosas muy especiales que solo tú sabes. No le entiendo a su cuerpo. Ella no tiene forma.

Por suerte, Andrés no había llegado, si no quién sabe qué le hubiera dicho a mi abuelita.

Las caras de mi mamá y de mi abuelito se encendieron de coraje, pero Lucero, ni tarda ni perezosa, intervino:

—Sí tengo *folma, abelita,* ni que *fela* amiba. *¿Vedá,* mamita chula que las amibas no tenen *folma* y yo sí *polque* soy una niña? —Mi mamá iba a decir algo, pero ella continuó—: La que *padece* amiba eles tú, *abelita...*, *pedo* una amibota así de *golda* —le dijo extendiendo los brazos.

—¡Lucero —exclamó mi mamá sin poder contener una risita—, no le digas así a tu abuelita!

—Te *etás liendo*, mamita —dijo socarronamente—. Y tú *tambén* —me dijo a mí.

—¡No sé cómo le consienten sus malcriadeces! —mi abuelita estaba fuera de sí—. ¡Esta niña no va a caber nunca en ningún lado!

—La que no cabe *eles* tú —dijo enseguida Lucero, volviendo a extender los brazos, diciéndole *gorda* una vez más.

—No digas eso, chiquita —intervino mi mamá—, pídele una disculpa a tu abuelita.

—Dame una discupa, *abelita* —dijo Lucero.

—No, chiquita —corrigió mi mamá—, dile que te disculpe.

—*Que te discupe* —repitió ella.

—¡Déjalo así! —vociferó mi abuelita—. Está claro que esta niña no entiende nada de nada. —Y furiosa se salió al patio, empujando al pasar a mi abuelito Jorge. Él, sonriendo con la mirada, le dijo a Lucero:

—¡Bien hecho, muñequita!, no dejes que nadie te ofenda.

—¿Que me *ofenan e* que me digan cosas feas?

—Sí, nenita, es eso mismo. —Se acercó a ella y la abrazó.

—No, *abelito*, no me dejo... Yo *tambén sé decil* cosas feas —respondió Lucero, correspondiendo al abrazo—. ¡Ay, *abelito*, a ti sí te *quelo* y nunca, nunca te voy a *decil* cosas feas!

30

Y A ERA de noche cuando mi papá regresó a la casa. Traía una caja envuelta para regalo y se la dio a Lucero. Ella la cogió con emoción.

—¿Qué es? ¿Qué es? —preguntaba mientras arrancaba el papel de la envoltura.

Al mirar la muñeca, dijo desconcertada:

—¿*Ota Feluca?*

Ferruca se llamaba la muñeca que mi papá le había regalado el año anterior, cuando cumplió doce años.

—¿Son gemelas? —preguntó Lucero confundida.

—Sí, chiquita, son gemelas —se adelantó mi mamá a contestarle.

Mientras Lucero la sacaba de la caja, mi mamá miró a mi papá con reproche y le dijo en voz baja:

—¿Por qué le trajiste una muñeca idéntica a la anterior?

—¿Es igual? No me fijé —dijo él.

Lucero fue a su recámara, trajo a su vieja Ferruca y la puso junto a la nueva en la mesa del comedor.

Mi mamá caminó hacia la sala y mi papá la siguió.

—*Mila, Feluca* —dijo Lucero a la muñeca que ya tenía—, papá *tajo* tu gemela; se va a *llamal Feluca Dos.* No te *pocupes, olita* se ve más bonita que tú *polque etá neva, pedo* voy a *jugal* mucho con ella *pada* que *tambén* se haga viejita y *tambén* le voy a *coltal el feco,* como a ti.

Mi papá le dijo quedo a mi mamá:

—Está contenta con la muñeca. Se ve que le gustó.

Ella lo volteó a ver con desprecio y le respondió, quedo también:

—A Lucero le gusta todo lo que le regalan, pero no se trata de eso. No sé por qué no le tienes más atención y pones más cuidado en las cosas de ella. Nada te costaba haberle comprado algo novedoso. Se me hace increíble que le hayas traído una muñeca idéntica a la otra.

—No me acordaba de esa muñeca —se disculpó él.

—Pero si tú mismo se la regalaste —le dijo mi mamá, cada vez más disgustada.

—Pues no me fijé —dijo él.

—Eso es lo malo —le recriminó ella—, tú nunca te fijas en Lucero... Parece que tienes una sola hija, y ¿sabes qué, Alfredo?, me das lástima. Te estás perdiendo de algo maravilloso. —Se dio la vuelta y se metió en la cocina.

Yo ya estaba con Lucero y ella me estaba diciendo, emocionada, cómo iba a jugar con Ferruca y con Ferruca Dos.

—Y yo voy a jugar contigo, chiquita —le dije.

—*Pedo* tú usas a *Feluca* y yo a *Feluca* Dos, *polque* como yo soy tan *destuyona*, así más *lápido* Feluca Dos se va a *hacel* viejita y Feluca no va a *sentil* feo de *velse* más feíta.

—Tú no eres destructora, Lucero; tú eres muy cuidadosa y, además, muy buena mamá con tus muñecas —le dije.

—¡Ay, cómo *qués*, Alelita!, yo siempe *lompo* las cosas y nada más ando haciendo *ciosidade*s, si no *pegúntale* a mi mamita chula —me cogió de la mano y me dijo angustiada—: ¡*Polfavol*, Alelita, usa tú a *Feluca* y yo a *Feluca* Dos!

—Está bien, hermanita, como quieras; pero ya no te preocupes. Vas a ver qué bonito vamos a jugar las dos juntas —le dije, sintiendo mi corazón lleno de ternura.

31

CUANDO acabé la prepa, entré en conflicto porque no estaba segura de qué carrera escoger. Decidí quedarme un semestre sin estudiar. Mi propósito era ponerme a leer, a tomar cursos de orientación vocacional, porque aquí entre nos casi en ninguna preparatoria toman en serio lo de orientarte bien y ayudarte a descubrir cuál es tu verdadera vocación y para qué tienes más aptitudes. Casi siempre la materia de orientación vocacional te la da el maestro menos preparado y solo la ponen como de relleno, nomás para cumplir con el número de materias que les exigen y salir del paso. Pues mis intenciones de tomar cursos y demás, cada vez fueron disminuyendo por una sola razón: Lucero. Me convencí de que mi vocación era ayudar a personas con problemas mentales, personas con conflictos o que están sufriendo internamente y que es muy difícil que los demás los comprendan y los ayuden a ser felices. La verdad, me decidí a estudiar psi- cología para ayudar a Lucero.

Curiosamente, estando ya en la carrera, me di cuenta de que Lucero era la que menos ayuda necesitaba. Éramos nosotros, los que estamos a su alrededor, los más necesitados, los más confundidos y los más tontos. Sobre todo, el pobre de mi papá. En varias ocasiones yo traté de hablar con él, pero siempre salía con evasivas o se hacía el enojado y me intimidaba. Hasta que un día me di valor y lo enfrenté:

—¿Por qué eres así con Lucero, papá? ¿Por qué no la aceptas?

Él me miró disgustado y me dijo casi a gritos:

—¡Ya estoy harto de que tu mamá y tú me reclamen por todo lo que pasa en esta casa! ¡Estoy harto de que siempre me culpen a mí de todo! ¡Como si yo hubiera deseado que Lucero tuviera tantos problemas! ¡Como si yo tuviera la culpa de...!

Lo interrumpí:

—¿Por qué siempre hablas de culpas cuando se toca el tema de Lucero? —Recordé en ese momento las pláticas que hacía años él tenía con mi tía Rosario y otras muchas que, también hace años, porque ahora ella ya no lo permite, tenía con mi mamá—. Aquí no hay culpables —le dije—, aquí solo hay gente que la quiere o que no la quiere, que la acepta o no la acepta.

—¡Claro que la quiero y la acepto! —se justificó—. ¿Cómo no la voy a querer si es mi hija?

—Eso no es suficiente —le dije—, el que tú seas su padre no quiere decir que ya por naturaleza sepas cómo tratarla, sepas comprenderla y aceptarla como el ser único, independiente, puro y cariñoso que es, y no la veas como algo vergonzoso que, en tu egoísmo, culpas por haber nacido así. Como si ella lo hubiera hecho a propósito solo para echarte a perder tu vida perfecta. Das la impresión de sentir por ella un gran rencor y un gran resentimiento.

—¡Estás mal! — protestó—. Yo no siento ninguna de esas cosas que estás diciendo. Hace mucho que superé la angustia y la pena de ver a mi hija enferma; de saber que nunca se va a curar... de... La voz se le quebró y empezó a llorar. ¡Me dio tanta tristeza! Me acerqué a él y lo abracé con ternura, con lástima, y también con un amor que hacía mucho que ya no sentía por él, o que creía ya no sentir.

—Cálmate, papá —le dije—. Yo creo que si para mí es terrible que Lucero esté enferma, para ti debe ser mil veces peor, porque ella es tu hija.

Él se abrazó a mí y sollozó largamente. Cuando ya estaba más tranquilo me dijo:

—Tienes razón, hija, todo lo que me has dicho es exactamente lo que siento. No sé qué hacer para pensar en ella como quiero pensar... Para aceptar su enfermedad como la quiero aceptar... Para quererla como deseo... Desgraciadamente creo que ya es tarde para remediar las cosas...

—Yo creo que no —le dije—, nunca es tarde... Les queda toda una vida por delante.

—¡Qué puedo hacer, hija? ¡Dime tú qué hago! —me dijo desesperado.

—Piensa en ella con alegría, mírala como tu niña que no va a crecer, pero no importa, porque ella solo trata de dar felicidad a los demás, de no dar molestias, hasta donde le es posible. ¡Disfrútala, papá, no te la pierdas!

32

MI PAPÁ en verdad cambió de actitud con Lucero. Al principio, ella lo veía con desconfianza y no dejaba que se acercara a ella; pero poco a poco fue cediendo y ahora se lleva, se puede decir, mejor con él, aunque todavía guarda sus distancias. Él se ha mostrado muy preocupado ahora que Lucero está enferma. Se le han presentado problemas cada vez más serios. Empezó a estar delicada de los riñones y a sentirse desanimada y débil. Los doctores nos dijeron que los padecimientos renales son comunes en las personas con síndrome de Down.

Mi papá se pasa tardes enteras con ella, leyéndole algún cuento o algún tomo de sus enciclopedias. Ella a veces nos llama a mi mamá o a mí y nos dice como haciendo un aparte, como para que mi papá no la oiga:

—Ya me cansé de que me lea ya sabes *quén*. —Y mira a mi papá disimuladamente—. *Quero* una voz finita.

Entonces, mi papá, sin ofenderse, dice que tiene algo qué hacer y nos pide a nosotras que le sigamos leyendo.

—Sí, papá, no te *pocupes*, vete a *hacel* muchas —le dice—, mañana me lees ota vez.

—O al rato regreso, hija —le dice mi papá.

—¡No!, no te *pocupes, mejol hata* mañana. Yo te voy a *etañal mucho, pedo me guanto hata* mañana. ¡Vete, vete, papito, no te *pocupes po* mí!

Y mi papá se sale de la recámara aguantándose la risa.

Muchas veces he pensado en lo maravilloso que sería si ella pudiera leer. Desgraciadamente, nunca podrá aprender; uno de los muchos problemas que tiene es que no puede fijar la vista para mirar cosas pequeñas, así es que no distingue las letras, aunque sí las ilustraciones. Es asombroso cómo le gustan los libros. Tiene una muy buena colección, entre los cuales estaba su favorito: *El quinto Sol*. Digo estaba, porque el otro día lo echó a la taza del baño.

—*Cántame ota* vez la *histodia* del Nana —me pedía con frecuencia, refiriéndose a *El quinto Sol*, en donde Nanahuatzin, el dios pobre, feo y llagado, valientemente se arroja al fuego y se convierte en el Sol. Al llegar a esta parte, Lucero aplaude y salta de gusto.

Hace poco, Lucero me dijo:

—Hoy yo te voy a *lee* a ti, *Alelita*.

Cogió el libro de *El quinto Sol* y comenzó a hablar, fingiendo que leía:

—*Eda* una niña que no *eda* nada bonita *polque* se ensuciaba mucho cando comía, y tapoco *eda* nada *lita polque* le daba *me do* que su mamita chula *apagada* la luz y que la *dejada* sola, y se *sustaba cando* el cielo hacía *luido*, anque *Alelita* le *dijela* que eran *teños* y que no le iba a *pasá* nada; *tonces* le *lijelon* los *doses* que se *aventala* a la *lumbe* pada que *nacela* la *etella* más bonita, y *Lucedo* se aventó y se quemó y le *lolió* mucho, *pedo* no *lloló*, y se fue volando y los *doses dijelon* que *ahola* ella *ela* Venus y que *tambén* se iba a *llama Lucedo*.

Su relato se me hizo maravilloso, me dio tanta ternura que se me formó un nudo en la garganta y se me salieron las lágrimas.

—¿*Pol* qué *llodas, Alelita*? —me preguntó preocupada—. Te hizo *llolá ete libo*, ¿*vedá*? ¡*Libo tonto, libo tonto*!

Antes de que yo le pudiera decir o hacer algo, rápidamente se dirigió al baño y lo aventó a la taza y le jaló. Como vio que no se iba, metió la mano y lo sumió, tratando de echarlo por el hoyo. Total, que su Nana se echó a perder y, es increíble, pero no he podido conseguirle otro como ese. Aunque a Lucero no le ha importado mucho, porque desde que cumplió dieciséis años solo le gusta que le leamos novelas de amor.

33

CUANDO conoció a Raúl, un amigo de Roberto, todo en la vida de mi hermanita cambió, porque, por primera vez, se enamoró.

Era un domingo y Roberto me había invitado a comer a un restaurante nuevo en la Zona Rosa. Mientras me arreglaba, Lucero se sentó a mi lado contemplando cómo me pintaba.

—¿Te quieres pintar? —le pregunté.

—¡Ay, cómo *qués, Alelita*! Yo no me *sé pintá*.

—¿Te pinto yo?

Se quedó pensativa, nerviosa, frotándose las manos, respirando muy agitada.

—¡Ándale —le dije—, te pinto!

—¡Ay, *Alelita*! ¿Cómo me *velé*? —Se empezó a limpiar sin cesar la nariz y la boca con su pañuelito, frotándose hasta irritarse.

—No te hagas así tu carita —le dije—, ya estás muy limpia. A ver, ven para acá, siéntate aquí.

La acomodé frente al tocador y se miró en el espejo.

—¿*Pedo* cómo me vas a *pintá* con los lentes puestos? —me preguntó.

Le quité los lentes y le dije:

—Claro que con los lentes puestos no te puedo pintar, ¿pero qué tal así?

—Sí ¿*vedá*? *Anque* no vea nada no *impota* —me dijo feliz.

Le pinté los ojos, la boca, y le puse tantito colorete; como ella es muy pálida, así, chapeadita, se veía de lo más mona.

—¿Cómo *quelé*? ¿Cómo *quelé*? —me preguntó.

—Pues mírate en el espejo —le dije.

Se acercó al espejo casi hasta chocar con él y me dijo:

—Yo *queo* que *quelé* bonita, ¿no?

—¿No te ves? —Le puse los lentes—. Ahora sí, mira qué linda estás.

—¡Ay, qué bonita! Me *palezco* a Bancanieves, ¿*vedá*?

—Más bonita que Blancanieves —le dije abrazándola.

En ese momento, tocaron el timbre.

—¡Es *Lobelto*! —dijo Lucero y se bajó de la silla de prisa—. ¡Yo le *abo*! ¡Yo le *abo*! —Y se fue corriendo hacia la puerta.

Roberto la vio y exclamó:

—¡Pero qué hermosa señorita me vino a recibir! ¡Qué cuñadita tan guapa tengo! —Y le dio un beso en la mano—. ¿Cómo está usted, señorita?

Lucero se puso roja. Era la primera vez que yo veía que le pasaba eso. Sonriendo y limpiándose la nariz con mucho cuidado para no despintarse, le dijo:

—¿No me conoces? Soy *Lucedo*.

Mi mamá salió de la cocina y Lucero caminó hacia ella moviéndose coquetamente.

—*Mila*, mamita chula, *mílame* qué guapa *toy*.

—¡Estás preciosa, chiquita! ¿Tú te pintaste? —le preguntó mi mamá, extrañada de verla así.

—¡Ay, mi chula, cómo qués! Me pintó *Alelita*. ¿No ves que yo no me sé *pintá*? —Mi mamá se le acercó y Lucero le dijo muy apurada—: ¡*Cuilalo*, mamita chula! ¡No me vayas *a tocá polque me pedes despintá*!

—No, mi amor, no te preocupes, no te voy a arruinar el maquillaje.

—No, *polque* los *mallicajes* no se deben de *auliná*, ¿*veda*? —le dijo Lucero—. ¿Qué es *auliná*? —le preguntó enseguida.

—Arruinar, chiquita, arruinar —la corrigió—. Quiere decir *descomponer, desbaratar...*

—¡Ay, no! ¡Ni Dios lo *mane* que me *desbalates* mi *calita* de Bancanieves! —Y se hizo para atrás.

—Bueno, nosotros nos vamos —dije—, te portas bien, chiquita; hasta luego, mami.

Roberto se despidió y en la puerta me dijo:

—Vamos a llevar a Lucero, ¿cómo la vamos a dejar aquí así de guapa?

—¿Crees que quiera? —Es que a veces Lucero si no va mi mamá ella tampoco quiere ir.

—Pues vamos a preguntarle —dijo Roberto.

—Chiquita —le dije—, ¿quieres ir a comer con nosotros? Ella, de inmediato, volteó a ver a mi mamá.

—Si quieres ve, mi cielo —le dijo ella.

—¿Y tú? ¿Te vas a *quelal* solita?

—Al ratito va a venir tu tía Rosario y tu papá no tarda en regresar —le dijo.

Lucero se empezó a frotar las manos, muy nerviosa y, después de pensarlo y pensarlo, dijo que sí.

Roberto nos tomó a cada una del brazo y nos abrió las puertas del coche.

—Adelante, bellas damas —nos dijo exagerando la cortesía.

—Gacias, píncipe —le respondió Lucero muy seria.

Roberto y yo nos volteamos a ver y sonreímos con ternura.

Llegamos al restaurante y el encargado nos preguntó que si queríamos zona de fumar.

—¿De *fumá*? —dijo Lucero—. ¿Que no sabes que *fumá* hace *laño*? ¿Tu mamita no te ha *licho* que no debes *fumá*? —le preguntó enojada.

El encargado sonrió y le dijo:

—Tiene razón, señorita, fumar es muy malo. Pásenle por aquí.

Y nos llevó a una mesa en zona de no fumar.

Acabábamos de pedir, cuando Roberto me dijo:

—¡Mira quién está ahí! —se levantó y gritó—: ¡Raúl! ¡Raúl Sanvicente! ¡Cuánto tiempo sin verte!

El muchacho se levantó de su mesa y vino hacia él con los brazos abiertos. Se abrazaron efusivos y Roberto le dijo:

—Mira, te presento a mi novia y a mi cuñadita. Él es Raúl Sanvicente, un buen amigo de Veracruz —nos dijo.

—Mucho gusto —me dio la mano. Cuando vio a Lucero, le dijo—: ¡Qué señorita tan guapa! ¡A sus órdenes! —Y le tomó, con cariño, su manita entre las suyas.

Lucero se quedó embobada. No pudo contestar nada. Solo cogió su pañuelito y, con mucho cuidado, se limpió la nariz.

—Siéntate con nosotros —le dijo Roberto.

—Vengo con unos amigos —respondió Raúl—, pero sí me tomo un refresquito con ustedes. —Volteó a ver a sus amigos y les hizo señas de que lo esperaran tantito.

Lucero estaba fascinada con Raúl, no le quitaba la vista de encima. No abrió la boca para nada, solo lo hizo cuando él le preguntó:

—¿Cómo te llamas?

—*Lucedo*, como las *estellas* —respondió, poniéndose colorada.

—¡Qué nombre tan bonito! —exclamó Raúl—. ¿Sabías que Lucero es mi nombre favorito?

Lucero no respondió. Solo lo miraba embobada, abriendo la boquita más que de costumbre.

Raúl es un muchacho alegre, como todos los veracruzanos; estuvo haciendo bromas y nos tenía muertos de la risa. Lucero estaba muy seria, pero cuando veía que nos reíamos, ella también lo hacía, pero exageradamente. Raúl la veía con simpatía. Cuando se despidió le dio un beso y ella se cogió el cachete con la mano, como para guardarlo ahí para siempre. Roberto y yo nos volteamos a ver, dándonos cuenta de lo que Raúl había despertado en ella.

A partir de ese día la conducta de Lucero cambió. Se veía pensativa y taciturna y a veces hasta lloraba sin razón.

Le conté a mi mamá lo que había pasado y a ella se le llenaron los ojos de lágrimas.

—Pobrecita de mi niña —me dijo—, pero, mira qué bueno que conozca el amor... Aunque los amores imposibles son horrorosos. Lo bueno es que yo creo que ella no se da cuenta de eso y pronto se le va a olvidar —agregó.

Pero mi mamá se equivocaba. Unos días después, vi a Lucero muy pensativa mirando por la ventana.

—¿Qué haces, chiquita? ¿En qué piensas? —le pregunté.

—*Laúl* no va a *vení* nunca, *¿vedá?* —me dijo con tristeza.

—Quién sabe, chiquita, tal vez algún día venga. —Yo sentí que mi corazón se encogía.

—¡*Cómo qués*! El no va a *vení* nunca, ya lo sé. Él se va a casar con una munchacha bonita. Yo no *pedo tenel* un novio como él. —Su ronca voz tembló y sus ojos se llenaron de lágrimas. Yo no sabía qué decirle. Estaba tan conmovida que no me salía la voz—. *Pedo* no *impota* —continuó—, de *tolos molos* yo lo *quedo* y *sempe* lo voy a *quedé*. ¿Sabes, *Alelita*? Yo ya sé que nunca me voy a casar, *pedo* sí *pedo soñá* con *Laúl* y ahí sí voy a *podel casame* con él y *llevalo a vivil* a Venus. —Se puso la mano en el cachete—. *Alemás* aquí tengo el beso que me *lió*.

Los razonamientos de Lucero siempre me han maravillado. Tiene mucha conciencia de su realidad y también sabe cómo suavizarla. ¡Ya quisiéramos nosotros poder hacerlo!

Desde entonces, también le gusta que le leamos poemas de amor.

34

VOLABA alto, en las nubes,
fue lo más bello en mi vida,
era el reflejo del cielo,
el color de la alegría.
Pero era muy pequeña,
muy pequeña fue mi vida,
fue muy leve, casi nada,
el tiempo en que yo reía.
La distinguí en el inmenso,
la conocí por hermosa;
era tenue, casi nada,
mi pequeña mariposa.
Por ella conocí el cielo,
por ella volteé al azul,
por ella miré lo eterno,
con ella, llegaste tú.
Pero una mañana fría
ella se fue tras el Sol,
se hizo pequeña... pequeña
y quedó sola la flor.
Se esfumaron mis colores
y mi cielo se alejó;
mi pequeña mariposa
fue con Dios y no volvió.

Como extraño sus colores,
como murieron las rosas,
voy a sembrar en mi vida
un árbol de mariposas.

Este es uno de sus poemas favoritos, otro:

Amor es un pájaro cruzando el cielo,
es una flor roja en tu pelo;
es un beso, una palabra,
es retener un momento
sin querer pensar en nada.
Puede ser una sonrisa
o algún lucero lejano...
¡El amor somos nosotros
al tomamos de la mano!

Y el que ya se aprendió y, de repente, con su voz ronca, declama a todo pulmón, en el baño, en su recámara, o donde esté que piense que no la estamos oyendo, es este:

Tú que formaste los mares,
Tú que hiciste el firmamento,
Tú que nos diste la vida,
que nos diste pensamiento...
¡Señor, que todo lo puedes,
no dejes que yo me muera!
 Señor de los imposibles:
¡Tú pídele que me quiera!

Nos sorprende lo bien que lo dice. Claro que las palabras las pronuncia a su modo, pero le da una entonación buenísima; además, le pone tanto sentimiento que conmueve.

35

LUCERO le pidió a Roberto una foto de Raúl. Nosotros estuvimos pensando si era conveniente o no. Tal vez a Lucero no le haría bien hacerse ilusiones. Tal vez estarlo mirando torturaría aún más su corazón.

—Roberto no sabe dónde vive Raúl —le dije.

—Vive en *Velacrú* —me respondió con firmeza.

—Pero no sabe su dirección y su teléfono.

Se quedó callada y sus ojos se pusieron tristes.

—Déjame ver qué podemos hacer. Cuando llegue Roberto le preguntamos, ¿sí, chiquita?

No soporto verla triste. Cuando le dije esto último, sus ojitos brillaron otra vez.

En cuanto llegó Roberto, Lucero corrió a abrirle, lo saludó de prisa y le dijo:

—¿*Vedá* que tú sí *pedes dame* una foto de *Laúl*? ¿*Vedá* que tú sí sabes *lónde* vive? ¿*Vedá* que tú *pedes hacé* todo, *Lobelto*? ¿*Vedá* que no hay nada que tú no *pedas hacé*?

Roberto me volteó a ver y yo le dije que sí con la mirada.

—Sí, Lucero, claro que yo te voy a conseguir una foto de Raúl —le dijo Roberto.

—Una donde *eté* muy guapo... *Beño*, él de *tolos* modos sale guapo, ¿*vedá*?

—¡Te voy a conseguir una donde salga guapérrimo! —le dijo Roberto.

—¡*Gualépimo*! ¡*Gualépimo*! Sí, sí, ¡*gualépimo*! —se entusiasmó Lucero, dando saltos y aplaudiendo.

Cuando le dije a mi mamá que Roberto le iba a conseguir la foto de Raúl, ella se preocupó:

—¿No la angustiará tener esa foto, estarlo viendo, hacerse ilusiones?

—Yo creo que ella de todos modos está angustiada. Está enamorada, mamá, ¿no sabes lo que es estar enamorada?

—Lo supe, hija, lo supe.

—¿Ya no?

—¡Ay, hija, para nada!

—¿Ya no quieres a mi papá?

—¡Ay, Adelita!, con todo lo que ha pasado, tu papá me ha caído tan mal. Se puede decir que ahora que ha cambiado ya lo estimo un poco, pero nada más.

—Pues yo creo que Lucero va a estar feliz con esa foto, vas a ver —le dije.

—Ojalá —respondió mi mamá—, ojalá.

Raúl le envió a Roberto una foto, donde sale en verdad guapo. Se la mandó por e-mail, y también una carta para Lucero.

Ella recibió la foto con adoración; la veía con tal devoción, como si fuera un santo, la besaba una y otra vez y la apretaba contra su pecho con fervor. Me pidió un portarretratos para ponerlo en su buró. Le dije que si quería ir conmigo a escogerlo y, muy entusiasmada, aceptó.

La carta la guardó quién sabe dónde y no quiere que se la leamos.

—Las *catas* de *otos* no se *peden leé*. Esa es mi *cata* y solo es *pada* mí —me dijo muy seria.

—¿Y no quieres saber lo que te dice Raúl? —le pregunté.

—Ya lo sé.

—¿Ah, sí? ¿Y qué dice?

—*Pes* que me *quede*, que ese día me veía bonita y que va a *vení a velme*... ¿El día que venga me *pedes vovel* a *pintá*? —agregó, limpiándose la nariz y la boca con su pañuelito.

—Claro que sí, chiquita, claro que sí —le prometí.

Ese mismo día, por la tarde, fuimos a comprar el portarretratos. Nos llevó toda la tarde buscar, en cantidad de tiendas, uno que le gustara a Lucero.

—¡*Ete*! —dijo y lo abrazó.

—A ver, déjame ver el precio —le dijo la señora de la sección de portarretratos.

Lucero se lo enseñó, pero no lo soltó. Le dio un poco de trabajo a la señora anotar el número de la etiqueta y ver el precio, porque Lucero estaba aferrada a él.

El portarretratos es de porcelana de colores, tiene unos pajaritos a los lados; en la parte de arriba y todo alrededor del marco, estrellitas y corazones.

Regresamos a la casa y Lucero, antes de saludar a mi mamá, cosa rara, corrió a su recámara a colocar en el portarretratos la foto de Raúl.

—¡Mamita chula, ven! ¡*Alelita*! ¡*Lobelto*! ¡Papá! —gritó angustiada.

—¡Ya se le rompió! —dijo mi mamá y todos corrimos a ver qué había pasado.

El portarretratos estaba bien, la foto de Raúl era la que estaba un poco arrugada.

—¡Ya se me *lompió Laúl*! ¡Ya se me *lompió*, mamita chula! —Estaba desesperada.

—Cálmate, chiquita —le dijo mi mamá—, ahorita lo arreglamos.

—¡Que lo *alegue Lobelto*! ¡Él sabe *alegal tolo*! —su voz temblaba.

—A ver, Lucero, cálmate y préstame la foto. Yo la voy a arreglar —le dijo él.

La parte de abajo de la foto estaba hecha chicharrón. Roberto la cogió y trató de alisarla, pero no pudo.

—Déjame a mí —dijo mi papá. Cogió la foto y salió del cuarto.

—¡A *onde* llevas a *Laúl*! ¡No te lo lleves! —gritó Lucero.

Mi papá regresó y le dijo:

—Ahorita te lo traigo, lo voy a poner derechito para que lo puedas poner en el portarretratos.

—¿Yo? —dijo Lucero sorprendida—. ¿Que no *vites* que yo no lo sé *poné*? ¿Que no *vites* que lo *lompí*?

—No lo rompiste, chiquita —le dijo mi papá—, solo se arrugó un poco; pero ahorita va a quedar como nuevo, ¿me dejas llevármelo para arreglártelo?

—*Beño... pedo* si lo *lompes* ya no te voy a *quelel* nunca más —respondió mi hermana con seriedad.

Mi papá entró a la cocina, bajó la tabla de planchar, puso un trapo húmedo sobre el reverso de la foto y la planchó. Es la única vez en mi vida que he visto a mi papá coger la plancha.

En verdad quedó como nueva. Cuando Lucero la vio, exclamó:

—¡*Gacias*, papá! ¡Ya te *volvites güeno*! —Y lo abrazó.

Él correspondió emocionado al abrazo, después colocó la foto en el portarretratos y se lo dio. Lucero lo cogió suspirando largamente y dijo:

—Los *pajaditos* te van a *cantal*, *Laúl*.

Luego, lo apretó contra su pecho, le dio un beso y lo puso de una manera extremadamente cuidadosa sobre su buró.

36

Los preparativos de la boda, para mí, han sido emocionantes, pero a la vez tristes. Me preocupa alejarme de mis papás y de Lucero. Sobre todo, me preocupa demasiado el que Lucero esté enferma. Casi todo el día se la pasa en la cama y no tiene ganas de hacer nada y, como tiene una dieta especial, no quiere comer porque lo que le dan no le gusta. El doctor Del Valle dice que, si sigue así, la van a tener que volver a internar y darle de comer por vía intravenosa. Yo me muero de la aflicción al pensar que se tenga que llegar a eso.

Mi pobre mamá está angustiadísima; en pocos días ha envejecido como veinte años y eso me preocupa mucho, tengo miedo de que también ella se enferme.

Roberto y yo le preguntamos al doctor si sería prudente seguir con los preparativos de la boda o si sería recomendable suspenderla hasta que Lucero esté mejor; pero él nos dijo que no, que siguiéramos adelante, que eso iba a animar a Lucero y que su estado de ánimo era importantísimo para su recuperación.

Nosotros tratamos de integrarla a todas nuestras actividades, pero ella, aunque se ve que quiere hacerlo, no puede porque no se siente bien.

Ayer le dijimos que tenía que ir con nosotros para buscar su vestido, pero no quiso.

—Me lo *compan* de *Bancanieves* —nos dijo—. Ya te *lije* cómo lo *quedo,* con el moño del pelo y *tolo,* ¿eh? —le dijo a Roberto.

—Claro que sí —le respondió él—, el día de la boda tienes que estar guapísima, porque voy a bailar una pieza con Adelita y otra contigo.

—Pues *mila, Lobelto* —le respondió ella—, vas a *tené* que *bailá* con *Alelita* y con mi *abelita Espedanza, pobe* de ti, *polque* yo voy a *bailá* con *Laúl.* —Y abrazó la foto.

37

DESDE que mi primo Andrés se enteró de los serios padecimientos de Lucero viene de Baja California mucho más
seguido.

—¡Acaba de llegar Andrés! —le dije a Lucero.

—¡Ay, qué beno! —se sentó en la cama, muy animada—.
¡*Segulo* que *vene* con ese papá que se *encontó tilalo* en el *mad*!
—me dijo, como siempre dice cuando viene Andrés.

Lucero no puede dejar de relacionar el hecho de que mi
primo siempre sí tuviera papá, con su ida a Baja California.
Y como le hemos explicado que Andrés trabaja estudiando
a los peces, ella piensa que su papá vivía dentro del mar y
que ahí lo había encontrado.

Yo le digo siempre:

—No lo encontró en el mar, él vive allá, en Baja California.

Y ella, invariablemente, me contesta:

—Sí ¿*vedá*?... ¡Qué *beno* que lo sacó *polque* si no se *biela
ogado*!

Cuando Andrés llega a la casa, Lucero no tiene ojos para
nadie más; ni para Roberto. Hasta quita de encima del buró
la foto de Raúl y la guarda en el cajón. Piensa que, como ella
no soportaba que él tuviera novia, él tampoco soportaría al
suyo. Andrés se sienta en la cama, ella le coge la mano y se
recuesta sobre ella.

—¿Me haces un lugarcito? —le pregunta Roberto.

—*Olita* no *pedo* —le dice Lucero—, ¿no ves que ya no cabes? —Y se aferra con mayor fuerza a la mano de Andrés—. ¿*Vedá* que te vas a *quedal* comigo muchos días? ¿*Vedá* que ya no te vas a *il* con tus *pecados* ni con ese papá que en*contaste* en el *mad*?

Andrés le tiene que explicar que tiene que regresar a trabajar, porque cuando se tiene un trabajo no se puede estar faltando.

—Es como tú en tu escuela, chiquita —le pone de ejemplo Andrés:— no puedes faltar muchos días.

—¡Ay! —le responde Lucero—, yo sí *faito* mucho a mi *equela*, ¿vedá, mamita chula, que yo sí *faito chísimo* a mi *equela*? —le pregunta, buscando apoyo.

—No, chiquita —le dice mi mamá—, tú no faltas mucho, solo cuando es necesario, y tu primo Andrés tampoco puede faltar a su trabajo.

Lucero hace pucheros y Andrés la consuela:

—Pero todavía no me voy. Voy a estar contigo muchos días.

Y, en verdad, todo el tiempo que Andrés viene a México se la pasa con Lucero. Ahora que está enferma se sienta en su cama y platica con ella, con su mano entre sus manitas.

Por supuesto que Andrés tiene que irse a escondidas. Esta última vez nos dio mucho trabajo consolarla. Increíblemente, quien ha ocupado estos días el lugar de Andrés ha sido mi papá. Se sienta en su cama toda la tarde, le lee las novelas de amor que tanto le gustan y también los poemas.

Cuando mi papá le está leyendo, ella coge la foto de Raúl, que apenas se había ido Andrés ella volvió a colocar en su lugar, la mira amorosamente y la aprieta contra su pecho.

Los pocos momentos que está sola en su recámara, habla sin parar con la foto de Raúl, y los besos que le da se oyen en toda la casa.

38

CUANDO Andrés tuvo su primera novia, resultó todo un problema. Lucero se puso celosísima.

Se llamaba Natacha; era una muchacha muy bonita. Andrés llegó a la casa con ella y nos la presentó:

—Miren, ella es Natacha, mi novia.

—¿Tu *nova*? —dijo Lucero—. Tú no *tenes nova, Andés*.

—Sí, Lucero, ella es mi novia. Salúdala —le dijo Andrés.

Ella se puso a gatas y empezó a hacer: "¡Mau! ¡Mau!", fingiendo no haberlo oído.

—Lucero —le dijo Andrés con seriedad—, te estoy diciendo que saludes a Natacha.

—¡Guá! ¡Guá! —empezó hacer Lucero—. Toy *haceno como pedo* —dijo, porque sabía que a Andrés le molestaba que dijera *pedo*, en vez de *pelo*.

—Me voy a enojar contigo —le dijo Andrés—, ya te he dicho que no digas así. ¡Saluda a Natacha!

Lucero se puso de pie y cantó:

—*Lo pollito dice pío, pío, pío, cando tenen hambe, cando tenen fío... Layayina...*

—¡Basta, Lucero! —le dije—. ¡No seas grosera, saluda a la novia de Andrés!

Natacha la miraba divertida, hizo una seña para indicar que no importaba y nos saludó de beso a mi mamá y a mí. Se acercó a Lucero, pero ella se retiró caminando para atrás.

—¡Ay, esta niña! —le dijo mi mamá, apenada—. Pasa, hija, pasa, estás en tu casa.

—¿Qué, mamita chula? —dijo Lucero—. Ella no *etá* en su *casha, eta e mi casha*. Mi *casha no e de eta Nacha*.

Andrés le iba a decir algo, pero Lucero corrió a abrazarlo, diciendo:

—*Andés e* mío, *Andés e* mío. ¡No *quelo* a ninguna *Nacha*! —luego, le dijo a Andrés, visiblemente alterada—. ¡Tú me *queles* a mí, *Andés*, tú no *queles* a *Nacha*! ¿Tú ya no *queles* a *Lucedo*? —Miró a mi mamá—. ¡Mamita, chula! ¿*Andés* ya no me *quele*? —Y empezó a llorar.

Andrés la abrazó con cariño y le acarició la cabeza.

—¡Claro que te quiero, chaparrita! ¿Cómo no te voy a querer? Aunque tenga mil novias a ti siempre te voy a seguir queriendo.

—¿Mil novias? —le reclamó Natacha.

—Es un decir... —le dijo Andrés, acariciándole el brazo.

—¡No la *coques*! ¡Esa *Nacha e muy fea*! ¡No la *coques*! —le dijo Lucero quitando la mano de Andrés del brazo de Natacha.

—Ya, chiquita —le dijo mi mamá—, tranquilízate; Natacha no es novia de Andrés, solo es su amiga. —Les guiñó un ojo.

—*Andés* dijo que es su *nova*, no su *miga*.

—Es que me equivoqué, Lucero —le dijo Andrés—, ¿verdad que somos amigos? —miró a Natacha.

—Sí, solo somos amigos —afirmó ella.

Lucero se tranquilizó, se limpió la nariz y la boca con su pañuelito y quitó la cara de enojo.

Nos sentamos. Mi mamá, con Lucero en el sillón grande; Andrés y Natacha, en el de dos plazas; y yo, en el individual.

Andrés pasó un brazo sobre los hombros de Natacha y le cogió la mano.

—¡Los *migos* no se *abazan*! —gritó Lucero—. ¡Los *migos* no son *pada gadase* la mano!

Y voló al sillón donde estaban ellos.

—*Pemiso, pemiso...* —le dijo a Natacha—. A *ve, Nacha, hate pallá.* —Y se sentó en medio de los dos.

—Lucero —le dijo Natacha—, yo también te quiero. No te voy a quitar a Andrés. Él nos quiere a las dos.

—¿*Andés?* —preguntó extrañada—. ¡*Andés* nomás me *quele* a mí. ¿*Vedá, Andés*, que tú no *queles* a *Nacha* y a mí sí, *polque tú queles* mucho a *Lucedo*?

—Lucero —le dije seria—, no seas así con Natacha, las niñas envidiosas son muy feas.

—Yo no soy *vidiosa...* ¿*Vedá,* mamita chula, que yo no soy *vidiosa* ni fea? —dijo a punto de llorar.

—No, muñequita, tú no eres envidiosa y mucho menos fea —le dijo mi mamá—, pero deja a Andrés y a Natacha; vente para acá conmigo.

—¡No, mi chula! ¡Si voy *cotigo* ellos se van a *besá!* —Se abrazó de Andrés—. ¡Yo no *quelo* que *Andés* bese a *Nacha!* ¡*No quelo!* ¡*No quelo!*

Andrés la abrazó y le dijo:

—Cálmate, chiquita, no voy a besar a nadie, solo a ti. —Y la besó en el cuello, en la pancita, en las costillas, y Lucero, feliz, se moría de risa.

Nunca volvió Natacha a la casa. Después supimos que terminaron cuando Andrés decidió irse a Baja California.

Hasta la fecha, Andrés nunca platica frente a Lucero de Lucía. Es la novia que tiene allá, con la que se piensa casar.

39

HACE un mes, Lucero se puso grave. El susto que nos dio nos sacudió violentamente a todos, de la cabeza a los pies. Estaba sola en su recámara, declamando su poema favorito, con la foto de Raúl entre sus manos, cuando empezó a toser insistentemente. Mi mamá y yo estábamos en la cocina, preparando la comida. De pronto, la tos paró. Nos tranquilizamos. Pasaron unos minutos y volvió a toser; pero de una forma muy rara: cada vez que tomaba aire se escuchaba un silbido que parecía salir desde el fondo de su pecho.

Mi mamá aventó la ensalada con todo y platón; y yo, el sartén donde estaba guisando la carne. Salimos de prisa de la cocina y llegamos con Lucero. Estaba morada. Se estaba ahogando. Mi mamá la sentó violentamente y la sacudió de los hombros una y otra vez, desesperada. Lucero estaba desfallecida y no podía tomar aire.

—¡Chiquita, mi vida, respira!... ¡Respira, por favor, mi amor! ¡Lucero! ¿No me oyes? ¡Ay, Dios de mi vida, que respire, que respire, por favor!... —Y la zarandeaba con violencia.

—Cálmate, mamá —le dije lo más ecuánime que pude, aunque yo también estaba asustadísima—. Vamos a llevarla al hospital. A ver, déjame cargarla.

Mi mamá parecía no oír, estaba fuera de sí.

Literalmente le arrebaté a Lucero y la cargué. No sé de dónde me salieron tantas fuerzas.

—¡Vámonos! —le dije a mi mamá y corrí hacia la puerta, con Lucero en los brazos.

Mi mamá se había quedado paralizada en la puerta de la recámara. Me dio miedo. Pensé que le iba a dar un infarto.

—¡Mamá! —le grité lo más fuerte que pude—. ¡Reacciona! ¡Lucero te necesita!

Ella pareció volver en sí y caminó hacia nosotros a toda prisa.

—Coge las llaves del coche —le dije.

Ella las tomó del portallaves que está a un lado de la puerta y salimos corriendo, con Lucero medio muerta. Se la di a mi mamá en el coche, y arranqué.

¿Cómo llegamos al hospital? No lo sé. Cuando me di cuenta, Lucero estaba en una camilla y dos enfermeras la llevaban a toda prisa hacia terapia intensiva.

Mi mamá y yo nos quedamos en la salita, sin saber qué hacer.

Nos miramos y nos abrazamos llorando.

De pronto, mi mamá recobró su fortaleza:

—Háblale a tu papá y dile que le hable al doctor Del Valle. También que les avise a tu tía Rosario, a tus abuelitos, a tu abuelita Adela, a Roberto, y que trate de hablar con Andrés. Dile que pase a la casa por la foto de Raúl, porque, seguramente, ahorita que Lucero se componga es lo primero que va a pedir.

—Sí, mamá —le dije sintiendo en el fondo de mí una duda inmensa y dolorosa de que Lucero se pudiera componer.

Fui al teléfono y hablé con mi papá. Cuando le dije lo que pasaba, se oyó como si el teléfono se le hubiera caído; después de un momento, me dijo:

—¿Se va a morir? —su voz temblaba.

—No sé —apenas le pude responder, porque el nudo que tenía en la garganta casi no me dejaba hablar.

—No me hagan ir a la casa por la foto. Voy a perder mucho tiempo —me suplicó.

—Tráela, papá, mi mamá se va a sentir más tranquila. Ella está muy mal.

—Está bien —aceptó—, voy para allá.

Ya no le dije que le avisara a nadie, yo misma les hablé a todos y también a mi abuelita Adela y a Andrés. Él me dijo que vendría en cuanto pudiera, pero se notaba muy preocupado. Ya estaban todos en el hospital, menos Andrés, cuando llegó el doctor Del Valle y, sin saludarnos siquiera, entró a terapia intensiva. Se tardó bastante tiempo en salir. A nosotros se nos hizo eterno.

—Lucero está muy delicada —nos dijo.

Nos miramos unos a otros, sin decir nada, y lloramos.

Fueron unos días muy estresantes; horribles. Nos dejaban entrar a verla de uno por uno y solo unos minutos. Lucero estaba inconsciente. Aunque yo sabía que no se daba cuenta de mi presencia, le hablaba y le pedía que, por el amor de Dios, se aliviara. Una mañana, después de casi tres semanas, estaba yo con ella, cogiéndole la mano y mirando el monitor que captaba los latidos de su corazón, cuando escuché:

—*Alelita*.

Yo salté del susto; casi me caigo de la silla. La miré y me encontré con la Lucero de siempre. Adoré sus ojitos bizcos, su pelito ralo, su boquita medio abierta y su naricita con algo de escurrimiento. .

—¡Nenita! ¡Mi chiquita! —la abracé—. ¡Ya despertaste, hermanita! ¡Ay, Dios mío, qué bueno eres! —exclamé.

—Ya no tengo sueño —me dijo—; no *toy* en mi *cuato* ¿*vedá*? —Miraba con extrañeza el cuarto del hospital. Vio el buró y me preguntó—: ¿*Onde etá Laúl*?

—Ahorita te lo traigo.

Le acomodé sus manitas sobre su regazo y le dije:

—Regreso enseguida, hermanita, no me tardo.

Salí del cuarto y, al verme, todos se levantaron de prisa de los sillones donde estaban sentados.

—¡Ya está consciente! —grité como loca—. ¡Ya está bien!

Todos corrieron a abrazarme, llorábamos y reíamos sin parar.

—Quiere a Raúl —les dije, y todos rieron.

Mi mamá sacó el portarretratos de su bolsa y, sin decir nada, se fue a toda prisa.

En esos momentos llegó el doctor Del Valle. Su cara se iluminó al mirar las nuestras.

Yo fui a su encuentro.

—Doctor, ella ya está bien, ¡gracias, gracias! —lo abracé y le di un beso.

El doctor nos había dicho que había estado a punto de darle un infarto, que le había dado un paro respiratorio y que era muy posible que, si sobrevivía, quedara en estado de coma por quién sabe cuánto tiempo... Quizás para siempre. A todos nos llegó como rayo fulminante esa noticia, pero, más que a nadie, a la pobrecita de mi mamá. Andaba como zombi y no le importaba nada. De pronto, de estar aparentemente bien, se ponía a llorar con tanta tristeza y desesperación, que nos desgarraba el alma.

Por eso el doctor se puso contentísimo cuando le dijimos que Lucero ya había reaccionado. Él es como parte de la familia. Desde que nació mi hermana, siempre ha estado cerca de nosotros; así como Luchis, su esposa.

Cuando llegan a visitarnos, Lucero se esconde detrás de mi mamá y le pregunta al doctor:

—¿No *tajiste tu jilinga*?

—No, Lucero, no la traje —y le enseña las manos.

Ella demuestra un inmenso alivio y entonces ya lo saluda.

Luego, cuando nos sentamos a platicar, el doctor siempre le dice que se siente junto a él, ella invariablemente responde:

—No, *dotol*, *mejol* me *sento* con Chuchis. —Luchis la abraza; se quieren mucho. Lucero siempre le dice en secreto—: ¿*Vedá* que tu no vas a *dejá* que tu *dotol* me *iyete*?

—Claro que no —le responde Luchis al oído—, si trata de inyectarte, yo lo inyecto a él.

Lucero se muere de risa y dice con su voz ronca:

—¡Sí, Chuchis, tú lo inyetas! ¡Ay, doto!, te va a lolé, te va a lolé!

Ese mismo día, en cuanto reaccionó, la sacaron de terapia intensiva y la cambiaron a un cuarto. Ahí podíamos estar con ella todo el día, así que nos turnábamos. Lucero repelaba solo cuando le tocaba estar con ella a mi abuelita Esperanza.

—Ya me *sento ben*, abelita —le decía—, si *queles pedes ite* a tu casa. Yo aquí *me toy* con *Laúl*.

—No, chiquita, voy a estar contigo un ratito. Mira, te traje una novela buenísima, de puro amor; te la voy a leer.

Solo así lograba que Lucero la aceptara.

Mi abuelita, con el tremendo susto que nos dio Lucero, reaccionó y cambió de actitud.

—He sido tan tonta, hija. Me he portado tan mal... No me había dado cuenta de cuánto quiero a Lucero —me dijo un día.

40

FALTAN tres meses para la boda, pero Roberto y yo hemos decidido que solo nos casaremos en esa fecha si Lucero se mejora; si no, lo aplazaremos hasta que ella esté bien. Yo no podría irme, no digamos a Michoacán sino a cualquier lado, y dejarla enferma.

Hace cuatro días la dieron de alta en el hospital, pero todavía sigue un poco delicada, aunque ya no está en cama todo el tiempo. Se levanta a comer, a dar unos pasos y todas las noches, como antes, se pone en la ventana de su cuarto a contemplar las estrellas, solo que ahora lo hace con Raúl. Pone la foto mirando hacia el cielo y platica con él sobre las constelaciones, sobre la luna y sobre Venus.

Raúl habló con Roberto y él le dijo que va a venir a México dentro de quince días. Todavía no sabemos si sea conveniente que venga a ver a Lucero, lo vamos a pensar bien. Tal vez sea mejor que ella siga personificándolo en su fotografía, que siga soñando con él, que siga despertando feliz y que casi todos los días nos cuente que soñó que se casaba con Raúl y que los dos se iban volando hasta Venus.

41

ANDRÉS llegó asustadísimo a la casa. Entró directamente al cuarto de Lucero, sin saludar a nadie. Yo fui tras él.

Ella tenía en sus manos la foto de Raúl y, en cuanto vio a Andrés en la puerta, la escondió.

—¿Cómo estás, princesa? ¿Te sientes mejor? —le preguntó.

—¡*Andés*! —dijo Lucero, feliz—. ¡Qué *güeno* que *llegates*! ¡Ya te *etaba epelando* desde hace mucho! ¿*Pol* qué no *bías* venido? ¿No sabías que *taba enfema*?

—No había podido venir, chiquita, pero en cuanto pude me lancé para acá como rayo...

—Como *layo*... como *layo*... ¡Ay, *Andés, tú eles* bien chitoso!

—¡Como rayos y centellas! —le dijo él.

—*Quentellas... Quentellas...* —Se rio con ganas. Sus roncas carcajadas alegraron mi corazón. Hacía mucho que no se reía así.

Entró mi papá a la recámara y saludó a Andrés con mucho gusto.

—¡*Andés* vino como *layo*, papá, como *layos* y *quentellas*! —dijo Lucero, todavía riendo.

—¿Cómo qué? —preguntó.

—Como rayo, tío, como rayos y centellas —le aclaró Andrés.

—¡Ay, qué rápido vino a verte, Lucerito! —le respondió mi papá, riendo también.

Andrés le pasó el brazo por los hombros y lo miró como dándole a entender que le daba mucho gusto la nueva relación que existe entre Lucero y él. Mi papá asintió y miró a Lucero con ternura.

—¡Mamita chula, ven! —gritó Lucero—. Mi mamá llegó y mi hermanita le dijo—: ¿*Qués* que es *Andés*? Pus no, mi chula, es *lavos* y *quentellas*.

—¿Qué dices, chiquita? —le preguntó mi mamá sin entender de qué le hablaba.

—¡*Lile* a mamita chula, *Andes*! ¡*Lile* cómo *vinites*! —le pidió Lucero, divertidísima.

—Vine a verla tan veloz, como rayos y centellas, tía.

—¡Ah! —dijo mi mamá—, con razón llegaste echando humo.

—¡*Jumo*!... ¡*Jumo*!... ¡Ay, mi chulita, *eles* bien chitosa! —No paraba de reír—. *Jumo... Jumo...* —repetía.

Andrés se sentó junto a ella en la cama y le dijo:

—¿Y qué no te vas a levantar? ¿Por qué estás de fodonga?

—No toy *folonga, toy* enfema. ¿*Pus* que no sabes? —le dijo ella.

—Pero ya no estás tan enferma... ¡Anda, levántate!, vamos a caminar un rato para que me platiques qué has hecho últimamente y qué has soñado. —Y la destapó.

Lucero se puso nerviosísima y trató de meter bajo la almohada el retrato de Raúl.

—¿Qué tienes ahí? —le preguntó Andrés—. ¿Qué me estás escondiendo?

—¡*Nala*! ¡*Nala*! —dijo Lucero.

—¿Cómo que nada? ¿No me vas a enseñar qué tienes ahí?

—Es que te vas a *enojá* conmigo —dijo Lucero, angustiada.

—¿Por qué? —le dijo Andrés—. ¿Pues qué es?

—¡Ay, *Andés*, me vas a *legañá*!

—Tú sabes que yo no te regaño... ¡A ver, enséñame eso!

Lucero sacó el retrato y con su manita temblorosa, se lo enseñó.

—A ver..., a ver... —dijo Andrés, examinando a Raúl—. ¿Y quién es este cuate? —le preguntó.

—¡Naide! ¡Naide! —respondió Lucero muy preocupada.

—Chiquita —intervino mi mamá al verla tan nerviosa—, no tiene nada de malo que le digas a Andrés quién es.

—¡Ay, cómo qués! ¡Sí teñe malo! ¡Sí teñe malo!

—No, Lucero —le dije—, no tiene nada de malo... Dile a Andrés quién está en esa foto, dile quién es.

Lucero bajó la cabeza y sin atreverse a mirar a Andrés, le dijo:

—E mi novo.

—¿Tu qué? —le preguntó Andrés, haciéndose el asombrado.

—... Novo —repitió Lucero, apenada.

—¡Ay, chamaca, descocada! ¡Conque ya tienes novio! ¿eh? ¿Y cómo se llama?

—Se ama Laúl —respondió Lucero, y suspiró.

—¿Raúl? Pues mira qué nombre tan a todo dar... —le dijo Andrés y luego agregó—: ¿Así que tú sí puedes tener novio y a mí no me dejas tener novia, verdad?

—No... Yo... E que... —no sabía qué contestar.

La abrazó y le dijo:

—No te pongas nerviosa, chiquita; claro que tú puedes tener novio y yo no me enojo; pero tú tampoco te vas a enojar si yo tengo novia, ¿de acuerdo?

Lucero se quedó pensativa y luego respondió:

—Güeno, Andés, etá bien, te doy pemiso de que tengas Nacha.

—No, mi reina, ya no es Natacha, ahora es Lucía —le dijo Andrés.

—¿Lushía? ¿Quén e Lushía?

—Mi novia.

—¡No Andés! ¡Tu nova e Nacha! —le dijo Lucero, enojada.

—No, chiquita, te estoy diciendo que Natacha ya no es mi novia. Ahora mi novia se llama Lucía.

—¿Dos *novas*? ¡No. *Andés*! ¡Dos *novas* no se *pede*!

—No son dos, nenita —dijo mi papá—, es solo una: Lucía.

—*Andés etá diceno* que dos, papá. ¿Poco tú *tenes* dos *posha*s? Tú nomás *tenes* a mamita chula.

—Por eso, chiquita, así como yo nada más tengo una esposa, a tu mamita chula, Andrés tiene una sola novia y se llama Lucía. Natacha ya no es su novia —le explicó.

—¡Ah, *beno*! —se tranquilizó Lucero—. Así sí te doy *pemiso* de *tené nova* —le dijo a Andrés.

—¡Vaya! —descansó Andrés—. Gracias, princesa —le dijo, y los dos se miraron con amor.

42

CUANDO Andrés ya se iba, yo lo fui a despedir. Me preguntó quién era Raúl, estaba intrigadísimo.

Le conté lo que había pasado. Le dio gusto, pero, a la vez, se sintió apenado.

—No sabes la tristeza que me da que, siendo Lucero como es de preciosa, no pueda tener un novio de verdad; no pueda ser amada como cualquier otra muchacha... claro, todos nosotros la amamos, pero me refiero al amor de pareja, al amor hombre-mujer.

—Sí, te entiendo —le dije—. ¿Y tú crees que yo no siento igual? Me da rabia pensar que ella no pueda hacer una vida normal. Con lo inteligente, simpática y buena que es... ¿Sabes?, yo creo que a veces la vida es muy injusta... ¿Por qué condenó a mi hermanita a sufrir para siempre este tremendo mal? ¿Por qué a ella? —Los ojos se me llenaron de lágrimas.

Andrés me abrazó, conmovido.

—Pues no te creas, Adelita —me dijo—, la vida a veces hace cosas incomprensibles para unos, pero todo tiene su razón. Mira, francamente, yo pienso que Lucero es una muchachita feliz. Aunque, claro, ella está consciente de que es distinta, pero, si te das cuenta, lo acepta y no se amarga la vida; al contrario, es una persona cien por ciento positiva y no hace más que dar alegría a los demás. Cuando me pongo a pensar en ella llego a la conclusión de que Dios nos la mandó para hacemos felices... Tal vez yo esté mal... Tal vez sea un egoísta...

—No, Andrés, tú menos que nadie puedes decir que eres egoísta. Tú nos has alegrado la vida y nos has hecho ser optimistas ante el problema de Lucero... Además, yo pienso igual que tú. Creo que la vida nos premió regalándonos a Lucero.

43

ROBERTO y yo también hemos contemplado la posibilidad de llevamos a Lucero a Michoacán, pero sabemos que mi mamá no va a querer y casi estamos seguros de que Lucero tampoco... ¡Qué va!, ellas no pueden separarse.

Mi mamá no quiere que nos vayamos; piensa que Lucero nos va a extrañar demasiado y, aquí entre nos, yo creo que también lo dice por ella. Aunque puede arreglar en la escuela que Lucero se quede ahí algunas horas más mientras ella sale del trabajo, sabe que ya no será lo mismo sin nuestro apoyo.

También podría cambiar de tiempo completo a medio tiempo, pero no sería justo para ella, ya que significa menor sueldo y, además, a ella le encanta su trabajo.

Mi papá dice que él va a apoyar a mi mamá; que él puede salir más temprano de su oficina y quedarse con Lucero el tiempo que se necesite. Nosotros, francamente, dudamos de que Lucero quiera quedarse sola con él, pues, aunque su relación ha mejorado bastante, no es para tanto; ella tiene memoria de elefante y todavía es un poco recelosa con él.

Mi tía Rosario nos opina que sí está de pensarse, que los ofrecimientos de trabajo que tenemos allá son muy buenos, pero que nos comprende, porque para ella siempre fue más importante Andrés. Y es verdad, me acuerdo que ella tuvo algunos ofrecimientos de trabajo con mejor sueldo y mayor jerarquía; pero se trataba de irse a vivir lejos, sola con Andrés, sin mi mamá cerca; cambiarlo de escuela, de ambiente, dejar a sus amigos, a nosotras, y prefirió no aceptarlos.

Mi abuelita Esperanza dice que ella está dispuesta a cuidar a Lucero mientras mi mamá no esté, pero nosotros sabemos que con ella, de plano, no hay ninguna posibilidad de que Lucero esté de acuerdo, ¡qué va!

Mi abuelita Adela nos aconseja que pensemos bien las cosas, que no actuemos hasta estar convencidos de lo que en verdad queramos hacer. Ella también se ofrece a cuidar a Lucero; dice que ahora que ya traspasó su negocio no tendría ningún inconveniente de venirse a vivir aquí. Aunque no a la casa, porque ella es muy independiente y muy respetuosa. Sería incapaz de perturbar la rutina y la vida de mis papás.

Mi abuelito Jorge nos aconseja que nos vayamos. Dice que no debemos desaprovechar la oferta de trabajo que le han hecho a Roberto, porque en verdad es una chamba bastante superior a la que ahora tiene en el periódico. Que las oportunidades a veces se presentan solo una vez en la vida y que de un sí o un no, depende muchas veces el futuro de las personas, que él podría ayudar a mi mamá con el cuidado de Lucero, y no dudamos que así sea; además, con él, Lucero estaría feliz.

Andrés opina lo mismo que mi abuelito Jorge, dice que no debemos depender tanto de Lucero, ni ella de nosotros; que al principio va a ser difícil, pero nos vamos a acostumbrar a verla de vez en cuando, y que ella va a responder igual; que todo es cuestión de tiempo.

—Acuérdense cuando yo me fui. Era un suplicio para los dos. Ahora, claro que nos extrañamos, pero ya no sufrimos, al contrario, esperamos con gusto el poder vernos y gozamos, a más no poder, cada momento en que estamos juntos.

Nosotros lo estamos pensando bien, creemos que mi abuelito y Andrés tienen razón, pero queremos estar seguros antes de decidir.

44

DE PRONTO, pensamos que con el apoyo de toda la familia, el que nos vayamos no va a ser algo tan terrible como pensamos; después, recapacitamos y volvemos a dudar. Porque, si ahora que está en recuperación nos necesita tanto, cuando se alivie y vuelva a su vida normal nos va a necesitar todavía más.

La imaginamos nerviosa, esperando, por la tarde, el timbrazo de Roberto.

Callada, mirando por la ventana, aguardando verme llegar para gritarme: "¡*Alelita,* ya te vi!".

Esperándonos para llevarla a tomar un helado y regresando para leerle un rato sus novelas de amor o sus poemas.

Deseando que Roberto le platique una y otra vez la misma historia de cómo y dónde conoció a Raúl y desde cuándo son amigos.

Despertándome por la mañana, tempranísimo, para contarme sus sueños y para decirme qué se le antoja desayunar; para que la ayude a bañarse y a peinarla y, mientras lo hago, que le vuelva a relatar, con detalles, el día que conocimos a Raúl, como si ella no hubiera estado ahí.

Diciéndonos que ahora que se alivie quiere que vayamos por ella a la escuela para que Roberto les diga a sus amigos, sobre todo a Roland, que es verdad que tiene *n*ovio, que se llama Raúl y que es el muchacho del retrato.

"*Polque siempe* lo voy a *lleva comigo.*" Diciéndome que quiere que la vuelva a pintar. "Pala tené mi cadita de Banca- nieves."

Esperándonos, por las noches, a que vayamos a despedir- nos de ella y recemos juntos antes de darle el beso de bue- nas noches y persignarla.

Creemos que no va a ser fácil su vida sin nosotros.

Pero, lo que más nos angustia es imaginar nuestra vida sin Lucero.

A Roberto y a mí se nos destroza el alma cuando pensa- mos en alejarnos de ella.

¿Cómo vamos a poder vivir sin sus ocurrencias, su voz ronca, su inteligencia, su carita, aparentemente igual a la de tantos niños con su mal, pero tan única, tan singular? ¡Cómo vamos a extrañar sus indiscreciones, su alegría, su forma de hablar, su cariño, sus razonamientos tan sencillos, tan ge- niales, tan de ella! Creemos que a nuestra vida le va a faltar emoción, sabor, sorpresa; pensamos que se va a volver mo- nótona, común y corriente, sin chiste...

¿Cómo puede una persona, aparentemente tan frágil, ser tan importante y darle a la vida de los demás un sentido tan especial? ¿Cómo vamos a llenar ese vacío que Lucero deja- rá en nosotros? ¿Quién nos conmoverá con tanta inocencia? ¿Quién, de repente, nos dará tremendas lecciones de huma- nismo, de grandeza de espíritu y de amor a la vida? ¿Quién nos llenará de ternura y nos pondrá al borde del llanto con una sola palabra o con solo una mirada? ¿Quién nos hará reír y nos llenará de alegría? ¿Qué sentiremos cuando por las noches miremos el cielo y veamos brillar a Venus?

CLAUDIA CELIS sabe disfrutar el lado sencillo y cotidiano de la vida. Le encanta estar con su familia, salir a tomar un café con sus amigos o invitárselo en su casa. Le gusta caminar por las calles de su pueblo (Texcoco), cuidar sus plantas y consentir a sus gatos. Le fascina leer, pues piensa que no hay cosa más maravillosa que un buen libro. La literatura la ha llevado de la mano hacia el camino que hoy recorre con tanto gusto y le ha brindado la for- tuna de poder estar cerca de los lectores, contándoles historias.

Claudia Celis nació el 6 de abril de 1951 en Tepexpan, Estado de México. Estudió la carrera de Educadora en la Normal de Puebla y el diplomado de creación literaria en la Escuela para Escritores de la SOGEM. La mayor par- te de su vida la ha dedicado a la docencia, tanto en preescolar como en pre- paratoria, y ahora imparte talleres de escritura creativa y escribe literatura para niños y jóvenes. Otras obras suyas son Donde habitan los ángeles, Las vacaciones de Sinforoso y Doro, la niña enamorada.

Atados a una estrella
se terminó de imprimir en junio de 2016
en Impresora Tauro S.A. de C.V.
Av. Plutarco Elías Calles 396, col. Los Reyes,
Iztacalco, Ciudad de México.
En su composición se empleó la fuente Celeste.

AMERICAN CRIMINAL JUSTICE POLICY

American Criminal Justice Policy examines many of the most prominent criminal justice policies on the American landscape and finds that they fall well short of achieving the accountability and effectiveness that policy makers have advocated and that the public expects. The policies include mass incarceration, sex offender laws, supermax prisons, faith-based prisoner reentry programs, transfer of juveniles to adult court, domestic violence mandatory arrest laws, drug courts, gun laws, community policing, private prisons, and many others. Optimistically, Daniel P. Mears argues that this situation can be changed through systematic incorporation of evaluation research into policy development, monitoring, and assessment. To this end, the book provides a clear and accessible discussion of five types of evaluation – needs, theory, implementation or process, outcome and impact, and cost efficiency. In addition, it identifies how they can be used both to hold the criminal justice system accountable and to increase the effectiveness of crime control and crime-prevention efforts.

Daniel P. Mears is a professor at Florida State University's College of Criminology and Criminal Justice. He has published widely in criminology, including more than ninety articles, chapters, and reports, and has examined a wide range of criminal justice policies. His work has appeared in *Criminology*, *Journal of Research in Crime and Delinquency*, and *Law and Society Review*, among other journals, and his views, including editorials, have been frequently cited in such media outlets as the *Boston Globe*, *Los Angeles Times*, and *USA Today*.

American Criminal Justice Policy

An Evaluation Approach to Increasing Accountability and Effectiveness

Daniel P. Mears
Florida State University

CAMBRIDGE UNIVERSITY PRESS
Cambridge, New York, Melbourne, Madrid, Cape Town, Singapore,
São Paulo, Delhi, Dubai, Tokyo

Cambridge University Press
32 Avenue of the Americas, New York, NY 10013-2473, USA

www.cambridge.org
Information on this title: www.cambridge.org/9780521746236

First published 2010

Printed in the United States of America

A catalog record for this publication is available from the British Library.

Library of Congress Cataloging in Publication data

Mears, Daniel P., 1966–
American criminal justice policy : an evaluation approach to increasing accountability
and effectiveness / Daniel P. Mears.
    p.   cm.
Includes bibliographical references and index.
ISBN 978-0-521-76246-5 (hardback)
1. Criminology – United States.   2. Justice, Administration of – United States.   I. Title.
HV6025.M376   2010
364.973 – dc22   2009047360

ISBN 978-0-521-76246-5 Hardback
ISBN 978-0-521-74623-6 Paperback

Contents

Preface

In this book, I argue that American criminal justice is flawed but redeemable. I argue that straightforward, feasible, and pragmatic steps can be taken to diagnose and solve many of the problems with the criminal justice system and the policies, programs, practices, and decisions that comprise it. Not least, I argue that policy makers, administrators, practitioners, and researchers can and should use evaluation to increase criminal justice accountability and effectiveness.

The motivation for the book stems from a desire to help elevate debates about criminal justice policy and to improve the criminal justice system. All too frequently, this system fails to hold offenders accountable, reduce crime, help victims, or operate efficiently. The fact that much of the system's inner workings occur within what might be termed a *black box* contributes to these problems. Many times, for example, we have little evidence about how, or even whether, policies have been implemented. The "black box" nature of criminal justice is problematic because of the tremendous growth in the size and costs of the criminal justice system. Moreover, it is troublesome because of the risks – such as increased crime, victimization, injustice, and inefficiency – that may result when this system operates with little credible information or evidence about its policies.

Still, strong grounds exist for being optimistic. For example, policy makers and the public increasingly have called for smarter, more effective ways to reduce crime and help victims. In addition, "government accountability" no longer constitutes a buzz phrase; rather, it now stands as a critical goal embraced by local, state, and federal agencies. The change in 2004 in the name of the U.S. General Accounting Office, which operates as the research arm of Congress, to the U.S. Government Accountability Office symbolizes this shift.

Against this backdrop, and while teaching criminal justice policy evaluation, the idea for developing this book materialized. Before entering a university setting, I worked at the Urban Institute, a nonprofit research organization. There I undertook evaluations of many criminal justice policies and learned several lessons. One was that evaluation research could provide important information about such questions as whether to adopt or abandon a policy and how to design or improve policies. Another was that evaluation involves both art and science, including the need to tailor research to fit the questions most important to criminal justice policy makers, officials, and practitioners or to debates about particular policies. A third was that criminal justice officials, practitioners, the agencies within which they work, and researchers frequently have limited training in policy evaluation. Not least, a fourth was that evaluation research, if applied on a widespread basis, had considerable potential to improve policy.

When I entered a university setting and began trying to teach policy evaluation, I realized that no books described the nuts and bolts of an evaluation framework – as applied to criminal justice – in an accessible manner and to a large number of policies. Evaluation research texts certainly existed. However, I wanted a discussion that focused on criminal justice policy, used criminal justice examples, and identified how evaluation research questions must be tailored to fit specific criminal justice policies. My experiences with criminal justice administrators, practitioners, researchers, and especially students made it clear that an evaluation approach makes more sense and is more meaningful if the audience can see how it applies to policies of interest to them. A focus on a diverse range of policies thus was critical.

As I thought about how to proceed, I realized that the systematic application of an evaluation approach to criminal justice policies could be used not only to show how such research can be applied to these policies. It also could be used to develop a powerful critique of them and of the criminal justice system more generally. Not least, it could be used to identify a relatively straightforward solution for helping to produce more accountable, effective, efficient, and evidence-based criminal justice policy.

Collectively, these observations led me to write this book, with the hope of contributing to efforts to improve criminal justice policy. I want to emphasize that this book is an argument about the state of criminal justice policy and how to improve it. Training in research methodology is not required to understand the argument or to understand and apply evaluation research. Such training will help, but it is not necessary. Indeed, as I emphasize throughout the book, the conceptual rather than the statistical underpinnings of evaluation research are what is most critical for assessing and improving criminal justice.

The contours of the book have taken shape over several years, and any strengths it may have come from the support and influence of many people. Special thanks go to Emily and Eli, who inspire and tolerate me. Emily has been a most gracious sounding board throughout the writing of this book and offered innumerable helpful suggestions for improving it. To my broader family, idealists and pragmatists alike, I am also most thankful – collectively, they provide perspective on what matters. I owe a debt of gratitude to Bill Kelly and Mark Stafford, both of whom I am fortunate to count as friends and mentors. I also am very fortunate to have been able to rub elbows with Jeremy Travis and Christy Visher. They have taught me more lessons than they likely realize about research and the broader policy context in which it occurs. I am indebted to my colleagues at the Urban Institute, especially John Roman for his review of the cost-benefit analysis chapter, and at Florida State University. I also am indebted to Christina Mancini, who helped collect material for the book, to my students, and to the many officials and practitioners who have taught me about the policies, programs, practices, and operations of the criminal justice system. Not least, many thanks to Ed Parsons at Cambridge University Press, who encouraged me to undertake an endeavor that I otherwise would not have tackled, and to the reviewers, who provided excellent advice. Any flaws in the book are, of course, my responsibility and mine alone.

Grateful acknowledgment is extended to the following publishers for permission to draw on, reprint, and excerpt from my previous work and articles: the American Correctional Association in Alexandria, Virginia; Blackwell Synergy; the Center for Juvenile and Criminal Justice; Elsevier; Sage Publications; Taylor & Francis; University of California Press; University of Houston Law Center; and the Urban Institute. Special thanks are extended to Elsevier for permission to develop several ideas that I briefly presented in an article in *Journal of Criminal Justice* ("Towards Rational and Evidence-Based Crime Policy," Vol. 35, No. 6, pp. 667–682, 2007). I thank not only these publishing companies but also the editors of their journals and the reviewers who took time to help improve the original articles. I also thank Sage Publications for permission to create a modified version of Exhibit 3-C from *Evaluation: A Systematic Approach* (2004:80) by Peter H. Rossi, Mark W. Lipsey, and Howard E. Freeman.

1

Introduction

The Problem

After several decades in which an ever-wider array of new and costly policies has emerged, America's criminal justice system stands at a crossroads. On the one hand, the United States can continue to invest billions of dollars in policies that may not be needed and may not work. On the other, it can heed recent calls for increased government accountability and reliance on evidence-based strategies. The latter path holds the promise of helping to place criminal justice policy on a solid foundation that cost-effectively reduces crime, helps offenders become contributing members of society, increases justice, and assists victims and the families and communities affected by crime.

Some signs suggest that the country is pursuing accountability and evidence-based policy, and thus indicate grounds for optimism. Many states, for example, are increasingly committed to identifying and implementing "best practices" for working with offenders.[1] Also, the very fact that the terms *accountability* and *evidence-based policy* frequently turn up in policy discussions underscores that policy makers and the public want the criminal justice system to be held to a high bar.

Even so, significant cause for alarm exists. Consider the rapid expansion of the U.S. prison population, which grew by more than 370 percent between 1980 and 2008[2] and far exceeded growth in the general population or in crime. This growth has generated increased costs for the correctional system, with expenditures that have increased 7.5 percent annually since 1990.[3] Such growth may have been warranted and may have produced, or will produce, dramatic returns, but to date there is little research to support such assertions. Much the same can be said of many other popular crime policies, including "get tough" sentencing laws, the spate of recent sex crime

1

laws, the widespread adoption of specialized courts, the proliferation of super-maximum ("supermax") security prisons, and the emergence of a range of faith-based prisoner reentry programs. These constitute but a few of the policies that have ascended into prominence in recent decades and yet remain largely unevaluated or, if evaluated, enjoy little or questionable empirical support.

Against that backdrop stands the fact that, even as calls for accountability and effective policy have increased, the bulk of what falls under the umbrella of the criminal justice system occurs within a "black box." We know little, for example, about many different facets of this system and the policies, programs, and practices that constitute it. That includes the day-to-day activities and decisions within criminal justice that directly affect the lives of millions of individual offenders and, ultimately, society.

This state of affairs is the motivation for this book, which argues for the systematic use and institutionalization of an evaluation research approach to assessing and improving criminal justice policy. By policy, I mean not only the various and sundry laws designed to guide sentencing decisions. I also mean the many crime-prevention and treatment programs, and the diverse set of court, law enforcement, and correctional system rules, protocols, and practices that collectively constitute the criminal justice system.[4] In short, *policy* is used here as a shorthand reference for characterizing a wide range of approaches aimed at achieving the goals of the criminal justice system.

The broad focus is purposeful. Discussions of criminal justice frequently center on particulars – a particular law or Supreme Court decision, a particular drug treatment program, a particular policing initiative, and so on. Whatever the merits of such discussions, and they are many, a downside is that we often lose sight of the forest because we are so preoccupied with the trees. By contrast, when we look across a range of policies, we may be better able to discern the forest – in this case, the state of criminal justice policy nationally. We can see certain patterns, for example, that may be cause for concern or for comfort. I believe that applying an evaluation research framework to many of today's most prominent criminal justice policies reveals two patterns of special importance. First, there is not a systematic, evidence-based foundation for many, if not most, of these policies; indeed, research all too frequently does not exist concerning a specific policy or reveals minimal to no positive effects. Second, many opportunities exist for increasing the accountability and effectiveness of the criminal justice system.

One opportunity bears mention at the outset. Increasingly, policy makers, criminal justice officials and practitioners, and the public have expressed interest in identifying and implementing cost-effective policies.[5] Corresponding with that interest is an increased emphasis in criminology and criminal justice and in university and college programs nationally on policy-focused research.[6] As but one example, in 2004 the American Society of Criminology created a special journal called *Criminology and Public Policy* aimed explicitly at forging a stronger link between research and policy. Perhaps more telling is the fact that, in recent decades, public policy has featured prominently as a theme in the society's annual presidential addresses.[7] Along a parallel track, the other prominent organization of American criminologists and criminal justice scholars, the Academy of Criminal Justice Sciences, has focused on forging ties between research and policy since 1963.[8] In short, a unique opportunity exists to improve criminal justice policy by capitalizing on the interest and willingness of these different groups to advance the goals of increasing accountability and evidence-based policy and, more generally, the effectiveness and efficiency of the criminal justice system.

Unfortunately, few sources exist that show how research and, in particular, evaluation research, can be used to inform and improve criminal justice policy. Certainly, textbooks on criminal justice research methods exist,[9] and so, too, do textbooks on evaluation research.[10] Books on policy development and planning also exist.[11] But there is little in the way of guidance about using an evaluation research approach to assess the most prominent criminal justice policies in use today.[12]

The Goals of This Book

One goal of this book is to fill this void and, in particular, to show how evaluation research can be used to contribute to efforts by policy makers, criminal justice officials and practitioners, researchers, students, and the public at large to improve criminal justice policy. To this end, the book is designed to be accessible to researchers and nonresearchers alike. As will become clear throughout this book, the art of evaluation research does not require extensive research or statistical skills, but rather an ability to ask relevant questions. Put differently, evaluation research involves asking good questions more than it does understanding or using sophisticated statistical techniques or research designs. For example, the first type of evaluation the book covers is a needs evaluation. To wit, is there a need for a given policy? Answering that question can be tricky, but not necessarily because of difficulties related to research design and methodology. Rather, the question itself raises a host of additional questions. For starters, consider this question: how much incarceration does a given state "need"? One might think that it depends on the amount of crime. That certainly is part of the equation. But other factors come into play as well. For example, presumably incarceration should be reserved for those who commit serious or violent crimes. What, therefore, is the prevalence of such crime? And how many years of incarceration are appropriate for a given offense, such as assault? Any assessment of need requires answering these and other questions, ones that anybody, not just researchers, can conceptualize if not answer. Indeed, researchers frequently do not know enough about a particular social problem or policy to ask the right questions, whereas others frequently do.

A second goal of the book is to make the argument that, in fact, many of our most prominent criminal justice policies lack a solid, evidence-based foundation.[13] Certainly, examples of effective criminal justice policy exist. However, I believe that, when viewed through the prism of an evaluation research perspective, far too much criminal justice policy fails to receive a passing grade. At the same time, I see a considerable basis for optimism in the fact that even small improvements in policy and practice could generate large returns to society in the form of reduced crime and more justice. The returns also include the potential for improving the life chances of individuals at risk of involvement in the criminal justice system or who are already in it, as well as for improving the lives of their families and the members of the communities from which they come or to which they will return.

A third and final goal of the book is to make the case that evaluation research should be much more and better integrated into criminal justice policy making and practice.[14] Indeed, without such a change, it is difficult to see how the accountability and increasing reliance on evidence-based policy and practice promoted nationally can emerge in criminal justice. Other factors besides research clearly must be in place for these goals to be achieved. As I discuss in Chapter 2, political dynamics alone play a critical role in which policies get adopted and which do not.[15] Even so, research constitutes an important part of any effort to improve criminal justice, especially if the goal is to increase the evidence-based foundation of policy. In the conclusion, I will highlight promising avenues for putting policy on a stronger research footing and end the book on what I believe is an optimistic note. Here, however, I will note that, at the most general level, there exists a unique juncture of pressures for institutionalizing evaluation research into all aspects of criminal justice policy and practice.

Organization of This Book

The organization of this book is as follows. Chapter 2 briefly introduces the evaluation hierarchy and provides an overview of the current crime and policy landscape nationally. It focuses particular attention on recent crime trends and the growth in all parts of the criminal justice system. The chapter emphasizes that there is little research to support current policies and, as importantly, that little is known about the implementation and effects of many of them. That situation, I argue, is irrational given the stakes involved and the opportunities for improving the effectiveness and evidence-based foundation of the criminal justice system. The chapter then discusses critical factors that can influence policy and also undermine accountability and effectiveness. These discussions set the stage for the argument that we need an institutionalized foundation for incorporating research into criminal justice policy design, implementation, monitoring, and assessment. This chapter, as with the others, includes discussion questions that can be used to review the material or to stimulate debate about particular issues.

Chapter 3 describes the evaluation hierarchy in detail, including its logic and benefits. It argues that the hierarchy provides a useful framework for conceptualizing what it means to have accountability or evidence-based policy and practice. The hierarchy creates the structure for the book. Thus, this chapter provides the cornerstone for understanding how the subsequent chapters relate to one another, how the different types of evaluation can be used to take stock of the state of criminal justice policy today, and how they can improve the accountability and effectiveness of the criminal justice system.

Chapters 4 through 8 apply and illustrate the five types of evaluation to some of the most prominent "hot topic" policies nationally. Chapter 4 focuses on needs evaluation, Chapter 5 on theory evaluation, Chapter 6 on implementation (or process) evaluation, Chapter 7 on outcome and impact evaluations, and Chapter 8 on cost-efficiency evaluation. In each chapter, the focus is on answering three questions. First, what is the particular type of evaluation? For example, what is a needs evaluation? A theory evaluation? Implementation or process evaluation? An outcome or impact evaluation? A cost-efficiency evaluation? Second, why is the particular type of evaluation important? For example, what exactly are the benefits of conducting needs, theory, implementation, impact, or cost-efficiency evaluations? Third, from the perspective of a particular type of evaluation, are the policies that currently feature prominently in national criminal justice systems warranted? For example, do the policies rest on a clear establishment of need? Are they well grounded theoretically? Are they implemented well? Have they been shown to have demonstrable impacts on critical outcomes? And are they cost-efficient?

To illustrate each of the types of evaluation, each chapter includes two case studies per type of evaluation: mass incarceration and sex crime laws

(Chapter 4), supermax prisons and faith-based reentry programs (Chapter 5), juvenile transfer and domestic violence mandatory arrest laws (Chapter 6), drug courts and gun laws (Chapter 7), and community policing and private prisons (Chapter 8). Throughout the chapters, I provide many examples of how the different types of evaluation could be or have been applied to a range of other criminal justice policies.

The case studies and examples serve to illustrate each of the types of evaluation and the need to tailor evaluations to the specific characteristics and nuances of particular policies. They also serve to highlight that little evidence exists for many of the most prominent policies on the criminal justice landscape today and, in turn, to highlight the need and room for improvement. My main criteria in selecting the policies were timeliness, prominence, and range. That is, the policies are widespread or are becoming so, and they collectively convey a sense of the contours of American criminal justice. Certainly, additional policies could have been included. In the end, though, the goal of the book is to show how an evaluation research framework can be used to improve criminal justice policy and to make an argument about the need for more systematic reliance on such a framework. In that respect, it is not necessary, much less possible, to discuss every major criminal justice policy.

Finally, Chapter 9 concludes by briefly summarizing some of the critical problems that largely preclude the systematic emergence of accountability and evidence-based policy in criminal justice systems throughout the country. It then turns to a discussion of concrete recommendations through which criminal justice policy could be improved.

2

Irrational Criminal Justice Policy

A CENTRAL GOAL OF THIS BOOK IS TO CONTRIBUTE TO EFFORTS TO improve criminal justice policy and to do so by showing how the systematic use of evaluation research can lead to less bad policy and more good policy. The ultimate aim is to help place criminal justice policy on a more rational footing, one where it has a chance of providing the accountability and the effectiveness that the public expects of it. At present, and as detailed in subsequent chapters, too many criminal justice policies are ill founded, ineffective, or inefficient, or they lack sufficient evidence to support them. Put differently, we have too much irrational criminal justice policy. I argue that increased reliance on the evaluation hierarchy in all parts of the criminal justice system and in the development and assessment of policy provides one critical platform for correcting this situation and fulfilling the public's desire for effective government.

This chapter sets the stage for this argument and the subsequent chapters in several ways. First, it briefly introduces the evaluation hierarchy as a framework for critiquing current policy. The details of the hierarchy are discussed in Chapter 3, but a discussion here provides a foothold for understanding the context – in particular, the lack of accountability and effective criminal justice policies – that motivates this book. Second, it provides a portrait of national crime and justice system trends, and, specifically, the dramatic increase in criminal justice populations and expenditures. This discussion serves to illustrate the stakes involved and to highlight the need for creating the types of research that can allow for accountability and evidence-based policy. Third, it describes some of the prominent factors that have been argued to influence criminal justice policy. This discussion highlights the fact that many barriers to research-based policy exist. In so doing, it underscores the importance of institutionalizing evaluation research as a critical part of an effort to place the criminal justice system on a more rational – that is, a more accountable and effective – foundation.

The Evaluation Hierarchy and the Irrationality of Criminal Justice Policy

Imagine someone tries to sell you a used car. Before responding, you may well ask yourself five questions. The first question is, "Do I actually need a car?" Perhaps you do. But perhaps you do not. In some areas, having a car is practically a requirement for getting to and from work. In others, especially metropolitan areas, public transportation may suffice.

Assuming that you do need a car, the second question presents itself: "Is this the *kind* of car I need?" For example, if you have a daily two-hour commute, you likely would want a car with good gas mileage, so a large pickup truck might not be the best option, all else being equal. Even so, gas mileage may not be the only relevant consideration. If you are more than six feet tall, some gas-efficient cars may feel uncomfortable. In addition, your work may involve shorter trips and carting large equipment from one place to another. A compact vehicle may not be the best option in such cases.

If you determine that the car indeed is appropriate for your purposes, you then likely will ask a third question, namely, "What is its condition?" That is, how has it been used and how well has it been maintained? For example, if it is a manual-shift vehicle, did the person shift in a way that wore the clutch down? If so, you may need to pay for a new clutch soon. Was the car ever in an accident? If so, there may be problems not immediately evident that could surface and lead to many costly repairs. Conversely, if the owner supplies detailed records, including regular tune-ups, oil changes, and the like, you may have more trust that the car will be reliable and that it will perform in the way you expect.

Should you determine, upon inspection of the car, that it passes muster, you might well entertain a fourth question: "What do reviews about this type of car say about its performance?" For instance, are claims about the car's gas mileage supported? How often are repairs typically needed? Put differently, how much can you trust that the car will get you where you want to go on a regular basis with minimal maintenance?

In the event that all of the preceding questions lead you to believe that the car is indeed worth purchasing, you typically will ask a final question: "Do the benefits of this car outweigh the costs, especially as compared to other cars or to other pressing needs that I may have?" Presumably, if another car passed all of the previously mentioned criteria comparably well but cost less, you would go with it. Similarly, if you determined that some other pressing need was more important – say, payment for a medical procedure not covered by insurance – you might well pass on what otherwise seems to be a good deal.

This example is by no means accidental. Car ownership is widespread in America, and so such questions are far from academic. Even so, the reality is that most of us make similar sets of calculations about many decisions in our everyday lives. I work in a university setting and students typically need to take classes to graduate. But they do not need to take all of them. Rather, they will want to select those courses best suited to help them complete their major. They also will want courses that are taught well, and they will want to learn something as a result of taking them. At a more general level, by attending a university, they, or their parents, are proceeding on the assumption that the benefits of additional years of schooling offset the costs of not immediately entering the workforce.

Such calculations are the stuff of life and affect even our most mundane decisions. Each week, my son and I go grocery shopping and must select from what seems to be about fifty or more different types of toothpaste. We have determined (or, really, I have) that we definitely need toothpaste. We are not entirely clear why toothpaste helps, but we proceed on faith. We are pretty clear that we need to put the toothpaste on the toothbrush for it to have any chance of having an effect. However, we have not the foggiest idea which toothpaste produces the best effects. Does brand X produce fewer cavities? How about brand Y? Even if brand X is better at reducing cavities, perhaps it is not as good at preventing tartar buildup, which seems like a good thing to avoid. Perhaps it is a draw when it comes to whitening teeth. Is one brand better at reducing tooth sensitivity? Then there is the whole question of how well it freshens your breath. After making many assumptions about the relative benefits of one brand versus another, we then consider the cost of the toothpaste. Some toothpastes seem to do everything at once, but they also tend to cost more, and there is the concern that perhaps they do some things (e.g., cavity prevention) less well than others (e.g., tartar reduction). In the end, I am not at all sure we end up making the best choice. But, the steps we go through – that all of us go through in making decisions throughout the course of every day – involve a logic and sequence highly relevant to policy debates.

In particular, most of us employ an evaluation hierarchy in our decision making, especially if it involves serious financial investments. Indeed, viewing our everyday decisions as policies, and the evaluation hierarchy, as depicted

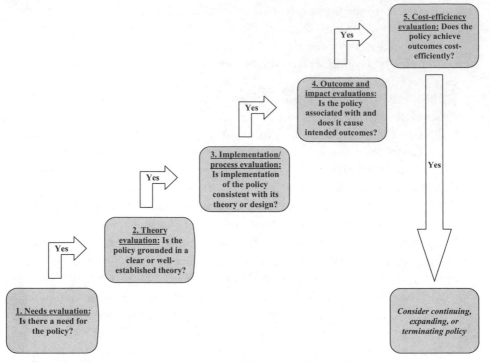

Figure 2.1. The evaluation hierarchy. Adapted from *Evaluation: A Systematic Approach*, by Peter H. Rossi, Mark W. Lipsey, and Howard E. Freeman, 7th edition, 2004, p. 80. Used with permission from Sage Publications.

in Figure 2.1, proceeds as follows. First, we assess whether a need for a policy exists; this is a *needs evaluation*. Second, we then assess whether the theory underlying the policy is logical; coherent; and, ideally, supported by research; this is a *theory evaluation*. Third, we assess how well a policy is implemented; this is typically termed an *implementation* or a *process evaluation*. Fourth, we assess (1) whether the policy actually is associated with intended outcomes (this is typically termed an *outcome evaluation*) and (2) whether it likely causes the outcomes (this is typically termed an *impact evaluation*). Fifth, we assess whether the policy's benefits outweigh its costs and whether the benefits, relative to costs, are substantially greater than those of another policy; this is a *cost-efficiency evaluation*. The first type of cost-efficiency evaluation is a cost-effectiveness analysis, which compares the costs of two or more policies aimed at achieving the same goals. The second type is a cost-benefit analysis, which compares the costs and benefits of two or more policies that have different goals. In a cost-benefit analysis, the impacts on goals are monetized (i.e., we assign monetary values to them) so that we can make apples-to-apples comparisons between two or more policies.

Each type of evaluation can be viewed as involving a particular question. In the car example, the five questions are: (1) Do we *need* a car? (2) Does the *theory* for selecting the car make sense? That is, are particular types of cars best suited, by design, to meet our needs? If so, what are the relevant considerations (e.g., appearance, comfort, gas mileage)? (3) Has the car been *implemented* well in the sense that it has been well maintained? If not, we can be reasonably sure that we may not obtain the benefits (e.g., low-cost transportation) that we want from the car. (4) Does the car actually achieve the *impacts* that we expect? Does it, for example, actually get the expected fuel savings, and is it as comfortable as reported? (5) Is the car the most *cost-efficient* way to travel from one place to the next or are there other options that would be as effective but cheaper? Alternatively, is there another, more pressing need (e.g., medical care) that, if addressed, would result in more benefits than would be gained by better transportation?

The basic logic of the hierarchy is that we do not typically want to proceed with a policy if the questions associated with each level of the hierarchy have not been adequately answered. Consider, again, a car purchase. We typically would proceed with buying a car only if we needed it. If we do need a car, most of us would buy one that fit our particular need (e.g., a compact car for commuting or a pickup truck for carting heavy equipment). Even then, we likely would not make a purchase unless we felt confident that the car had been well maintained and needed no expensive repairs. We would also be likely to refrain from a purchase if we learned that the car's performance was or would be poor. For example, a car may be touted as getting thirty miles per gallon, but perhaps independent tests establish that, in reality, the true performance lies closer to twenty miles per gallon. Finally, most of us would hold back on buying a car that performs no better than another but costs twice as much; similarly, most of us would not buy a car when the money could be used to pay for a life-saving surgery that we need.

Needless to say, when we employ the evaluation hierarchy in our day-to-day lives, we may not make accurate assessments, and we may lack sufficient information to make good judgment calls. (In all likelihood, I have been using the wrong toothpaste for many years.) But that does not negate the importance of the hierarchy in guiding our decision making and helping us to arrive at better decisions.

Here is the catch – even though most of us proceed through the evaluation hierarchy in our day-to-day decision making, criminal justice policy typically proceeds without recourse to it. That is, quite simply, irrational. The pursuit of crime prevention and justice constitute critical societal goals. No one wants to be a victim of a crime. No one wants a society in which justice is arbitrarily meted out. And, of course, no one wants to expend scarce resources willy-nilly without obtaining some type of return, ideally the most possible one, especially when the stakes are high.

The Policy Context and the Stakes Involved

A central aim of this book is to argue, through the use of the evaluation hierarchy, that many of the nation's most prominent criminal justice policies lack a solid theoretical and empirical foundation and that the necessary ingredients for holding the criminal justice system accountable and making it effective do not yet exist. I elaborate on this argument in subsequent chapters. Here, however, I want to turn to the national criminal justice policy context to highlight some of the stakes involved in allowing criminal justice policy to be irrational.

Crime Rates

To begin, let us first focus on crime rates. Many different sources of data can be used to examine crime. For example, arrests and calls to the police frequently serve as the basis for establishing whether crime has increased, decreased, or remained stable. Many news accounts focus on such data. If the number of robbery arrests increases from, for example, 100 to 110, a news account may well report that crime is up 10 percent. That would be incorrect. Law enforcement data reflect two factors: crime and law enforcement behavior.[1] Observe, for example, that a community's true crime rate could decrease, but if the number of police officers doubled you likely would see a dramatic increase in arrests and possibly reported crime. So, a more accurate news account would say that arrests have gone up 10 percent and that the increase reflects increased crime, increased law enforcement activity, or both.

If we want to determine what the true rates of crime are, it would be far better to conduct offender and victimization surveys.[2] The first would allow us to determine how many offenders exist and how much crime they commit, while the latter would allow us to identify the total number of victims of crime. No large-scale, nationally representative offender surveys exist in the United States, though a number of small-scale studies exist. By contrast, the U.S. federal government has invested a considerable amount of money and effort into conducting a large, nationally representative victimization survey, titled, appropriately enough, the National Crime Victimization Survey (NCVS). The first data collection for the study began in 1973 and today

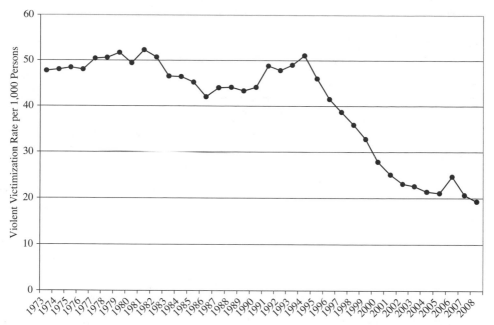

Figure 2.2. Violent victimization, 1973–2008. The increase from 2005 to 2006 is not likely a reflection of a true increase in victimization, but rather reflects a change in the methodology used with the National Crime Victimization Survey, the source for the victimization estimates (Rand 2008:2). *Sources:* Rand, Michael R. 2009. *Criminal Victimization, 2008.* Washington, D.C.: Bureau of Justice Statistics. Rand, Michael R. 2008. *Criminal Victimization, 2007.* Washington, D.C.: Bureau of Justice Statistics. Rand, Michael R., and Shannan Catalano. 2007. *Criminal Victimization, 2006.* Washington, D.C.: Bureau of Justice Statistics.

includes more than 60,000 households and the victimization experiences of persons ages twelve or older.[3]

When we examine the trends in violent crime (rape or sexual assault, robbery, and aggravated and simple assault), which typically seem to garner the most concern among the public and policy makers, we see that such crime remained relatively stable throughout the 1970s and declined in the early 1980s, as shown in Figure 2.2. Then, around 1986, it began to rise steadily, peaking in 1994 before beginning a steady decline during the next decade. The victimization survey entails the interviewing of individuals and so does not capture homicides. However, for that offense, law enforcement data tend to be relatively accurate; analyses of such data reveal that the trend in homicides during the same time period largely mirrored the trend for violent crime generally.[4] When we turn to property crime (burglary, motor vehicle theft, and theft) – as depicted in Figure 2.3 and as measured by the NCVS – we see a steady decline over three decades.[5] In short, except for the

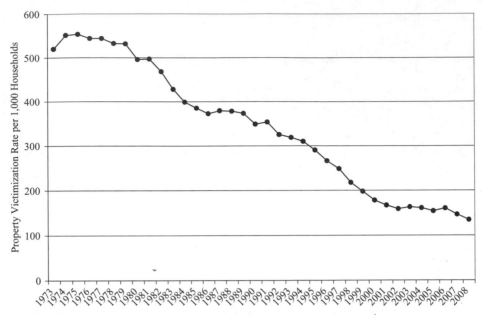

Figure 2.3. Property victimization, 1973–2008. *Sources:* Rand, Michael R. 2009. *Criminal Victimization, 2008.* Washington, D.C.: Bureau of Justice Statistics. Rand, Michael R. 2008. *Criminal Victimization, 2007.* Washington, D.C.: Bureau of Justice Statistics. Rand, Michael R., and Shannan Catalano. 2007. *Criminal Victimization, 2006.* Washington, D.C.: Bureau of Justice Statistics.

rise in violent crime from 1986 to 1994, crime has been stable or declining since 1973.

Correctional System Growth

On the basis of analysis of these trends, we might reasonably hypothesize that the criminal justice system would have increased modestly in the 1980s to early 1990s to address the rise in violent crime but that it otherwise would have remained stable and perhaps even decreased in size. Such a prediction would be wrong. Juxtaposed against the overall decline in violent and property crime has been unprecedented growth in the criminal justice system. The growth in corrections alone is striking, as can be seen in Figure 2.4. In 1980, there were 1.8 million individuals under some form of state or federal supervision or incarcerated in jail or prison. By 2008, that number more than quadrupled, rising to 7.3 million.

By far, the biggest driver of that growth has been the increase in the probation population, which has risen from 1.1 million to 4.3 million. Even so, the

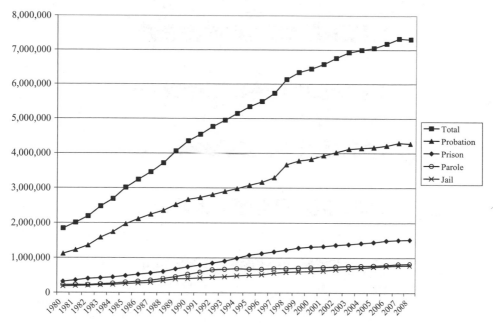

Figure 2.4. U.S. correctional populations, 1980–2008. *Source:* Bureau of Justice Statistics. 2009. *Correctional Populations in the United States.* Washington, D.C.: U.S. Department of Justice. Available online: http://www.ojp.usdoj.gov/bjs/glance/tables/corr2tab.htm (accessed December 15, 2009).

jail and prison populations increased at higher rates. For example, the number of individuals in jail grew from 183,988 to 785,556, an increase of 327 percent. Prison populations grew even more, increasing from 319,598 inmates to more than 1.5 million, or 375 percent. That growth is striking given that jails and prisons typically cost considerably more to build and operate compared with the costs of probation and parole or various types of community supervision and intermediate sanctions. They also, for all intents and purposes, constitute permanent investments. For example, once a prison is built, it generally will remain in use for decades. So, any expansion in prison capacity essentially represents an indefinite commitment to increased prison costs. Why? When states decide to expand prison capacity, they cannot easily undo that decision if, at a later point, they determine that less capacity is needed.

Prisoner Reentry

The large-scale increase in the number of individuals incarcerated in jails and prisons translates into a new social problem – namely, the return of large numbers of ex-prisoners back into communities, what has been termed

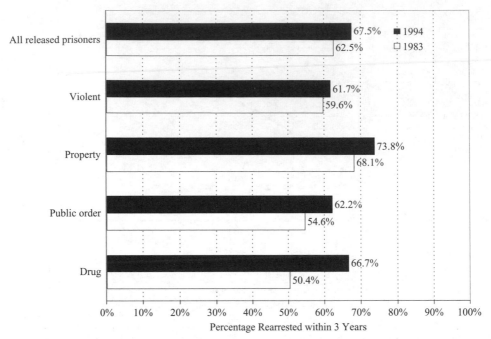

Figure 2.5. Recidivism of prisoners from 15 states released in 1983 and in 1994. *Source:* Langan, Patrick A., and David J. Levin. 2002. *Recidivism of Prisoners Released in 1994.* Washington, D.C.: Bureau of Justice Statistics.

"prisoner reentry."[6] Annually, more than 735,000 inmates leave state or federal prisons[7] and undergo the process of transitioning from institutional life to a context in which they have few opportunities for employment and frequently suffer from a number of problems, including mental and physical health problems, substance abuse, family dysfunction, histories of physical and sexual abuse, and spotty educational and employment histories.[8] Of particular concern is the high likelihood that these individuals will recidivate. Figure 2.5 shows the rates of recidivism from one of the largest national studies ever conducted. It reveals that, in 1994, more than two-thirds (68 percent) of released prisoners were rearrested within three years.

Remarkably, after the large-scale increases in the correctional system and the spate of "get tough" crime policies in the 1980s and 1990s, this level of recidivism was higher than it was a decade earlier. (In 1983, "only" 63 percent of released prisoners were rearrested within three years.) It remains unclear why the increase occurred, although it may have stemmed in part from a decline in educational, vocational, and treatment programming in prisons during this time period.[9] It also may have reflected more vigorous law enforcement activity. For example, numerous efforts were taken to target drug crimes, which would have increased drug arrests. Indirect support for that explanation can be seen at the bottom of the figure – the percentage of drug offenders rearrested increased from 50 percent to 67 percent between 1983 and 1994. Observe that recidivism in the study was measured using rearrest. That means that the study included only those crimes for which a released prisoner was arrested. If measured using self-reported offending data, the recidivism rate assuredly would have been higher.

In short, America now faces a situation in which ever-greater numbers of individuals are returning to communities and almost all of these individuals continue to commit crime. The "glass half full" view of the situation is that considerable room for improvement exists, especially given the ubiquity of reoffending among people released from prison. The "glass half empty" view, however, is that we may not be able to make much of a dent in recidivism rates given the commitment to increased incarceration. Of course, it can be argued that incarceration helps society by reducing crime through incapacitation or general deterrent effects. So, even if recidivism rates remain high or increase, perhaps that negative is offset by the positive of overall decreased rates of crime. There is some evidence – although far from compelling – to suggest warrant for such optimism, as will be discussed in later chapters. Regardless, recidivism stands as a concern in its own right – few of us want someone who may reoffend moving next door to where we live.

Criminal Justice Expenditures

Putting aside such concerns, the stakes involved in criminal justice policy can be highlighted by turning to economic considerations. Given the growth in the criminal justice system, it perhaps should come as no surprise that criminal justice expenditures have dramatically increased as well, as is evident from Figure 2.6. From 1982 to 2006, the United States increased its investment in police more than fivefold, from $19 billion to more than $99 billion. It increased its investment in corrections almost eightfold during the same time span, from $9 billion to $69 billion. And it increased its investment in the judiciary – which is required to process the large influx of new cases – from almost $8 billion to $47 billion. Adding all functions together, from 1982 to 2006, criminal justice expenditures rose by 500 percent, from $36 billion to $215 billion. Inflation accounts only for $30 billion or so of that increase.[10]

The burden of these new costs has largely fallen to local jurisdictions and to states, not the federal government. Figure 2.7 depicts the trends in criminal justice expenditures by level of government. The most dramatic increase,

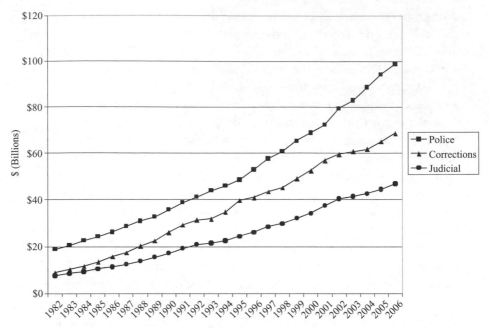

Figure 2.6. Criminal justice expenditures by function, 1982–2006. *Source:* Bureau of Justice Statistics. 2009. *Justice Expenditure and Employment Extracts*. Washington, D.C.: U.S. Department of Justice. Available online: http://www.ojp.usdoj.gov/bjs/glance/tables/exptyptab.htm (accessed October 1, 2009).

in absolute amounts, clearly lies with local jurisdictions. In 1982, localities had $21 billion in criminal justice expenditures. By 2006, their expenditures increased to $109 billion. States' investments in criminal justice rose almost as dramatically during this same time period, from $11 billion to $69 billion. And federal expenditures rose from $4 billion to $36 billion. As of 2006, roughly 51 percent of all criminal justice expenditures were borne by local jurisdictions, 32 percent by states, and 17 percent by the federal government.

Evidence for Current Criminal Justice Policies

Set against a backdrop of dramatic increases in criminal justice funding and in federal funding for a wide range of crime prevention and crime control policies is the pressing concern that too little research exists to support the selection and continued support of many of these policies. Several criminal justice policy reviews that have emerged in recent years suggest, in fact, that most criminal justice policies lack a strong empirical foundation. A National Academy of Sciences review found, for example, that "scientifically strong impact evaluations of [crime prevention and crime control] programs,

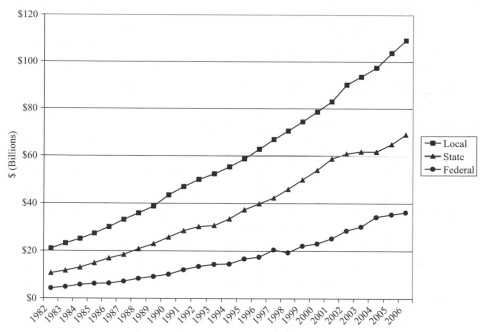

Figure 2.7. Criminal justice expenditures by level of government, 1982–2006. *Source:* Bureau of Justice Statistics. 2009. *Justice Expenditure and Employment Extracts.* Washington, D.C.: U.S. Department of Justice. Available online: http://www.ojp.usdoj.gov/bjs/glance/expgov.htm (accessed October 1, 2009).

while improving, are still uncommon in the context of the overall number of programs that have received funding."[11] Similar critiques, discussed in later chapters, have been leveled against many different parts of the criminal justice system.

In various ways, this book will tackle the question of whether the criminal justice policy investments of the past several decades have been wise choices. What I will argue is that, by and large, local and state governments, and the country as a whole, lack an institutionalized foundation for conducting the types of research necessary to produce wise choices, much less to show that existing choices are sensible. The result? Too little evidence exists to support many if not most of the policies and practices that constitute the nation's criminal justice system.

Ultimately, the failure to use research to inform criminal justice policy constitutes a profound mistake with real-world consequences. Society spends a great deal of resources on catching and punishing as well as treating offenders. It has spent even more in recent decades. Even so, a limited supply of funds exists. We cannot, for example, build enough prisons to house every person who commits a crime. As with our individual financial decisions, mistakes about the allocation of large amounts of time and money can have dramatic affects. They can, for example, contribute to a lack of accountability; to a failure to identify or implement evidence-based policies; and, more generally, to ineffective and inefficient criminal justice policies.

Influences on Criminal Justice Policy

Given the pronounced increase in calls for greater government accountability and evidence-based practice, why does so much of the criminal justice system and the laws, practices, programs, rules, and protocols that constitute it remain unexamined and largely hidden in the equivalent of a "black box"? Why, more generally, is there a seemingly large disjuncture between calls for accountability and evidence-based policy and the realization of these calls through the research base necessary to have accountability or to identify evidence-based policies that are effective and cost efficient?

Many scholars have tackled these questions, including the broader one of why any criminal justice policy is adopted.[12] In the following discussion, I describe several possible explanations. In so doing, I recognize that any adequate account about the emergence of specific policies or policy trends typically must reference a multitude of social and economic conditions and their interactions with one another over time.[13] Nonetheless, this discussion serves to highlight the many and varied forces that can conspire against rational, evidence-based policy. In turn, it underscores the need for systematic integration of evaluation research into policy development, implementation, and assessment to help address this situation.

Politicization of Crime

One prominent explanation for why many criminal justice policies emerge can be summarized in one word – *politicization*. From this perspective, policy makers focus on crime to advance their interests. That is, they are motivated more by the thought of political gain than by a sincere belief that crime will be affected.[14] Of course, many policy makers sincerely believe that crime merits attention not because of any political gain that may accrue to them but because, in their view, it constitutes a substantial problem.[15]

Nonetheless, the politicization of crime has featured prominently in many compelling accounts of crime policies. What benefits, though, does this strategy – what some scholars characterize as "symbolic politics" – confer upon policy makers? Among other things, it may enhance their electability and divert attention from other, more divisive social problems.[16] It also, as scholars have argued, may enhance state power and the interests of an elite social class at the expense of the socially disadvantaged. For example, David Garland, who has written at great length about the crime policies of the 1980s and 1990s in the United States and in Great Britain, has noted: "Crime – together with associated 'underclass' behaviors such as drug abuse, teenage pregnancy, single parenthood, and welfare dependency – came to function as a rhetorical legitimation for social and economic policies that effectively punished the poor and as a justification for the development of a strong disciplinary state."[17]

Why would crime serve as a convenient target for generating political capital among policy makers and, more generally, for increasing state power? Garland's work highlights that the ideological rhetoric employed in policy discussions in the 1980s and 1990s viewed individual behavior as resulting largely, if not exclusively, from self-discipline and moral character, not from the social contexts and conditions in which individuals reside. Such a view, which represents a philosophical orientation more than a scientific one,[18] dovetails with the more general political ideologies of the conservative governments that prevailed in both the United States and the United Kingdom during these decades. Garland and others have argued that support for a broad array of conservative policies at this time was facilitated by focusing on crime and, in particular, by framing crime policy decisions using the language of conservative political ideologies.

Crime served as a useful target for additional reasons. One is that violent crime worsened during the 1980s. Another is that little political fallout occurs when policy makers focus on criminals. In fact, a failure to establish a record of being tough on criminals can substantially limit a policy maker's career, as occurred when George H. W. Bush ran the now-famous Willy Horton advertisement in his campaign against Massachusetts Governor Michael Dukakis for the presidency. Horton, incarcerated in a Massachusetts prison for murder, was released on furlough during Dukakis's time as governor; while on furlough, he raped a woman.[19] The advertisement was widely viewed as contributing to Dukakis's defeat. Another prominent example arose in Texas in the early 1990s. Ann Richards, a Democrat, ran against George W. Bush for governor in 1994 and, unlike Dukakis, attempted to compete in part on the basis of her ability to be tougher on crime than her opponent.[20] Ultimately, she, too, lost out to a conservative candidate who more strongly emphasized a tough-on-crime platform.

Arguments about the politicization of crime have emerged in an era in which conservatives arguably have had a greater role in dictating the tenor

of criminal justice policy. Concomitantly, "get tough" approaches to crime
and punishment have predominated.[21] It would be reasonable, therefore, to
assume that conservatives politicize crime and liberals do not. The assumption would, however, be incorrect. Crime has been and can be politicized by
conservatives and liberals alike, as the Ann Richards example illustrates and
as research attests.[22]

False Dichotomies

Whether one accepts arguments about the politicization of crime, politics
may influence criminal justice policy in other ways. For example, the nature
of political debates, especially in contexts where two political parties pre-
dominate, tends to create false either-or dichotomies. In any democracy,
policy makers must strive to gauge the public will and determine which social
problems merit attention and what should be done about them. Necessarily,
then, policy makers must reduce a great deal of complexity to simplified
descriptions of the problems and the options for addressing them. Such an
approach unfortunately lends itself to creating overly simplified distillations,
and, indeed, to two-scenario options – there is X way of doing things or
Y way of doing things. That approach neatly accords with a conservative-
liberal dichotomy. Even so, it frames discussions and debates in terms that
frequently misrepresent reality.

One prominent example consists of the rehabilitation versus punishment
divide in American politics.[23] Media accounts present anyone who promotes
rehabilitation as a liberal and anyone who promotes punishment as conservative. The problem lies in the fact that few policy makers hew exclusively
to one or the other dimension but instead differ in the extent to which they
support both approaches to managing and sanctioning offenders. In a class
I teach on juvenile justice, students frequently express surprise that the public strongly supports punishment of violent offenders *and* that the public
also strongly supports providing rehabilitative services to such offenders.[24]
On the face of it, the students seem justified in their surprise. How could
the public support both punishment and rehabilitation? Observe, however,
that nothing about one view precludes the other. Consider, for example,
that parents typically employ many different strategies – including a diverse
array of "carrots" and "sticks" – for managing children who break rules and,
more generally, for socializing them into the ways of the world. Few of us
would level the critique that doing so is necessarily inconsistent or odd. By
extension, there should appear nothing especially notable or contradictory
about the public supporting diverse approaches to addressing juvenile or
adult crime.

Such nuances frequently get lost in the policy-making arena, which all too often glosses over nuance and substitutes in its place dichotomies that not only simplify but also distort public views. To illustrate, a policy maker who holds the view that punishment and rehabilitation should be weighted equally may nonetheless feel compelled to emphasize one more than the other. The tenor of a political debate may require such a packaging of one's views. Recent news accounts about, say, a felon who committed a violent crime while on probation, may force policy makers to articulate more extreme versions of their viewpoints. As the Willy Horton example illustrates, such possibilities are far from hypothetical. During the 1980s and 1990s, it would have been difficult for many policy makers to be elected or reelected if they argued for policies that equally balanced rehabilitation and punishment.[25]

Long ago, Benjamin Franklin held up as a virtue the notion that we should do everything in moderation. Following that dictum may not always lead to good outcomes, but in some cases it would appear to be the better part of wisdom. In the case of criminal justice policies, extreme policies constitute the equivalent of stock-market speculation, where you sink all your eggs into one company's stock in the hopes that it will produce fabulous returns. That may happen. However, it may not, and on the face of it, such returns seem highly unlikely. Criminology offers little by way of research that establishes whether punishment or rehabilitation produces the most or greatest impact.[26] Clearly, punishment seems like the hands-down winner if the goal is retribution. Not everyone weights retribution in the same manner, however. More relevant is the fact that if our goal is reduced recidivism, the research evidence to date would suggest that either can be effective, depending on how they are implemented. That is, punishment can reduce recidivism, but it also may increase it, and rehabilitation may reduce recidivism, but it also may have no impact. Much rests on the precise type of punishment or rehabilitation and how exactly it is implemented.[27] In short, when policy makers create or are pushed into accepting false dichotomies, the likelihood increases that ineffective and inefficient criminal justice policies will emerge.

Swings from One Extreme to Another

The false dichotomy problem is compounded by a similar yet slightly different political dynamic. Specifically, the nature of many political systems, and certainly of America's political system, leads to dramatic swings in policy. In the United States, for example, the country's crime policy approaches have changed dramatically from one era to the next, most recently transitioning away from the rehabilitation-oriented, crime-prevention approaches that prevailed in the 1960s and 1970s and toward the more punishment-oriented approaches that have prevailed since.[28] Thomas Bernard has illustrated the problem in his account of the juvenile justice system, noting that, regardless of juvenile crime trends, policy makers and the public become increasingly disenchanted with the current set of policies in place and substitute in their place policies that lie at the other end of the philosophical spectrum. As a result, juvenile justice tends to cycle back and forth between lenient policies and harsh, punitive policies.[29] Such transitions frequently occur with little to no assessment of the precise problems, the effectiveness of the current set of policies, or the best mix of strategies for addressing crime and improving criminal justice operations. The end result is a costly transitioning from one set of approaches to another and the whole-cloth adoption of many new strategies that have been unevaluated and that, after implementation, remain so.

As the preceding discussions have indicated, the latest swing in American criminal justice policy has been toward "get tough" punishment-oriented philosophies. The effect of this swing arguably has been and will be greater than earlier ones given the dramatic growth in America's prison population and the attendant fixed commitment of resources for incarceration. It is relatively easy to dismantle a particular law or program. Politically, however, it is not easy to generate support for dismantling prisons, and indeed, one rarely reads accounts where a given state's prison capacity declines. In the past decade, many policy makers have derided the growth in prison populations, noting that it cannot be sustained and calling for "get smart" rather than "get tough" options. Even so, prison populations have steadily continued to grow.[30] One benefit of the situation may be that it reduces the likelihood of a dramatic swing toward a different set of policies. Yet it also reduces the ability to achieve what might constitute a more balanced and ultimately more effective portfolio of strategies for managing, reducing, and preventing crime and for achieving justice.

Bad Cases Make for Bad Policies

Another influence on policy is a political dynamic in which cases that are not representative of most others serve as the basis for new laws and policies. The expression "bad cases make for bad laws" captures this idea. In any given year, atrocious examples – such as the Willy Horton case – exist of the criminal justice system having failed. The problem arises from the fact that virtually any policy, no matter how effective, will include failures. Consider that, on average, and as shown in Figure 2.5, roughly two-thirds of individuals released from prison will be rearrested within three years.[31] Suppose a program in a particular state could reduce that rate of recidivism to 50 percent. Such a reduction would be greater than many of the best programs.[32] Still, a large number of released inmates would still go on to commit more crime, providing endless fodder for complaints that somehow the criminal justice system is "broke" and requires fundamentally new responses. Of course, if one is going to complain, it helps to focus on the most extreme cases. The problem lies in the fact that such cases not only always occur but also are just that: extreme and not representative of the overwhelming majority of offenders or cases that enter the juvenile or criminal justice systems.

This situation is complicated by the fact that policy makers attempt to respond to the public and, at the same time, frequently must respond to issues as they are depicted in media accounts. So, if the media, as much research attests, is biased toward publicizing the most sensational crimes, policy makers feel compelled to respond.[33] The public's lack of understanding of many aspects of the criminal justice system, including the amount of crime and the levels and quality of punishment and rehabilitative services,[34] further compounds this problem. A dynamic thus ensues in which sensational cases, not the everyday ones, drive criminal justice policy. Indeed, one might argue that a "perfect storm" of distortion emerges because many public opinion polls ask only a few questions, focusing on sensational cases, and then the media publicizes these responses. Policy makers proceed to interpret such results as representative of public opinion about crime and its solutions, although the findings speak only to public views about a very particular type of crime.

In reality, public views about crime and justice are complicated, nuanced, and highly variable depending on such factors as the issue involved and the nature of the question wording and the response options. For example, support for the death penalty drops roughly 20 percentage points when respondents are asked to express their level of support in a context where life in prison without the option of parole is included as part of the set of options for sanctioning murderers.[35]

Symbolic Gestures

Paralleling and contributing to these problems is a situation in which policy makers frequently feel pushed into doing something – anything, in fact – that demonstrates their responsiveness to crime as a problem.[36] The result can be a penchant for responding to the latest crisis with some type of new, and typically extreme, response rather than to deliberate assessment of the problem and what can and should be done about it.[37] In recent decades, for example, many new penalties have been imposed on convicted felons, creating a penumbra of "invisible" or hidden punishments, such as restrictions on employment, housing, welfare, and voting, all of which go well beyond the traditional notion of having inmates serve their time and then reenter society as citizens with the full set of rights they had prior to incarceration.[38] Perhaps such restrictions were needed to create a more powerful general deterrent effect to would-be offenders, and perhaps they help to reduce the recidivism of the released prisoners. There is, however, little theoretical or empirical research to support such a claim.

These additional invisible punishments arguably emerged not from a considered assessment of the need for them or their effectiveness, but rather from policy makers' desire to provide symbolic gestures of their responsiveness to public concern about crime. Here, again, it is important to recognize that such arguments assume a level of political calculation that does not necessarily accord with reality. For example, many policy makers clearly want to serve the public interest and do so with a sincere commitment to pursuing policies that they feel are needed and will be effective.

Public Opinion and Policy Makers' Misunderstanding of It

Reviews of public opinion research consistently reveal that public views about crime are, as discussed earlier, complicated and nuanced.[39] Studies typically show that the public supports a range of strategies, some rehabilitative in nature and some punishment oriented, for reducing crime and that the level of support varies over time.[40] They show that the majority of the public views prison as a breeding ground for crime but that they also, while supportive of rehabilitation,[41] have doubts about the effectiveness of rehabilitation as it occurs in practice. As Julian Roberts and Mike Hough found in their review of public opinion research on views toward rehabilitation in the prison system, "People around the world support the principle that prisons *should* rehabilitate offenders, however, they do not believe that in practice it succeeds in doing so."[42]

The public also tends to know very little about the criminal justice system as it operates in practice. With respect to prisons, for example, "the public around the world underestimates the severity of life inside prison."[43] Indeed, many view prisoners as having an "easy ride" that amounts to a vacation with no work responsibilities and innumerable opportunities to play and watch television in well-heated or air-conditioned housing.[44] Not surprisingly, then, studies frequently show that the public supports lengthier and tougher prison sentences.[45] The unfamiliarity with criminal justice extends to more than just prison, however. As Francis Cullen and his colleagues have noted, for many areas of criminal justice, "including knowledge of trends in crime rates, of the prevalence of violent crimes, of recidivism rates, of specific criminal laws, of legal reforms, of legal rights in the criminal justice process, and of the extent to which the insanity plea is used successfully – the lack of knowledge [among the public] is widespread."[46] This lack of knowledge "allows cynical use of simplistic slogans and policies that respond to the public's emotional needs but do not address the substantive challenge," as Alfred Blumstein has noted.[47]

Given this lack of knowledge and the complexity of public opinion,[48] it should not be surprising that the views of the public do not readily translate into simple either-or (e.g., rehabilitate or punish) options. As a case in point, studies find that even when the public believes prison time is too lenient and filled with too many amenities, they do not "necessarily want to make it more aversive," but rather want to do away with idleness and replace it with work.[49]

Policy makers appear to operate within a political context in which the complexity of public views sometimes must be downplayed or ignored.[50] As but one example, many of the "get tough" reforms of the 1990s emerged from policy makers' assumption that the public called for such reforms and not for any other approaches. However, studies have shown that policy makers overestimated how much the public wanted punitive sanctions and underestimated how much they wanted such things as vocational training; conjugal visits for inmates; counseling and therapy; and, more generally, rehabilitation.[51] One striking example of this phenomenon can be seen in a study of Michigan policy makers, which found that "while only 12 percent of policy makers believed the public would support rehabilitation as a criminal justice objective, in reality two-thirds of the public took this view."[52]

In a democracy, we expect that the public will should at least inform policy discussions and debates.[53] It should not necessarily dictate policy. Even so, public views are foundational to democracy. For that reason, one of the more striking findings from public opinion research is the fact that policy makers frequently misestimate or distort, whether consciously or not, public views about crime and its causes and solutions. Given the way in which political decision making occurs, such misunderstanding helps contribute to policies that not only reflect extreme and unrepresentative cases but also fail to reflect public sentiment.

Belief in "Silver Bullet" Causes and Solutions to Crime

Another factor that contributes to ineffective policy is the seemingly widespread belief among policy makers that there exist "silver bullet" causes of criminal justice problems and "silver bullet" solutions to them.[54] A silver bullet approach is effective when, among other things, the following conditions hold: the targeted cause is truly a cause of the outcome of interest (e.g., criminal behavior), the cause is widespread, and the cause is easily amenable to modification. These conditions rarely if ever hold true in criminal justice, and yet many – although certainly not all – policies take a largely single-minded focus toward reducing crime.

To illustrate, a plethora of laws and programs have emerged that focus on illegal drug use and selling. Many of these efforts create enhanced penalties for such crimes, or for committing other crimes while using illegal drugs, and are widely viewed as contributing to the dramatic growth in the correctional system in recent decades.[55] At the same time, drug courts, which specialize in handling drug offenders and drug-using offenders, have proliferated since the early 1990s.[56]

In part, the focus on drugs appears to be fueled by a belief that illegal drug use causes crime and that it does so in a dramatic way. Notably, however, it remains unclear how strong the relationship between individual drug use and offending is and whether the relationship is causal.[57] In asserting a causal relationship, one might point to the fact that many people in prison have or had drug problems or were using drugs at the time of their offense.[58] If that were the only problem that prisoners exhibited, the causal claim would be easier to accept. Yet the reality is that the profile of the typical prisoner leads to a host of factors – such as mental illness, homelessness, unemployment, abuse[59] – that could be the cause of their behavior, including their drug use. Complicating matters is the fact that, while various sanctions and treatments can reduce drug problems; resolution of these problems is not simple; relapse is common, and many interventions are costly, especially if implemented as intended.[60] In short, two of the conditions for an effective silver bullet solution do not appear to be present when it comes to drug-related offending. At the same time, a large body of research points to many other factors that cause crime and to the likelihood that the most effective approaches to crime prevention involve a focus on multiple causes of offending.[61]

To be clear, there seems little doubt that drugs play some role in crime and offending. It remains unclear, however, whether a largely exclusive focus on drug-related crime would substantially reduce overall crime or recidivism rates.[62] Certainly, a balanced approach to reducing crime might involve a focus on illegal drugs. The silver bullet approach, however, places a primary emphasis on drugs. For example, when a criminal justice system gives priority to drug treatment, it typically must reduce its emphasis on other approaches to resolving crime, if only because most systems operate within a zero-sum environment in which a limited pool of resources exist. So, if a jurisdiction decides to create a drug court, it necessarily will have fewer resources to devote specialized attention to other populations.

It may be argued that many jurisdictions and many correctional systems embrace a diversified portfolio of approaches, not a silver bullet approach, to fighting crime. In reality, however, priority is frequently given to a select few approaches. Consider, for example, that while drug courts have proliferated nationally, few other such specialized (e.g., mental health, drug, community) courts have enjoyed such popularity. Consider, too, at a national level, the dramatic increase in prison systems, which is tantamount to a belief that increased incarceration, more than a range of other approaches, can substantially reduce crime. Here, again, the point is not that such approaches are ineffective. Rather, it is that much criminal justice policy making is aimed at finding silver bullet solutions rather than at creating comprehensive, research-based approaches to crime reduction.

Limited Production of Policy Research

To this point, many of the factors that have been described as influencing criminal justice policy and that serve as barriers to research-based criminal justice policy making have centered on political factors. What about research itself, or, perhaps more precisely, the lack of research, as a barrier to better policies? As a general matter, most accounts – including American Society of Criminology presidential addresses – wax pessimistic about the influence of research on policy. They point to innumerable instances in which policies get adopted with little to no attention to prior research and in which poorly conceived policies continue unabated and unevaluated. Even so, a number of scholars have pointed to evidence that, at least on occasion, research influences policy.[63] If we were to average the two views, the situation might be aptly described as one where, by and large, research provides little by way of a positive influence on policy but where many exceptions exist. Assuming that this assessment is correct, the question emerges as to why research has had relatively little influence on policy. Here, I will briefly touch on some of the major factors scholars have identified.[64]

The first and perhaps most important problem is the lack of an institutionalized foundation for systematically integrating evaluation research into decisions about criminal justice policies and for monitoring and assessing the criminal justice system as a whole. For example, federal funding for crime and justice research is minimal relative to investments in other policy areas.[65] At the state, county, city, and municipal levels, few agencies allot much funding for research, and what funding exists typically is provided for compiling highly descriptive annual reports that say little about the need for or the design, implementation, effectiveness, or efficiency of a range of policies.

This situation is compounded by a second problem: specifically, policy evaluation research – what sometimes gets referred to as "applied research" because of the focus on applying research to policy – traditionally gets short shrift within universities.[66] Many factors have contributed to this dynamic. By historical standards, criminology is a newcomer in the academic world. As Joan Petersilia has noted, criminology was not offered as a major in universities until the early 1930s, and it was not until 1950 that the first criminology program formally emerged.[67] As a newcomer, considerable pressure existed to elevate the status of the discipline to a "science," which meant focusing on questions about the causes of crime and not necessarily the solutions to it.[68]

Not surprisingly, such circumstances can lead to a bias away from policy research and toward so-called basic research. In turn, not only do university scholars tend to shy away from policy research, but they also tend not to train graduate students in the art and science of evaluation research.[69] In addition, the orientation toward basic research diminishes the likelihood of developing strong institutional ties between university researchers and local, state, and federal criminal justice system agencies. Notably, when criminology programs first emerged, practitioners held more sway in the classroom, "but since the academic has largely replaced the practitioner in the classroom and in research, the link has grown weaker and, with it, that kind of immediate influence."[70]

Even when scholars undertake policy-related research, they typically do not translate their findings in a way that is accessible to policy makers and practitioners. Other researchers have the training and time to sift through myriad statistical analyses; policy makers and practitioners typically do not. Even so, translating sophisticated analyses so that nonresearchers can easily digest them can be challenging, especially if, as is frequently the case, many caveats and limitations bear emphasis. To illustrate, a study may show that a given program reduces recidivism, but that finding may apply only to similar programs, such as those that serve similar clients. It may be that the effect was not particularly large. It may be that only drug recidivism was reduced but not violent or property recidivism. It also may be that the effect only emerged when participants fully completed all aspects of the program. Scholars are trained to give considerable weight to such nuances and to stick closely to the limits of what the type and quality of data and analyses allow. Consequently, it can be a struggle to try to discuss the results in a way that runs counter to their training. That struggle can turn into resistance if they feel that policy makers or the media purposely or unwittingly distort such results.

A third problem is the limited funding for criminal justice and crime policy research. Petersilia has remarked that "the federal government is, by orders of magnitude, the largest funder of research on criminal justice policy."[71] However, federal funding for criminal justice research has been nominal and remains so. Consider the funding of the National Institute of Justice (NIJ), which serves as the main federal agency focused on criminal justice evaluation and policy researches. Writing in 1995, Blumstein and Petersilia observed that NIJ's budget "has been essentially flat (with slight declines in real terms) since 1981 and has stayed in the range of about $20 million to $30 million since then – well short of a priority."[72] By 2008, more than a decade after that observation, funding for the agency had increased to $37 million,[73] a modest increase but still well short of constituting a priority, especially in a context where federal and state criminal justice expenditures, well into the billions of dollars, escalated dramatically and where baseline levels of funding were minimal compared to federal investments in other social policy arenas. The point was made bluntly by Petersilia, who, in 1991, commented that "for every U.S. citizen, federal funders spend $32 on health research, but only 13 cents on criminal justice research."[74] That situation remains largely the same today despite the dramatic increases in violent crime and in criminal justice system expenditures that occurred during the decades after Petersilia made this observation.[75]

A fourth problem has been the relative lack of investment in high-quality impact evaluations that rely on experimental designs. The gold standard for impact evaluations is the experiment, precisely because, if well conducted, the results can be interpreted in a straightforward manner as indicating that a program "works" or does not. Most criminal justice policies go unevaluated, and the few that are evaluated typically get examined using nonexperimental research designs.[76] The use of the latter type of designs can be problematic because they tend to find positive impacts of programs in cases where the impacts are not real.[77] Consequently, the results of many studies rest on shaky foundations and so lead to a situation in which researchers must be highly cautious in reporting results. A typical example, created for illustrative purposes here, would be a study in which the hypothetical conclusion reads as follows:

> The results here suggest that program X may reduce the recidivism of moderate-risk male offenders but not necessarily affect the recidivism of high-risk or low-risk offenders or of female offenders. In addition, the results should be interpreted with caution given that the study sample consisted of a highly select group, including inmates who volunteered to participate in the study, and given that many acts of recidivism may have gone unreported to law enforcement. Indeed, because the study could not fully address important potential selection effects, the estimated effects of the program may be biased. Put differently, were the selection effects better addressed, the study may have found no difference between the treatment and comparison groups in their rates of recidivism.

A policy maker would understandably view such an account as not especially helpful in making a decision about whether to close down, continue, or expand the program.

The problem lies not just with a lack of experiments in criminal justice policy research but also with a lack of high-quality quasi-experimental research (i.e., studies that attempt to approximate an experimental design).[78] All too often, the design of such research is weak, and the result tends to be a situation in which the positive impacts of a program are overstated.[79] Frequently, too, experimental and quasi-experimental research designs rely on sample sizes that are too small to allow one to detect anything other than an extremely large impact.[80] Many policies and programs that may be effective thus are reported not to be. (These and related issues are discussed in Chapter 7.)

A fifth problem is that researchers frequently focus their attention on the problems and policies that policy makers emphasize or that constitute the "hot topics" of the day. In so doing, they ignore a wide range of important policies and policy emphases. Francis Cullen and Paul Gendreau have drawn attention, for example, to the fact that in the 1970s, a period when rehabilitation increasingly was viewed as ineffective, "the study of corrections became largely the study of social problems," and so "criminologists paid scant attention to 'what works' to change offenders."[81] Indeed, this bias was institutionalized through publishing biases: "[scholars] were praised and rewarded with opportunities to publish their research when they could show that an acclaimed program did not live up to its billing."[82] Criminologists thus tended to emphasize the negative over the positive and did so in part because of a political climate in which rehabilitation came into disrepute.[83]

Other barriers related to the production of research exist as well. For example, evaluations sometimes take years to complete, but policy makers frequently need and want results sooner. This problem is amplified by the lack of institutionalized linkages among universities, research organizations, and the agencies that constitute the criminal justice system, in part because the absence of such linkages delays access to data.

All is not bleak, however. As Petersilia has emphasized, research can and does exert a positive effect on policy. It has "helped shape the way police are deployed," "demonstrated the effectiveness of career criminal programs in prosecutors' offices," "improved the ability to classify offenders and to predict recidivism," "provided information about the relationship between drug abuse and crime" and "participation in rehabilitation programs [does not] necessarily [reduce] recidivism."[84]

That said, substantial improvements could be made for potentially little cost. In the book's final chapter, I will provide a discussion of specific steps – such as the use of systemwide, comprehensive performance measurement and monitoring – for making such improvements. In so doing, I will spotlight research-based efforts that hold promise for enhancing the contribution and role of research in criminal justice policy.

Conclusion

America stands at a unique juncture in the history of its criminal justice system. Unprecedented growth in this system and in criminal justice expenditures, along with an ever-growing panoply of policies, create substantial concerns about whether the growth, expenditures, and policies make sense. The evaluation hierarchy highlights some of the critical concerns. Have the growth and the investments been needed? Do the policies rest on sound theoretical grounds? Have they been well implemented? Do they achieve expected outcomes? And have the investments been allocated to the problems and policies where the greatest gain will accrue? By and large, and as subsequent chapters will argue, research is silent about such questions as they relate to the criminal justice system's many policies, practices, protocols, and rules. In those cases where research exists, it sometimes waxes positive. However, it all too frequently suffers from critical problems or provides pessimistic or equivocal assessments.

This situation is cause for particular concern, especially given the unprecedented growth in the size and costs of the American criminal justice system and the more than 735,000 prisoners released back into society annually, more than two-thirds of whom will recidivate. The very real possibility exists that this growth and the many policies enacted in recent decades have done little to make the public safer or as safe as might be possible with investments in other approaches to crime control and prevention.

Juxtaposed against this situation is a context in which myriad forces – such as the politicization of crime and the belief in silver bullet solutions to crime – lead to continued creation of and investment in criminal justice policies that may not be the most effective or efficient. Policies will always result from a constellation of factors. Nonetheless, efforts to make criminal justice more accountable or to place it on a more evidence-based foundation will not likely succeed without more and better research. What is needed is a systematic approach to developing, monitoring, and assessing criminal justice policy. That approach is the focus of the next chapter.

Discussion Questions

What have been the prominent crime and criminal justice system trends in recent decades?

What are the risks of adopting unnecessary, ineffective, or inefficient criminal justice policies?

How can greater government accountability or reliance on evidence-based criminal justice policies be achieved?

What factors influence the creation of criminal justice policies, and which ones matter the most? Why?

What role can evaluation research play in contributing to accountability in the criminal justice system and to more effective and efficient policies?

3

A Solution for Improving Criminal Justice Policy

Evaluation Research

THE CENTRAL ARGUMENT OF THIS BOOK IS THAT AN EVALUATION RESEARCH framework provides one solution for helping make criminal justice policy more accountable and effective. More precisely, application of an evaluation framework on a widespread basis throughout the criminal justice system and as part of policy-making efforts can help ensure that (1) the need for policies is clearly identified, (2) policies rest on a solid theoretical or logical foundation, (3) are implemented well, (4) are effective, and (5) achieve their goals in a cost-efficient manner. These five dimensions constitute the cornerstones of the evaluation hierarchy. Evaluation research is no panacea, but it nonetheless constitutes a critical part of any effort to place criminal justice policy on a firm foundation.

This chapter describes the history of evaluation research and what it is. In so doing, it focuses particular attention on describing each type of evaluation and the logic of the hierarchy. It makes the case that evaluation research can be used as a conceptual foundation for thinking about what accountability and evidence-based policy mean, and it highlights parallels between evaluation research and performance monitoring. It then discusses the benefits of evaluation research and the art and science of conducting it. The subsequent chapters describe each of the five types of evaluation in detail and illustrate them by examining criminal justice policies.

History of Evaluation Research

Although one can point to many historical examples in which some type of researchlike activity focused on social policy, it was not until the 1930s that such activity was undertaken using more rigorous research methods and for a wide array of policy areas.[1] This activity greatly escalated after World War II, in no small part because of the numerous federally funded initiatives aimed at alleviating a variety of social ills, including poverty and disease. Given the enormous sums of money involved, it should not be surprising that policy makers and the public wanted evidence that the initiatives generated positive results. The emergence of policy-focused research in the 1950s an era in which criminology began to emerge as a discipline – nonetheless was remarkable: "By the end of the 1950s, program evaluation was commonplace. Social scientists engaged in assessments of delinquency prevention programs, psychotherapeutic and psychopharmacological treatments, public housing programs, educational activities, community organization initiatives, and numerous other initiatives."[2]

The development of evaluation research as a social science endeavor grew directly out of this set of initiatives. Subsequent to the implementation of them, for example, scholars began to develop new approaches to policy evaluation and to publish how-to texts on evaluation. This work was stimulated even more by the War on Poverty in the 1960s, which contributed to a dramatic increase in evaluation research and to it becoming its own field of study in the 1970s. Since then, evaluation research has increasingly become central to policy-making efforts and to the monitoring and assessment of social policies aimed at bettering the lives of citizens. Indeed, evaluation divisions now exist in many federal, state, and local governmental agencies. Notwithstanding this situation, however, many agencies lack the resources and funding to conduct or contract for evaluations of more than a small fraction of the policies for which they are responsible.

Evaluation Research Defined

What exactly is evaluation research?[3] Different definitions exist. Here, I use one provided by perhaps the most widely used evaluation text on the topic: "[Policy] evaluation is the use of social research methods to systematically investigate the effectiveness of social intervention programs in ways that are adapted to their political and organizational environments and are designed to inform social action to improve social conditions."[4] In short, evaluation research aims to improve society by examining social policies through the use of various research methodologies. Research methodology is, of course, central to evaluation efforts, but it is not the focus; methodologies serve to achieve specific evaluation research goals.

Put differently, evaluation research is fundamentally driven by a focus on policy-relevant questions. It aims to answer critical questions that policy makers, administrators, and the public may have about specific social problems and policies. Does a given law, for example, reduce crime? It also clarifies issues relevant to policy debates. For example, does the law unfairly affect racial or ethnic minorities? What are the appropriate standards for evaluating the law? In each instance, evaluation research aims to produce empirically based evidence about policies, not anecdotal accounts that confirm opinions about them.

The Evaluation Hierarchy

The specific "nuts and bolts" of how to do evaluation research are described in great depth in many texts.[5] They describe, for example, the types of questions and methodologies that can be used, the range of problems that can arise and how to overcome them, and how to present evaluation results in a way that will have the greatest impact. My goal here is not to repeat such efforts but rather to apply an evaluation research approach to criminal justice policy, with the goals of (1) showing how evaluation research can be used to improve criminal justice policy; (2) making the argument that, in fact, many criminal justice policies lack a solid, "evidence-based" foundation; and (3) arguing that evaluation research should be much more and much better integrated into all criminal justice policy making and practice to increase government accountability, evidence-based practice, and the effectiveness and efficiency of the criminal justice system. To this end, the subsequent chapters describe each of the five major types of evaluation, why each is important, and how prominent criminal justice policies fare when viewed from an evaluation perspective.

Before proceeding to these chapters, the logic of the evaluation hierarchy, depicted in Figure 2.1 and described briefly in the preceding chapter, merits further discussion. The most critical observation is captured by the very notion of a *hierarchy* – that is, in a hierarchy, one level builds on a prior level, and if the prior levels are weak or shaky, then so, too, will be the ones that build upon them.[6] To use a different analogy, if we build a house on an off-kilter foundation, then the rest of the house will be off-kilter. The point may seem simple, but it cannot be understated how frequently it goes ignored.

Consider the first level of the evaluation hierarchy: a *needs evaluation*. Here, the basic idea is that the need for a social policy should be established before the policy takes shape or gets implemented. Frequently, however, one encounters criminal justice policies where no evidence of need has been established. Instead, a policy of some sort, such as the expansion of a prison system, gets enacted and, as a result, any discussion of assessment typically proceeds directly to a focus on implementation or impact evaluations. In so doing, however, we implicitly proceed on the incorrect assumption that the policy was needed. Perhaps it was, perhaps it was not. We cannot say unless the question of need gets asked and a study is undertaken to answer it.

The first level of the evaluation hierarchy emphasizes that absent the need for a policy, it makes little sense to fund it. By way of illustration, imagine seeing a doctor who tells you to undergo an expensive and time-consuming cancer treatment, and upon questioning the doctor, you learn that you actually have no cancer. Clearly, the treatment would not be warranted. At the same time, imagine a situation in which someone you care for has cancer but the cancer goes undetected. Just as clearly, treatment would be warranted but would not likely be sought if the problem went undiagnosed. The same logic applies to needs evaluations of social problems. A policy should be justified on the basis of some assessment of need, and the extent and cause of a social problem ideally should be monitored on a regular basis so as to know when to intervene.

Assuming that a social problem exists, the next progression – or the second step – in the evaluation hierarchy takes the form of a *theory* or *design evaluation*. Here, our focus is on developing a clear charting of what a policy will do and how its activities or services are expected to directly or indirectly contribute to an improved outcome. In developing this policy theory, we ideally will find that its logic accords with existing theory and research about the causes of the problem. Put differently, if we wish to intervene successfully with a problem, it helps greatly to know something about the contours of the problem and what causes it. To use a medical analogy, it helps to know where pain of some type is located and also what causes it. Knowing the location can help guide doctors to target treatment, and knowing the cause of the pain can guide selection of the treatment. Indeed, given the wide range of possibilities – physical abnormalities, stress, biochemical factors, and so on – knowledge of the cause is imperative if treatment is to have a chance of being effective.

The same can be said of social problems. Crime is, for example, caused by many factors, and so ideally a policy aimed at reducing it will take into account at least some of them. Similarly, criminal justice operations are influenced by many factors, and some may be especially relevant for alleviating a particular problem. To illustrate, case processing of youths referred to juvenile court may take many more months to occur in a given jurisdiction as compared with similar jurisdictions or compared with standards established by such organizations as the American Bar Association. Case-processing times reflect such factors as the volume and types of cases referred to court, the priority given to certain types of cases (and changes in the priorities of varying regimes of prosecutors and judges), the ratio of court personnel to cases, use of detention and alternatives to detention, extent of attention given to timely and speedy processing, and the presence or absence of case management monitoring systems.[7] Any one of these factors, or combinations of them, might slow processing. We might be tempted to target all of these factors. However, doing so would be ineffective and inefficient, especially if one factor (e.g., the presence of a case management monitoring system) caused most of the processing delays. A theory evaluation provides guidance about such possibilities. More specifically, theory evaluations help to ensure that a sensible causal logic – or, as Peter Rossi and his colleagues have described it, a credible policy theory – exists for tackling a problem.[8] Such a theory ideally is built on prior theory and research and empirical information about the precise scope and nature of the problem being targeted.

Given a situation in which the need for a policy intervention has been established and in which a credible theory for the intervention exists, it is reasonable to proceed to the third step in the evaluation hierarchy – namely, an *implementation evaluation*, sometimes referred to as a process evaluation. As the name connotes, this type of evaluation examines how well a policy is implemented, or, using the alternative terminology, how well the various processes that comprise the policy are undertaken. Once, again, a medical analogy may be useful. Perhaps we have identified that a patient indeed has pain and that it stems from poor posture. The doctor and patient then develop a treatment plan aimed at improving posture. Does the patient actually implement this plan? If so, perhaps he or she will get better. If not, even the most effective plan will not likely generate improved outcomes. This same logic applies to social programs. For example, the effectiveness of a drug court is premised in part on the idea that participants will receive drug treatment, but if participants do not receive treatment, we should not expect the program to be effective. If by some chance it is, we might well wonder why. In short, the evaluation hierarchy tells us that before we undertake any assessment of outcomes or impacts, we should first examine whether the policy of interest has actually been implemented as designed.

Implementation evaluations can be useful for several reasons. First, they can provide critical information about the level and quality of policy implementation and, at the same time, possible causes of and solutions to inadequate implementation. We typically refer to this undertaking as a *formative evaluation* because the underlying goal of the research is to help improve or "form" the policy.[9] Such an evaluation can be especially helpful during the early stages of implementing a new type of policy; however, it can be useful for many long-standing policies as well. Second, research on the implementation of a policy can be helpful as part of a *summative evaluation*, the aim of which is to assess whether a policy achieves its intended objectives.[10] This latter use accords with performance monitoring efforts, which aim to hold government accountable by documenting how well agencies perform their functions in accordance with expected standards. The main difference is that performance monitoring typically occurs on a regular, ongoing basis whereas evaluations typically constitute one time activities.[11] A third benefit of implementation evaluations is that they can provide information that helps us to interpret why impact evaluations may identify less-than-expected effects.

If we can safely assume or have shown that a need for a given policy exists, that its theoretical foundation or design is credible, and that the activities and services associated with it have been well implemented, the hierarchy indicates that the next step consists of conducting an *outcome* or *impact evaluation*. This type of evaluation is the one that most likely comes to mind when people think about policy assessment, and for good reason. A policy that ultimately does not produce expected changes is, at bottom, a failure.

The main goal of impact evaluations lies in showing, through empirical research, that any identified change in outcome is because of the policy and not to what evaluators term the *counterfactual* condition, or what would have occurred in the absence of the policy. As will be discussed in Chapter 7, evaluators typically view an impact evaluation as a special type of outcome evaluation, one in which some type of comparison group is used that enables one to make claims about actual impacts resulting from a given policy. From this perspective, outcome evaluations measure policy outcomes but lay no claim to establishing that a given policy causes the outcomes. By contrast, impact evaluations not only measure policy outcomes but also claim to assess whether the policy is the cause of any change in the outcomes. The latter approach requires the use of special research designs and methodologies aimed at uncovering what likely would have happened to the outcomes if the policy had never been implemented.

One might ask, what then is the use of an outcome evaluation? This question will be answered in more detail in Chapter 7. However, the short answer is that ongoing outcome evaluations – or outcome monitoring – can be useful for assessing an organization's or agency's performance. For example, if case-processing times improve from one year to the next, that does not necessarily mean that a particular court system is doing well or that the improvement results from some new activity undertaken by the court. It is, however, useful for identifying a potentially important trend and possibly an indicator that should be used to hold the court system accountable.[12]

The final step of the evaluation hierarchy consists of a *cost-efficiency evaluation*, which, as discussed earlier, includes two types: cost-effectiveness analyses (where two or more policies that try to achieve the same outcome are compared) and cost-benefit analyses (where two or more policies that try to achieve different outcomes are compared). Once, again, the logic of proceeding to this type of evaluation makes sense only if the prior types of evaluation have been conducted or we can safely make assumptions about them. Policy makers and the public clearly have a vested interest in knowing what the "bang for the buck" is for a given policy. Societies typically operate with a certain amount of scarce resources and so cannot afford to willy-nilly invest resources on any and all policies. Indeed, they have an interest in investing primarily in existing or proposed efforts that will achieve the greatest results at the least cost and terminating those that have little to no effect at great cost.

However, if we do not know what the "bang" is – that is, what the impact on a given outcome is – to what exactly do we assign a dollar value? The answer? Nothing. To illustrate, it remains largely unknown whether supermax prisons increase order and safety throughout prison systems, and there exists little theoretical or empirical research to allow one to safely assume a particular level of impact. For that reason, it would be odd to conduct a cost-efficiency evaluation because no reasonable statement of impact can be made. Certainly, we could develop estimates of the costs associated with supermax prisons.[13] But we would have no impacts to which to assign values. Put differently, if we cannot show that a policy is effective, how could we proceed to put a dollar value on the benefits associated with it? Perhaps, however, the state of knowledge about some policy is such that we can safely assume a particular level of impact. Alternatively, perhaps we want to explore whether some level of assumed impact would, in the final analysis, produce returns that offset the costs. In such a context, we might be justified in proceeding to a cost-efficiency evaluation.

Evaluation as a Way to Increase Accountability and Evidence-Based Policy

Accountability and *evidence-based policy* have become increasingly common terms used in discussions about a range of social policies. It may seem relatively straightforward – indeed, it seems like common sense – that we would want government to be held accountable for what it does or funds. Likewise, it seems only sensible that we would want social policies and practices to be grounded in knowledge or evidence about what works best.

However, only in the past few decades have these notions been prominently used to guide debates and decisions about social policy. The shift is considerable. Today, government accountability and evidence-based policy have emerged as near-national mantras in recent years, under both Republican and Democratic presidencies and throughout all parts of government.[14] Many reasons may account for this trend, but two key factors include greater demands on government and diminished funds. As Wayne Welsh and Phillip Harris have noted, "As public resources have dwindled, agencies have increasingly been called upon to demonstrate their effectiveness and efficiency in meeting their goals."[15]

Within the world of criminal justice, the urgency behind calls for more accountable and evidence-based policies stems from a number of pessimistic assessments. The most notable is the conclusion of a widely cited, federally funded review, published in 1997, of the scientific literature on the effectiveness of crime prevention programs: "This report found that some prevention programs work, some do not, some are promising, and some have not been adequately tested."[16] That assessment has been echoed by other reviews, including a prominent National Academy of Sciences study.[17]

What really is meant, though, by accountability and evidence-based policy? Some debate exists about which definitions are best. A relatively common view of *accountability* holds that it occurs when the government delivers on its promises.[18] What exactly are those promises? Much depends on how one defines the scope of government responsibility. From one perspective, accountability might simply be a situation in which the government actually delivers promised services. Observe, however, that such a view ignores the possibility that the government might be funding unnecessary services.

Accordingly, a more comprehensive view, one suggested by the evaluation hierarchy, argues that accountability occurs when government adopts policies that are needed and grounded in theory and research, when it implements them well, when the policies achieve their intended effects, and when they do so in a cost-efficient manner. Under the rubric of "implementation" fall several additional and important dimensions. From an implementation perspective, for example, we expect that a given policy will target the intended populations or areas; provide the expected services; and do so in a way that complies with any and all legal and financial constraints, rules, and auditing standards.[19]

Evidence-based policy, as typically depicted, consists of programs or practices that have been subject to impact evaluations that establish their effectiveness in achieving particular outcomes. This view is, I submit, too narrow. Consider, for example, that the use of empirical research to establish whether a particular policy is needed – not just whether it is effective – arguably constitutes a form of evidence-based policy. Certainly, it represents an advance over simply assuming, without credible evidence, that a policy addresses a real or pressing social problem.

Here, again, an evaluation research perspective suggests that a more comprehensive view be taken – specifically, evidence-based policy can be defined as the use of empirical research to guide the development, implementation, and assessment of the various laws, programs, practices, rules, and protocols that collectively make up the criminal justice system.[20] Viewed this way, evidence-based policy is not simply the adoption of *effective* interventions. It also is the use of empirical research to guide decisions about the other dimensions of the evaluation hierarchy, such as whether a policy is *needed*, whether it rests on solid *theory*, whether it is *implemented* well, and whether it is *cost efficient*.

Evaluation Research versus Performance Monitoring

In recent decades, considerable attention has been given to performance monitoring.[21] Most accounts of performance monitoring emphasize the use of empirical indicators (1) to document the extent to which intended activities and services are actually undertaken and (2) to measure outcomes that are supposed to result from these activities and services.[22] Performance monitoring involves the ongoing analysis of these process and outcome indicators. It does not establish the effectiveness of policies, or various services and activities, in achieving particular outcomes. Rather, it simply documents trends over time in such things as the activities and the delivery of services and the outcomes used to judge whether a given policy is effective.[23]

To use a sports analogy, monitoring the win-loss record of a team provides a basis for judging how well the team is doing.[24] Wins and losses are the relevant performance outcomes. At the same time, if we monitor how often a team works out, we have some basis for documenting whether the team practices as often as it should and whether a possible cause of good or poor performance is the frequency of practices. The latter could be viewed as an additional performance measure. In this example, we might place greater emphasis on outcome monitoring rather than activity monitoring, but each is an important area of performance. Observe, however, that even if the activities are implemented well and the outcomes accord with our expectations, we cannot conclude – in the absence of a particular type of research study (i.e., an impact evaluation) – that the activities (e.g., practice) necessarily led to the outcome (e.g., the number of wins).

Performance monitoring can be used to increase accountability and to identify if policies, whether effective or not, are being implemented well, and correspond to expected outcomes. It does not ensure that policies address actual needs, that they rest on credible theories, that they are effective, or that they are cost efficient. To achieve these goals, we need a more systematic approach to improving policy.

The evaluation hierarchy, if institutionalized into policy development, monitoring, and assessment, provides just such an approach. It includes implementation and outcome analyses and so is not essentially different, in these regards, from performance monitoring. The latter simply constitutes an ongoing effort, as opposed to a one time effort, to monitor activities and outcomes. However, an alternative view of the matter is to say that performance monitoring involves ongoing implementation and outcome evaluations. The main difference, and the one more relevant here, lies in the fact that the evaluation hierarchy leads us to take a much broader view of policy-relevant dimensions – the focus is on not just implementation but also on whether a need for a policy exists, whether it rests on credible theoretical foundations, whether it produces intended impacts, and whether it does so in a cost-efficient manner.

Benefits of Evaluation Research

An evaluation research framework provides a powerful foundation from which to think about, assess, and improve criminal justice policy. The five-fold emphasis – need, theory, implementation/process, outcome and impact, and cost efficiency – imposes a check against irrational policy. If, for example, agencies can provide no clear evidence that a policy is needed, there arguably should be no progression to the design and implementation of one. Similarly, if a policy cannot be defended on theoretical or empirical grounds – for example, if the design of it raises considerable questions about whether the changes will lead to improved outcomes or if prior research shows that certain assumed facts are incorrect – there presumably should be no implementation of it.

If evaluation research were institutionalized into policy-making efforts, including criminal justice system decision making, it would provide a critical platform to inform and improve governmental decision making. Alone, it would not be sufficient. As discussed in Chapter 2, many factors influence governmental decision making. Nonetheless, evaluation research constitutes a critical, and to date largely neglected, strategy for increasing

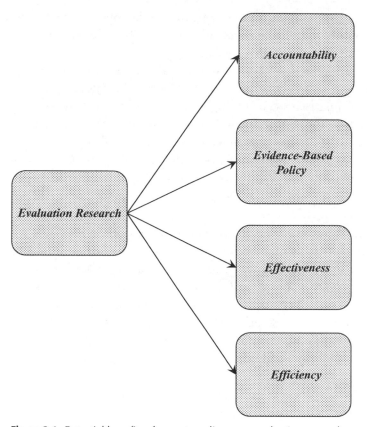

Figure 3.1. Potential benefits of a greater reliance on evaluation research.

accountability, evidence-based policy, effectiveness, and efficiency, as depicted in Figure 3.1.

Evaluation research may improve criminal justice policy directly and indirectly. The *direct* influence stems from the fact that the evaluation hierarchy provides a clear framework for establishing what accountable and evidence-based policies look like. In the parlance of an evaluation framework, criminal justice policies should be needed, designed well, implemented well, achieve their goals, and do so with as few costs as possible.

It is difficult to see how society can hold government accountable or how we can have any comprehensive or systematic use of evidence-based policy in the absence of evaluation research. In the world of criminal justice, research receives little by way of resources and funding and most decision making occurs without any relevant research. Indeed, research simply is not institutionalized in any systematic, meaningful way in most criminal justice systems.[25] I mean here not the one time research studies of this or that crime or policy, but rather the ongoing evaluation of all critical decision making and policies that occur in criminal justice.

Without more research, accountability and assertions about a reliance on evidence-based or effective policies – including the myriad practices and decision making that occur throughout the criminal justice system – necessarily have to rest on unverifiable claims. What is the check, then, against enactment of policies that are not needed? How can we know if the policies rest on sound theory or logic or if they are appropriately or well implemented? How can we know if they are effective or cost efficient? In each instance, the answer, by and large, is that we cannot know without empirical evidence.

The argument here is not that an evaluation framework should supplant recent emphases on accountability, evidence-based policy, or performance monitoring. *Rather, I argue that the framework is useful as a means of specifying what accountability and evidence-based policy mean and the uses to which performance monitoring can be put.* If evaluation research were institutionalized into the policy-making process and into everyday agency operations, it would, I submit, almost necessarily lead to improvements in accountability and evidence-based policy and improve the quality and benefits of performance monitoring.

Evaluation research also has the potential for *indirectly* improving criminal justice by helping to overcome many of the barriers to rational criminal justice policies. For example, efforts to politicize crime or to generalize from extreme and unrepresentative cases would be hindered if policy makers were required to demonstrate empirically the need for particular policies. They would have to show not only that a specific crime existed but also, among other things, that the prevalence of that crime and that its causes could readily be addressed by a particular policy. To be clear, considerable leeway would remain for politicizing crime and for enacting policies based on unrepresentative cases, but it would not be as easy to do.

A greater reliance on evaluation research also would likely reduce the ability of or pressure on policy makers to create and use false dichotomies concerning the policy options available for addressing a problem. In turn, there would be a greater chance for more balanced policies to emerge, and, by extension, for avoiding the swings from one policy extreme to another. In addition, evaluation research could be used to document the extent to which existing or proposed policies adequately address the range of crime problems or criminal justice problems that may exist. In so doing, it would make it more difficult for symbolic gestures or "silver bullet" solutions to prevail over more needed, well-designed, and effective policies.

Evaluation research that involves the systematic polling of public preferences could also be used to help ensure that policy makers' claims about public views more accurately accord with reality. Given the complexity of public opinion about crime and justice, it is at least possible that such polling would serve to check tendencies to enact extreme policies, whether they are liberal or conservative in nature.

Of course, evaluation research may not necessarily produce these benefits.[26] That idea remains largely untested. However, it is precisely this situation – a lack of research – that calls out for correction, especially given the calls for more accountability and evidence-based practice and the centrality of research for achieving such goals. Greater research would not supplant the range of forces that affect policy. However, it might well contribute to developing more defensible and effective policies. As Cullen and Gendreau have argued, "Corrections will never be the exclusive domain of 'what works'; policy discussions will reflect fundamental cultural values, organizational resources, and political realities – among other factors. Even so, an evidence-based approach would place research more systematically and prominently into the mix of factors that shape current correctional policies and practice."[27] I elaborate on these points in the book's conclusion. Here, I will state simply that, although greater use of evaluation research will not necessarily yield improvements in criminal justice policy, I am optimistic that it would do so.

The Art of Conducting Evaluation Research

Evaluation research sometimes is described as involving as much art as science. Why? Sometimes the policy questions and issues are not entirely clear. Imagine, for example, that you, as an evaluator, are asked by a local jurisdiction to evaluate the drug court. A typical request from the evaluation sponsor (i.e., the person requesting and typically paying for an evaluation) might be to help determine if the drug court is effective. That seems straightforward enough. However, perhaps the court has only just started and is suffering from a number of start-up problems. If so, the likelihood of achieving much of an impact diminishes. Here, a better approach might be to evaluate how well the various facets of the drug court are being implemented and to identify where improvements could be made. You might make this recommendation and run into resistance. Consequently, you step back and try to determine what exactly it is that the requester needs. In so doing, you must balance the immediate needs and understanding against your professional judgment about what is appropriate. Do you proceed with an impact evaluation that likely will contribute to an unfair and negative assessment of the court's effectiveness? Do you simply say, "No, I will do an implementation evaluation or nothing"? Here, as with many such examples, there is no one right answer. The "art" lies in helping the evaluation sponsors determine what they really need to know and what can be done with the resources that they have at their disposal. The "science" lies in applying the best methodological approaches one can to answer a given question given the available data, resources, and funding to support an evaluation.

In this vein, much has been written about the factors that influence the precise direction, scope, implementation, and presentation of results from evaluations. As but one example, political considerations may dictate which policies get evaluated and which dimensions of a policy receive the greatest scrutiny. Some organizations may exert greater political clout than others and use that to promote one type of evaluation over another. And local groups may have a vested interest in the outcome of an evaluation. Put differently, there may be a range of evaluation *stakeholders* – individuals, groups, communities, agencies, and organizations with a vested interest in the funding, implementation, or impacts of a policy – each of whom bring to the table different levels of interest in a policy and each of whom may have different goals that they wish to achieve or agendas that they wish to further.

Imagine, for example, a new policy initiated by a district attorney's office in which the practice is to prosecute all domestic violence arrests regardless of whether victims want to press charges or are willing to testify.[28] The district attorney's office might want an evaluation of the impact of the policy on crime, while court administrators might want an evaluation of the policy's effects on court processing and victims' rights organizations might want an evaluation of the experience of the victims. Within the district attorney's office, there may be disagreement about whether the new policy is needed, and some within the office may feel that a focus on gangs would be better. If so, they may call for an evaluation that examines whether a domestic violence problem actually exists and what its size is relative to, say, gang violence. Should any of these groups feel especially strongly about the issue, we can easily imagine that substantial disagreement might exist about the appropriate or best type of evaluation to pursue.

In such contexts – which are typical of policy evaluations – no one particular perspective represents the "correct" one. Not all views merit equal attention, but no one view should necessarily be given greater weight without first carefully considering the overall social and political context in which the evaluation is being requested. Even then, evaluators must attempt to be as responsive as they can to the diverse stakeholders while also maintaining a clear sense of what is possible within the resource and other constraints that they face. They must learn as much about the overall context; the stakeholders; and, not least, the policy, and they also must attempt to educate the different groups about the merits of various approaches, what is and is not possible to achieve with a study, what the potential disruptions or impacts on a policy may be, and what tangible results can be expected. This balancing act requires the ability to negotiate through potentially complicated social and political contexts while attempting to maximize the quality of the research to be undertaken.[29]

Conclusion

Despite calls for greater accountability and evidence-based criminal justice policy, there remains a large gap between these ideals and the realization of them. Use of the evaluation hierarchy – that is, the systematic use of each of the five types of evaluation, including needs, theory, implementation/process, outcome and impact, and cost efficiency – provides a foothold for identifying the problems with current criminal justice policies and also for conceptualizing these two concepts. For example, accountability and evidence-based practice can be defined as occurring when government adopts *needed* policies that rest on a credible *theoretical* or research foundation, that are *implemented* well, that are shown to be *effective*, and that achieve intended outcomes in a *cost-efficient* manner.

The logic of the hierarchy is simple yet important. If we determine that a need for a policy response exists, we should proceed to a theory evaluation. If we can develop or identify a credible theoretical foundation for a policy, we then should proceed to an analysis of policy implementation. If we find that a policy is well implemented, we should assess whether it is effective. And, should we find that the policy indeed produces intended outcomes, we examine whether it does so cost effectively. Should any problems arise along any step of the way, then we should pause and take stock. If, for example, no clear need exists, we should probably not bother to invest in a particular policy, no matter how effective research may show it to be.

Greater use of the evaluation hierarchy in the development, monitoring, and assessment of criminal justice policy is not likely to occur quickly. However, a starting point is recognizing how evaluation research differs from other kinds of research. The main difference lies in the fact that evaluators focus on policy-related questions and use various methodologies, ones that most researchers use, to answer them. It involves developing an awareness of the art of conducting policy research that meets and addresses the needs and concerns of diverse stakeholders. It involves efforts to expand performance monitoring to include all dimensions of the evaluation hierarchy. And, not least, it involves demonstrating that an evaluation approach to criminal justice policy can provide important insight and guidance into the need for greater accountability and effectiveness and how these can be achieved. The subsequent chapters focus on this task and the book's conclusion then discusses concrete steps that can be taken to increase the amount and quality of criminal justice evaluation research.

I do not think it is pie-in-the-sky thinking to believe that evaluation research funding could be increased dramatically or that such research could be institutionalized into everyday criminal justice decision making. Today, the United States invests billions of dollars in policies such as supermax prisons and has invested next to nothing in research on them. It is not, I submit, naïve but instead pragmatic – and in keeping with the numerous calls for more accountable and efficient government – to push for efforts to make evaluation research a central feature of the criminal justice system. For the foreseeable future, budget constraints alone may create the impetus for such a change.[30]

Discussion Questions

What factors contributed to the emergence of evaluation research?

How does evaluation research differ from other types of social science research?

What are the five types of evaluation?

What is the logic of the evaluation hierarchy?

How can evaluation research contribute to increased government accountability and evidence-based policies and practices? More generally, how can it contribute to effective and efficient criminal justice policies and practices?

What challenges might confront evaluators in their efforts to assess policies?

4

Needs Evaluations

F EW OF US WOULD BUY SOMETHING IF WE DID NOT NEED IT FOR SOME purpose. We might be impulsive perhaps, but even impulsive purchases typically meet some real or perceived need. Of course, our reasoning may be flawed. But that in no way detracts from the notion that real or perceived needs drive much of our decision making, especially when the decisions entail large amounts of resources or sums of money.[1]

A similar assertion can be made about criminal justice policies. That is, they presumably emerge from concern about a real problem, such as an increase in crime, or at least from what policy makers *perceive* to be a problem. Even so, what does it mean to say that there exists a sufficiently large problem, or that there exists a small but nonetheless important problem, as to create a *need* for a particular policy response, such as more prisons? What criteria should we use for assessing the amount of a social problem or the need for a particular policy response?

This chapter examines these questions by describing needs evaluations and what they entail. As will be detailed in this chapter, needs evaluations help to identify whether a problem exists and, in turn, whether and what type of a policy response is indicated. They provide guidance on prioritizing different problems. They point to research gaps that must be addressed before it can be determined that a policy response merits implementation and, if a response is warranted, which type. They highlight the dimensions relevant to assessing success. And, more generally, they clarify policy discussions. The chapter describes these benefits and provides two case studies – one focused on mass incarceration and the other on sex crime laws – to illustrate needs evaluations. Drawing on these case studies and other examples, the chapter concludes with a discussion of whether the prominent crime policies that populate today's current criminal justice landscape are needed.

What Is a Needs Evaluation?

Needs Evaluation: Step 1 in the Hierarchy

A needs evaluation constitutes the first step in the evaluation hierarchy, as shown in Figure 2.1 and described in Chapter 3. The reason should be clear: without an established need – that is, without clear evidence of a social problem – why proceed to develop and implement a policy? To use an analogy, if we don't have cancer, why spend money for a treatment that we don't need, that may draw funds away from real problems that we may have, and that may actually cause more harm than good in the absence of the disease? The answer? No good reason exists to do so. Treatment should be reserved for real diseases. So, too, with social policies – we should intervene only when a real social problem exists. To do otherwise risks misallocating scarce resources and failing to address as forcefully as we could real or pressing problems.

Crime clearly constitutes a social problem, so there perhaps would seem to be little risk involved in misdiagnosing it. In reality, and as will be discussed throughout this chapter, defining need can be quite complicated. How much crime exists, whether crime has increased, and what types of crimes have increased are all critical considerations. In addition, needs may arise that center around specific facets of the criminal justice system. For example, perhaps prison officers receive insufficient training for work with maximum-security inmates. Perhaps caseloads among defense counsel, probation officers, prosecutors, or judges greatly exceed reasonable amounts. Many other problems exist in criminal justice, some of them directly involving crime (e.g., an insufficient response to dramatic increases in violence) and some reflecting the specific demands and activities of components of the criminal justice system (e.g., inmate attacks on prison officers). An effective response requires first identifying these specific problems and their contours.

Given their importance, needs evaluations would seem to be likely candidates for the "most common type of evaluation" award, if such existed. Unfortunately, no census of types of evaluation exists. However, even a cursory review of the literature reveals that needs evaluations rarely occur in criminal justice. By contrast, implementation and impact evaluations, discussed in subsequent chapters, occur more frequently. Why?

A number of factors may be relevant. Many researchers lack any formal training in evaluation research and so hew to the two types that they most frequently see in journals and reports. Criminal justice administrators, too, may lack training in evaluation research and so not be sensitized to the importance of assessing the wide range of potential problems within their purview. In addition, policy makers have little to no training in evaluation research. Perhaps more important, they appear to be propelled toward action even when doing so is unnecessary or a mistake, what medical researchers term *action bias*.[2] For example, rather than slow down and evaluate a problem or refrain from acting until and unless a compelling case for a particular intervention emerges, a physician makes a diagnosis and starts treatment. Similarly, policy makers or criminal justice administrators may proceed with promoting a new policy or increasing an existing one (e.g., incarceration) even though they lack evidence about the precise nature of the problem they wish to address, its causes, or how best to reduce it.

Other factors may come into play as well. For example, each year thousands of new criminal justice policies and programs emerge. Because they already exist, researchers might reasonably prioritize implementation or impact studies rather than step back and examine whether a need for the policies existed in the first place. Within the scholarly community, research that simply describes a problem rather than explains its occurrence may not be viewed as an important endeavor. The more prestigious criminology and criminal justice journals tend to emphasize theoretical work, and tenure and promotion frequently depend on publication in such journals.[3] As a result, many researchers may feel pressured to avoid conducting studies that "merely" describe a social problem. Still other factors may be relevant as well. Regardless, needs evaluations can serve a critical – indeed, a foundational – role in improving criminal justice policy.

Defining the Problem: Size, Trends, Location, Causes

Social policies serve to address problems or what alternatively can be called needs. Crime constitutes one prominent social problem or need. Because it is ubiquitous, we might conclude that no assessment of need is warranted. Would that matters were so simple. Defining a social problem involves many considerations, including reference to the (1) size, (2) trends, (3) location, and (4) causes of it.

AN ILLUSTRATION. To illustrate this point, consider the differences in the following two scenarios, depicted in Table 4.1, that assume cities with the same population size and characteristics. In City A, the number of homicides rose from sixty to ninety during a two-year period, an increase of thirty homicides, or, alternatively, a 50-percent increase in homicides. Assume that forty-five of the year-2 homicides involved some type of gang-related

TABLE 4.1. The crime problem in two cities

	City A				City B			
	Year 1	Year 2	Change (No.)	Change (%)	Year 1	Year 2	Change (No.)	Change (%)
Homicide	60	90	+30	+50	20	30	+10	+50
Gang Homicide	10	45	+35	+350	1	1	None	None
Burglary	1,000	700	−300	−30	1,500	2,400	+900	+60

activity, up from ten the year before. In this scenario, gang-related homicides increased by 350 percent from one year to the next. Assume that almost all of the gang-related homicides occurred in three neighborhoods. Finally, assume that during the same time period (i.e., from year 1 to year 2), burglaries declined by 30 percent, from 1,000 to 700.

In City B, let us assume that the number of homicides rose from twenty to thirty during the same two-year period, an increase of ten homicides and an overall increase of 50 percent. Almost none of the past-year homicides appear to be linked to gang-related activity, and no evidence of a trend in gang-related homicides exists. However, three of the homicide events accounted for ten of the thirty year-2 homicides. These were events in which one person killed four people and the two other killers murdered three people each. In prior years, few homicide events involved the death of more than one person. Notably, most of the homicides seem to be relatively evenly dispersed throughout the city. Finally, during the same time period, burglaries increased by 60 percent, from 1,500 to 2,400.

A number of patterns in this highly simplified example can be identified. City A clearly suffers from a large violent crime problem relative to City B. Whether we look at year 1 or year 2, City A reported more homicides. In addition, in absolute terms, City A experienced a much greater change in the number of homicides – an increase of thirty homicides from one year to the next as compared with the increase of ten homicides during the same time span in the other city.

In this example, observe that despite the larger increase in homicides in City A, both cities experienced a comparable percentage change – a 50 percent increase – in the number of homicides. How could that be? City A experienced a greater number of homicides overall as well as a greater number of new homicides from one year to the next. However, City B had a relatively small number of homicides (twenty) in year 1. The result in such situations is that a city can experience a relatively small absolute increase in homicides from one year to the next (from twenty to thirty in the case of City B), and yet report a dramatic percentage increase in such crime.

Review of the two cities' crime statistics shows that, in City A, gang activity is implicated in the increase in homicides and that much of the gang-related murder occurred in a small handful of neighborhoods. In City B, however, the homicide increase does not appear to be readily linked to a single factor such as gang activity nor do the homicides appear to be concentrated in one area. Indeed, closer inspection of City B's crime statistics reveals a different story entirely – a large proportion of City B's year-2 homicides, one-third of them, resulted from just three events. That fact suggests that, in reality, no dramatic increase in violent killers occurred in the city.

Finally, we can see that City A experienced a decrease in burglary during the two-year period. By contrast, in City B, burglary not only increased, but it did so more than homicide, whether measured in absolute or relative terms. Specifically, from year 1 to year 2, there were nine 900 more burglaries, or a 60 percent increase in such crime.   ·

This illustration serves to highlight a number of considerations related to evaluating whether a social problem exists and, by extension, whether there is a need for a policy response of some type. First, numbers matter. More formally, the size of the problem matters. A big problem calls for more attention, whereas a smaller problem calls for less. City A experienced a large increase, in *absolute* and *relative* terms, in homicides, which would suggest a need to respond. Ideally, of course, we could address every problem. In reality, however, society typically must make triage decisions, focusing on the more urgent problems first and then turning to those deemed to be less urgent.

That challenge confronts City B, which faced an increase in both violent and property crime. Yet how we should proceed is less clear. Yes, homicide increased, but in absolute terms the increase of ten homicides is relatively small – indeed, it is considerably smaller than the thirty additional homicides that City A experienced. And it appears that most of the increase stemmed from three offenders. In fact, if we count crime events rather than specific victims, one might dispute whether any increase in violence occurred. At the same time, any increase in homicide victims stands as cause for concern. But what about the increase in burglary? City B was confronted by 900 more burglaries from year 1 to year 2, an increase of 60 percent. Burglary does not compare with murder in terms of severity. Yet it would be odd to allow such a dramatic increase in the frequency of property crime to go unchecked.

Second, absolute and relative *changes* in the *magnitude* of a problem should be taken into account. One or the other by itself can be misleading. For example, if we focused purely on absolute numbers, City B has little basis for focusing on homicide as aggressively as City A. However, if we focused on trends over time, then both cities appear to be facing comparable problems in terms of increased violent crime. Consider the matter from a state level. Both cities may claim that they have a comparable social problem – an increase of 50 percent in homicides. State policy makers might be inclined to treat the two cities equally, given this claim. However, when viewed in absolute terms, City A unquestionably has the far more pressing homicide problem. Which standard should local or state policy makers or law enforcement agencies use to guide their decision making? If they use both, how do they jointly consider the absolute and relative changes in homicide, relative to burglary, in quantifying the scope of the problem? No simple solution exists. Yet quantifying such dimensions as the absolute and relative magnitude of a problem – and comparing them over time across different areas within and across cities – can ground policy discussions in a better understanding of the problems at hand.

Third, knowing something about the *distribution* of a problem in social and geographic space can help us to delimit the contours of it and perhaps in turn guide our thinking when developing a policy response. For example, City A's increased homicide rate appears to stem from gang-related activity in a few select areas. That in turn suggests that a focus on gangs could help reduce homicides and, more specifically, that a focus on gangs in those areas could help reduce violent crime. Closer analysis of the problem may prove these inferences to be false, but we at least have some reasonable basis for creating a more targeted response. We could, of course, ignore such information. However, we then would risk dispersing our efforts in a diffuse manner to populations and areas that have not contributed to the violent crime increase.

City B faces a potentially more difficult situation in that the increase does not appear to stem from an underlying factor or to be concentrated in one area. Thus, should the city decide to step up its efforts to combat violent crime, it will want to develop a better understanding of what set of factors has contributed not only to homicides in general but also to the increase in homicides. At the same time, the fact that much of the increase may stem from three homicide events suggests that caution should be exercised in making too much out of the seemingly large percentage increase in violent crime. For example, a large investment in fighting gangs would appear unlikely to achieve much if anything by way of a reduction in homicides.

The two-city illustration highlights the essence of needs evaluations. Briefly, such evaluations aim to define a problem by (1) describing the nature and extent of it in absolute and relative terms, including (2) how the problem has changed, if at all, over time; (3) the distribution of the problem among different populations and places; and (4) what caused it.[4] Providing insight into the possible causes of the problem is important not only because doing so helps to describe the nature of the problem but also because it helps to establish whether there is a need for a particular type of policy response.

This last point bears elaboration. In the illustration, we can see that a more refined analysis of City A's crime statistics shows (1) gang activity to be a significant contributor to violent crime and (2) particular areas to be host to such gangs. Such information suggests that a more accurate depiction of the crime problem in the city is not that homicides have increased but rather that gang-related homicides in a select few areas have increased. That framing of the situation describes a quite different social problem from one where we say simply that "violent crime has increased in the city." The former depiction provides an arguably more accurate account of the problem and it also provides guidance about how we might intervene to reduce homicide. By contrast, the latter treats homicides in general as a social problem, which seems to downplay that a more precise problem (i.e., gang-related violence) exists. And, to make matters worse, it provides no guidance about how to intervene.

Investigation of the causes of a problem can, of course, go much deeper. For example, what caused the surge in gang activity? Was it a change in drug market activity? An influx of new gangs? Increased competition in the illegal drug market? A shift in the law enforcement department's approach to intervening with gangs or a shift in its emphasis on gangs to, say, one on domestic violence or to sex crimes? Should clear answers emerge in response to these questions, policy makers can develop more precise descriptions of the problem and, in turn, how to respond. For example, if one gang was the predominant instigator of gang-related violent crime, that suggests a very different problem (and the need for a very different response) from one where multiple gangs have been involved. In short, assessing the *causes* of a problem is an essential step both in defining what the problem is and in determining how best to respond.

THE NEED FOR ASSESSING MANY TYPES OF NEED. The previous example focused on homicide and burglary. In reality, of course, many more crimes exist. In addition, many problems arise in the criminal justice system that relate not only to crime but also to providing justice and, more mundanely, to executing everyday tasks (e.g., making arrests, defending and prosecuting individuals).

The problems in criminal justice defy any simple categorization. Even so, clarity about the types and levels of problems can help place policy on a more rational foundation. At the broadest level, there is, of course, the fact of crime. The two-city example underscores, however, that we typically will want to disaggregate the problem of crime by examining specific types (e.g., violent, property, drug). We also will want to map crime and its change over time as well as its distribution across different populations and places. For example, are there "hot spots" of criminal activity? Or populations that are "hot" in the sense that more crime occurs among them than others? At the least, we will want to identify what, in each instance, has caused it.

The same observations hold for individual-level offending. As with eco-logical-level crime (e.g., rates of homicide or burglary among cities), con-siderable variation in individual-level offending exists, which has implica-tions for describing what constitutes a "problem." Here, consider the range of ways in which we can measure individual-level crime problems. Partici-pants in a program aimed at reducing recidivism could be asked whether they committed any crime in the year after release. The outcome in this instance is a simple binary one – a crime was committed or it was not. We can measure offending in other ways, though. We could, for example, exam-ine types of recidivism (e.g., violent, property, drug). We also could examine the frequency of offending. Did participants in the program experience a greater reduction in the amount of crime they committed compared to sim-ilar inmates not exposed to the program? The *diversity* of offending might be of interest to us. Did participants commit less violent crime compared to similar inmates, or was the effect more diffuse, with the program reduc-ing the occurrence of all types of recidivism? Criminologists increasingly have become interested in examining the onset and desistance of offend-ing, and, more broadly, trajectories of offending.[5] So, a natural question is whether programs that deal with offender populations effectively alter these trajectories, such that participants become more likely to transition from higher-offending trajectories to lower-offending ones.

Beyond the focus on crime, there exists, of course, the entire criminal justice system and the varied set of policies and practices that constitute it. These aim not only to reduce crime but also to mete out justice and, more simply, to process large numbers of cases. Many types of problems can be found in criminal justice. To illustrate, law enforcement agencies may lack the resources to respond in a timely manner to 911 calls. They may focus too much attention on some crime and not enough on another. Some officers may abuse their authority. Others may be overworked. Domestic violence victims may be reluctant to contact law enforcement agencies for assistance. Communication and cooperation within and between units of these agencies may be minimal. And so on.

Narrowing our focus somewhat, we can see that much the same can be said of the courts – that is, a wide range of diverse problems can exist that can undermine their effectiveness and efficiency. Prosecutors may lack the resources to target high-impact crimes or they may expend resources on questionable cases. They may be overly aggressive in seeking tough sanctions or too lenient. Probation officers may produce low-quality case reports for judges. They also may suffer from morale problems stemming from an inability to execute the many and varied expectations placed upon them. Defense counsel and public defenders may have caseloads that preclude adequate representation of clients, and they may even refuse to take new cases or may delay acting on them for many months. Judges within a given jurisdiction may vary dramatically in how they sanction particular types of cases. Victims may receive little attention or assistance from court personnel. And so on.

Many problems also pervade, in varying degrees, correctional systems and their component parts. Prison officers may be poorly trained for managing violent inmates. The classification of inmates may rely on unvalidated assessment instruments and there may be too few facilities for accommodating different types of inmates. Prison graft may go largely unchecked. Unrealistic policy makers' demands may be placed on prison administrators. Parole officer caseloads may be so high as to limit "face time" with parolees to minutes each month. And so on.

"And so on" constitutes the operative phrase here. Each stage of the criminal justice system entails enormous potential to do good and also to cause harm. Many possible problems exist. In each instance, the size of the problem may vary from the negligible to the large; it may have decreased or increased over time (in small or large absolute or relative amounts); it may be widely dispersed or may be concentrated among a few select groups, units, places, and the like; and it may stem from a few specific causes or a wide range of them. In such a context, operating without any systematic needs evaluations of actual or proposed policies amounts to flying an airplane at night without any equipment and with one's eyes covered – an accident almost inevitably will occur. More concretely, it results in many problems going unidentified and unaddressed and it means that policy makers likely place too little or too much emphasis on the few problems that do get documented.

Determining the Type and Level of Response Needed

ASSESSING THE NEED FOR AN EXISTING OR PROPOSED POLICY RESPONSE. To this point, the discussion of need assumes a focus on some type of social problem. That is, we begin with determining whether a social problem exists and whether, by extension, a need exists that should be addressed by policy. Consider, however, a situation where we approach the matter from the opposite direction. Specifically, we begin with an existing or proposed policy and we determine whether a need for this specific policy exists. This is the second major type of needs evaluation. Here, rather than determine whether a social problem exists and then proceed to a broad-based focus on possible policy responses, we instead determine whether a particular policy is warranted. We end up examining similar issues. However, conceptually the task entails a different approach because we begin with a policy rather than a problem.

At first blush, this approach may seem odd. Presumably, legislators implemented the policy because of a real need. As the previous discussion highlights, however, and as the following case studies will reinforce, that assumption frequently may be incorrect. Regardless, investigation of whether existing or proposed policies are needed can provide critical information for determining whether a shift in direction is indicated. On the basis of the findings from a needs evaluation, we might determine, for example, that the policy should be terminated, that it should be modified, or that a different policy might better address the existing problem.

THREE QUESTIONS WHEN EXAMINING THE NEED FOR AN EXISTING OR PROPOSED POLICY. A policy-focused needs evaluation entails answering three related questions. First, are existing efforts insufficient to address some social problem? It defies common sense to create a policy merely for the sake of doing so, especially if other policies that address the problem exist. Consider the typical situation in criminal justice – most states have numerous policies in place to sanction offenders and to provide diversion and treatment services. A lawmaker may propose new legislation to toughen penalties for some class of offender. But any such effort assumes that the range of sanctions currently in place somehow are insufficient and that diversion or treatment services somehow do not work or are inadequate. Why else go to the trouble of creating more complexity in a system already overburdened by complexity? In short, to determine whether a particular policy is needed requires, in part, first determining how, if at all, existing policies fall short.

Second, are existing efforts to address some social problem not only insufficient but also not amenable to correction? Here, contemplate preparation for an exam, because most of us have had to take a test at some time or another. Perhaps someone comes along and tells you to adopt an entirely new approach to preparing for your exam. That's well and fine, but really, do you need to undertake a whole new strategy? The person responds by observing that you flunked in all of your previous efforts and so clearly something new is warranted. The logic seems self-evident. It is, nonetheless, specious. It may be that the strategy you used was entirely appropriate and that you simply failed to implement it well. That does not mean that you should continue with it as a strategy. For example, if the strategy was to study two hours every night, and if that strategy was unrealistic given competing obligations, another strategy might well be indicated. However, it may be that the poor implementation can be easily remedied. Perhaps, for example, you simply need to shift the time of day when you study, or spread the study time out over different periods of the day. In this situation, you might simply want to revise your current approach to exam preparation, not move on to a new one.

Third, in comparison to existing efforts to respond to some assumed or documented social problem, is a proposed or newly implemented policy a needed substitute or supplement? Here, assume that existing policies have been found to be insufficient and that their inadequacy is only partially remediable. The question remains – is a new policy in any obvious way more responsive in addressing a social problem? Answering that question is important because it makes little sense to invest scarce resources in policies that do not clearly address a problem in a more direct, effective, and cost-efficient manner than some other approach or set of approaches.

Doesn't this last question tip us into the land of conducting theory evaluations of different policies? In part, yes. As will be discussed in the next chapter, theory evaluations examine a policy's causal logic to determine if it rests on solid theoretical, logical, and empirical foundations. Theory evaluations thus necessarily entail investigation of how well a policy may remedy some social problem.

That observation underscores a critical point – needs evaluations and theory evaluations are inextricably intertwined. A well-conducted evaluation of the need for a particular policy typically will require delving into the theoretical logic and evidence for the policy. Similarly, a well-conducted theory evaluation typically will require delving into the evidence concerning the prevalence, distribution, and nature of a social problem. Consider, for example, that a well-designed policy may exist but the social problem it aims

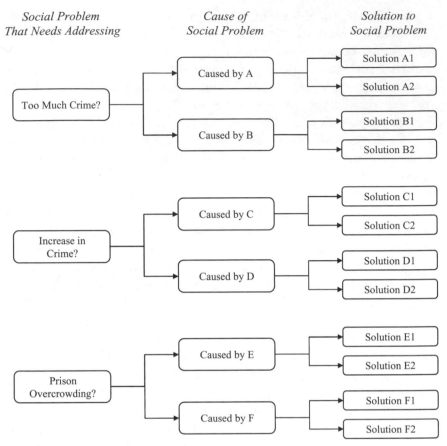

Figure 4.1. Defining need.

to address does not. In such a situation, we would not want to implement the policy because no problem exists.

EXAMINING WHETHER A PROBLEM EXISTS VERSUS THE NEED FOR A SPECIFIC POLICY. To clarify the distinction between a needs evaluation aimed at determining whether a social problem exists and one aimed at assessing whether a particular policy is warranted, let us turn to Figure 4.1. If we begin on the left side, we can see that our first task involves defining the social problem that we wish to address. Is it, for example, that we feel that too much crime exists? Or is it that there appears to be a sudden surge in crime? The two problems may be related but may not be, and so warrant separate treatment. For example, a community with low levels of crime may experience a doubling of crime from one year to the next and, as a result, decide to intensively implement policies aimed at addressing this new problem, one that is "new" not in the sense of crime existing but in the sense of its rising dramatically. In another community with higher levels of crime, there may have been little change in the crime rate from one year to the next, and so perhaps no new policies are implemented. Instead, attention may be centered on improving existing efforts to combat crime. Still another social problem that may constitute a concern is prison overcrowding, which may or may not be linked to levels or changes in crime. It, too, may warrant its own evaluation.

As part of a needs evaluation, we would want to clarify which of these problems merits the most attention. In that effort, we would want, as discussed earlier, to describe the nature and extent of the problem, how it has changed, and its distribution among different populations and places. We also would want to identify what caused it because doing so can help us define the problem more precisely and lead us to a targeted policy response. The second column depicts that focus and illustrates that multiple factors may cause a given problem. High rates of crime, for example, may be caused by poverty, unemployment, socially disorganized communities, weak social ties among neighbors, and so on.[6] Rapid increases in crime may be caused by increases in such factors but also may result from rapidly expanding drug markets, changes in the demographic characteristics in a given area, and many other such changes.[7] Prison overcrowding may result from increased crime rates and, in turn, incarceration of ever-greater numbers of offenders. It also may result from shifts in public opinion, concern about specific types of crimes, changes in the prevailing political philosophy in states or nationally, and, not least, mandating that inmates serve their entire terms of incarceration, which creates less capacity for admitting new offenders.[8]

Observe that specific causes lead to consideration of different solutions, as indicated by the third column in Figure 4.1. For example, if we find that high levels of poverty cause crime, then policies that alleviate poverty would be a logical focus. Of course, many different ways exist to reduce poverty, including various types of social welfare and efforts to bolster the economy. Which solutions get pursued would reflect many considerations. Perhaps the prevailing political climate rails against the notion that people should get "handouts"; in such a context, efforts to improve the economy presumably would garner greater political support.[9] Another cause of high crime rates may be a lack of social ties. If identified as the most salient or tractable cause, then policies that promote stronger community ties would make more sense. The same logic applies regardless of the type of social problem under consideration, whether it is high crime rates, increased crime, prison overcrowding, or any of myriad possibilities.

Revisiting Figure 4.1, let us now work from right to left. It frequently seems to be the case that policy makers assume that a particular policy must be needed. Perhaps they hear about a new policy developed in some other state. Perhaps they believe that innovations, as a general matter, should be adopted. Perhaps they think that nothing currently works and so something is better than nothing. Whatever the reason, policies frequently emerge without any clear statement or documentation of need. Instead, the need is assumed to exist. That assumption can lead to significant mistakes in the allocation of resources.

To illustrate, many states have implemented supermax prisons without clear statements of need. What problems do such prisons address? System-wide safety problems, disorder, riots, escapes, and recidivism are some possibilities.[10] Most state correctional systems experience these problems. So, the main one of interest would seem to be dramatic increases in these problems.

Here, observe that a basic challenge emerges as we work from the solution, supermax prisons, to the problem – namely, numerous problems exist for which such prisons could be viewed as a solution. In addition, in each instance we would want to ask what really is the scope of the problem, how has it changed; what is its distribution; and, critically, what caused it. Consider systemwide order and safety. Perhaps there has been a dramatic increase in these problems in some states, but perhaps the cause stems from prison management, not the behavior of a few "bad apples." In this case, supermax prisons do not seem to be a logical solution to the problem given that they primarily focus on incapacitating a relatively small number of the so-called bad apples, that is, those inmates thought to cause many of the problems in prison systems.[11]

Other questions quickly emerge as we try to work backward from the solution to the problem and the causes of it. Has disorder and safety actually increased in a given system? Are the causes of it primarily or only caused by the behavior of a few inmates? Is the problem instead increased escapes or higher rates of recidivism or even crime rates? If so, the question again is what has caused these problems and whether supermax prisons constitute an obviously superior policy choice over other possibilities.

Similar questions can be asked of virtually any policy. To wit, what exactly is the need that the policy addresses, and is it, upon closer inspection, the most logical solution? Consider another example: drug courts. This specialized, intensive form of processing, supervising, and treating offenders has expanded rapidly since the early 1990s. What problem does it actually address, though? The use of illegal drugs? Production and distribution of them? Drug-related offending among individuals caught by the police? Community-level drug crime? All of these possibilities constitute good candidates, but they each raise different questions. Intensive supervision and treatment would seem to hold the promise of reducing recidivism among drug offenders as a general matter, but would they do much to reduce it among those offenders whose offending careers predated any involvement in drugs? Would it do much to deter illegal drug production and distribution? More to the point, what causes each of these types of problems and do these causes naturally lead to a focus on drug courts? For example, if illegal drug markets prevail during downturns in the economy, it would seem that economic interventions would have a greater chance at reducing overall levels of drug production and distribution and, by extension, drug use and any drug-induced criminal behavior.

A careful investigation of the need for a drug court would not stop there, but also would situate the problem in relative terms. For the sake of argument, assume that a city has many thousands of people who use illegal drugs and commit crime to support their drug habit or because of it. From a criminal justice perspective, the fundamental concern lies with criminal behavior. So, our primary focus then would be on documenting how much drug-related crime contributes to overall levels or rates of crime in the city and to changes in such crime. Doing so would enable us to determine how much drug-related crime contributes to overall crime problems and in turn whether it merits special focus relative to a focus on other factors that may contribute to crime.

This example highlights an important axiom – any definition of need necessarily implies some basis of comparison. Pointing to particular drug-related crimes or to estimates about the large percentage of prisoners with drug problems does little to advance discussions of need precisely because of the lack of comparative context. However, pointing to such facts and then highlighting that no other "competitors" exist – like mental health problems, poor education, poverty, chronic unemployment and homelessness – would do so. One then could argue that drug-related crime clearly predominates over other crime and so merits special attention. However, if one finds that crime seems more associated with other problems, such as mental illness or poverty, then a stronger need would seem to exist for solutions focused on them, not drugs.

It bears emphasizing that the many and sundry criminal justice policies that exist today or are being contemplated, including supermax prisons and drug courts, may well be needed. Nevertheless, asserting that fact and show-ing it to be true are two different things. Ultimately, a science – or evidence-based criminal justice system – would err on the side of demonstrating need, not asserting it.

How to Conduct a Needs Evaluation

Needs evaluations – whether of social problems for which we think a policy response might be needed or of the problems we think an existing policy is intended to address – can be viewed as progressing through two stages. The first is a conceptual endeavor, one aimed at describing as specifically as possible the social problem thought to exist. The second stage involves the development of quantitative estimates of the problem. Following this sequence helps to ensure that we conduct the type of research relevant to identifying and addressing a problem. For example, if we determine first that supermax housing serves primarily to reduce disorder and violence throughout prison systems, we know then that we need information about the nature and levels of disorder and violence.

The sequence can be reversed, but significant risks arise in doing so. To illustrate, consider reading a report that shows that a state experienced no rioting after it constructed a supermax facility. We see this fact, which in turn leads us to think that the supermax prevented future riots and, more than that, to assume that the facility was needed. In reality, however, the relevant facts that we want for assessing need in this case would likely be trends in the amount and distribution of disorderly and violent acts throughout the prison system. If we collect information necessary to produce such facts, we might well find that disorder and violence were declining well before introduction of the supermax, suggesting that no need for the supermax existed. We also might find that the factors contributing to the riot had little to do with the types of inmates housed in the supermax facility, suggesting that the housing was not actually the type of policy response needed for responding to this particular problem (i.e., riots).[12]

No single approach exists for conceptualizing a problem. The main ingre-dients include efforts to state explicitly the nature of the problem, to com-pare that statement with accounts in the scholarly or policy literature of what seem to be similar problems, and to work toward a precise description that can guide research aimed at quantifying the problem. In such an under-taking, interviews with experts in the field and focus groups with different stakeholder groups can be invaluable.

There also is no single approach to quantifying a problem. Many needs evaluations begin with qualitative methodologies, such as interviews, focus groups, and ethnographies, because these can help us to identify the types of information we should collect.[13] A well-done qualitative study can be used to aid in designing survey questionnaires or in making tailored requests for agency or administrative records. These in turn provide the basis for establishing the prevalence – measured using counts, percentages, rates, or the like – of the problem. Numerous research methods and evaluation texts exist that describe these methodologies and how to undertake them.[14] Once, again, however, the conceptualization of the problem ideally should dictate the methods used.

The purpose of needs evaluations is to inform policy decisions. For that reason, they should clearly identify the target population that contributes to a problem or that can help alleviate it. For example, if we determine that violence has increased dramatically in a prison system, we will want to aid those charged with developing a policy response. To this end, we should go beyond showing that violence has increased and identify who should be the target of a response. The targets typically will be individuals or groups who contribute to the problem, which, in this instance, likely would include inmates who incite others to commit violence or those who actually engage in it.

Finally, in an effort to inform the development of an effective policy response, a needs evaluation also will want to describe the current efforts to address the problem and the causes of it. For example, have wardens implemented any initiatives to reduce violence? Have there been difficulties in implementing them? If instigators contribute to most of the prison violence, can they easily be identified? Would legal barriers inhibit a prison system's ability to use isolation as a means of controlling these inmates?

Why Are Needs Evaluations Important?

Needs evaluations serve a number of critical functions. First, and perhaps most important, they help us to identify whether a problem exists, and, if the evaluation is done well, the scope and nature of the problem. The point cannot be emphasized enough – expending resources on nonexistent problems not only is wasteful but also draws attention away from other, real problems.

Second, a needs evaluation can provide guidance about whether a policy should be retained. All too frequently, policies emerge in the absence of any systematic needs evaluation. In these cases, a needs evaluation can provide guidance on whether the problem to which the policy is addressed actually exists. Should there be no problem, then perhaps the policy should be terminated, especially if it entails considerable costs.

Third, well-done evaluations can also provide guidance about the type of policy response that should be considered. For example, they can show not only that homicides have increased but also that, say, gang-related homicides have dramatically escalated in certain areas of a city. Policy makers thus have information that can guide them, not to respond to violent crime "in general," but rather to focus on gang-related homicides in certain areas, and thus to develop policies that target gangs in them.

Fourth, needs evaluations can aid in efforts to prioritize the problems that merit attention. Typically, communities or criminal justice systems face a wide range of problems and so they must make the difficult decision to emphasize some over others. For example, a prosecutor's office may face what they perceive to be a large influx of juvenile delinquency cases and domestic violence cases, enough so that discussions emerge about creating specialized delinquency or domestic violence units. Ideally, such decisions would be informed by, among other things, information about the number of delinquency and domestic violence cases, changes in them relative to each other and to other types of cases, and the time and money required to handle each cases. A needs evaluation might reveal that in fact domestic violence cases have increased much more dramatically than delinquency cases and require far more resources. That information in turn can be used to guide decision making about specialized units.

Fifth, needs evaluations can highlight research gaps that ideally would be addressed before implementing a policy. A particular state may feel that prison overcrowding exists and must be addressed by building new prisons. However, before undertaking such a costly endeavor, it would help to know what caused the overcrowding. Is it due, for example, to larger numbers of admissions from the courts, from admissions in one county in the state, or perhaps to a new law mandating that any newly admitted inmates must serve a minimum of, say, 80 percent of their sentence in a context where traditionally only 40 percent of inmate sentences get served? Each of these sources suggests different policy responses. A needs evaluation could help to identify the source of the overcrowding, and if it could not, then it could draw attention to the fact that the new policy – building more prisons – proceeds from an unverified premise that the problem stems from a constant source of new pressure for beds rather than, say, a temporary spike in new admissions. Policy makers may still feel compelled to support prison expansion, but they would be able to make that decision in a more informed manner.

Sixth, needs evaluations can highlight the dimensions that should be used to assess a policy's effectiveness.[15] Consider community policing, which aims to reduce crime, an admittedly critical law enforcement priority. At least in part, however, community policing also aims to foster greater cohesion among community residents as well as to increase trust in and satisfaction with the police.[16] Such changes might ultimately reduce crime, but they also constitute important goals in and of themselves.[17] A needs evaluation would likely identify this fact and thus underscore the importance of including changes in community cohesion and trust in the police as important markers of success.

Finally, a more general benefit of needs evaluations is that they can help clarify policy discussions and debates. Policy makers and criminal justice officials face a strong mandate to take action, and so they quite reasonably tackle the problems that seem most prominent. However, policy makers and officials come and go while criminal justice systems remain. That creates a problematic situation. One group feels compelled to do something, yet taking action with incomplete information about the range and depth of public safety and criminal justice system problems creates potentially more problems. In such a context, needs evaluations, especially when aimed broadly at illuminating the spectrum of problems in criminal justice, can contribute to more informed discussions and debates about the direction that policy should go.

Case Studies: *Mass Incarceration* and *Sex Crime Laws*

To illustrate several of the aforementioned points, we turn now to two case studies, one focused on mass incarceration and the other on sex crime laws. In each instance, the discussion centers on a description of the policy and its goals and how need might be or is defined. Following the case studies, we then turn to the question of whether these prominent criminal justice policies and others like them appear to be needed.

Mass Incarceration

THE POLICY. Correctional populations in the United States have burgeoned, expanding almost four times in size from 1980 to 2008. If incarceration rates are the measure, the United States is the "most punitive country in the world."[18] In 1980, there were 319,598 individuals in prison; by 2008 that number had risen to 1,518,559. The latter figure does not count the 785,556 individuals who were in jail. Combining these two figures, there were more than 2.3 million individuals in jail or prison in 2008.[19]

People who hear about such increases frequently comment, "Yes, but over that twenty-eight year period of time the U.S. population grew, so doesn't the growth simply reflect that change?" The answer is no. Figure 4.2 shows the changes in incarceration rates, which adjust for population

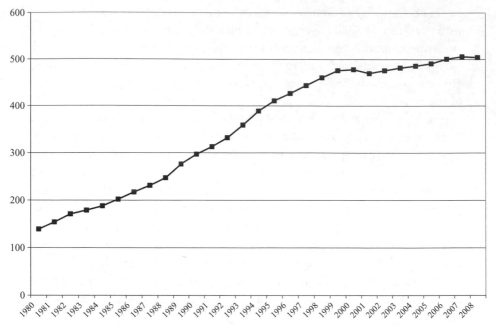

Figure 4.2. U.S. incarceration rates, 1980–2008. The rates refer to adult prisoners held for one year or longer per 100,000 residents. *Source*: Bureau of Justice Statistics. 2009. *Correctional Populations in the United States*. Washington, D.C.: U.S. Department of Justice. Available online: http://www.ojp.usdoj.gov/bjs/glance/tables/incrttab.htm (accessed December 15, 2009).

growth. In 1980, the incarceration rate was 139 per 100,000 residents. By 2008, the incarceration rate was 504 per 100,000 residents, an increase of 263 percent. In short, the use of incarceration relative to the size of the U.S. population increased dramatically in recent decades. (Perhaps the growth reflects increases in crime? As we will see next, that does not appear to be the case.)

Incarceration rates increased in all but two years (2000–2001 and 2007–2008) in that time span, but the most pronounced growth occurred from 1980 to 2000. During this period, the incarceration rate grew an average of 6.4 percent annually, with increases of 10 percent or more in some years. Many scholars refer to the historically unprecedented growth in incarceration, especially during the 1980s and 1990s, as mass incarceration.

This growth contributed to one of the critical challenges confronting America today – the reentry of more than 735,000 inmates annually back into families and communities nationwide. It also led to a large body of scholarship aimed at understanding the causes and consequences of this sea change in incarceration policy.[20] Much of this work sidesteps a basic question, however: When exactly does society need more incarceration?

TABLE 4.2. U.S. incarceration rates, nationally, regionally, and by state, 2008[a]

U.S. Total	*504*	Virginia	489
Federal	60	West Virginia	331
State	445	**Midwest**	*392*
		Illinois	351
Northeast	*306*	Indiana	442
Connecticut	407	Iowa	291
Maine	151	Kansas	303
Massachusetts	218	Michigan	488
New Hampshire	220	Minnesota	179
New Jersey	298	Missouri	509
New York	307	Nebraska	247
Pennsylvania	393	North Dakota	225
Rhode Island	240	Ohio	449
Vermont	260	South Dakota	412
		Wisconsin	374
South	*552*	**West**	*436*
Alabama	634	Alaska	430
Arkansas	511	Arizona	567
Delaware	463	California	467
Florida	557	Colorado	467
Georgia	540	Hawaii	332
Kentucky	492	Idaho	474
Louisiana	853	Montana	368
Maryland	403	Nevada	486
Mississippi	735	New Mexico	316
North Carolina	368	Oregon	371
Oklahoma	661	Utah	232
South Carolina	519	Washington	272
Tennessee	436	Wyoming	387
Texas	639		

[a] The rates refer to adult prisoners held for one year or more per 100,000 residents.

Source: Sabol, William J., Heather C. West, and Matthew Cooper. 2009. *Prison Inmates, 2008*. Washington, D.C.: Bureau of Justice Statistics, p. 30.

Before addressing that question, we should be clear that incarceration is a policy – it represents a decision to use long-term confinement of individuals to achieve some goal, such as retribution, rehabilitation, or public safety.[21] Not only that, but it constitutes a policy that regions of the country and states use in varying degrees. Examine, for example, Table 4.2. We can see that the national incarceration rate in 2008 was 504 per 100,000 residents. That combines the state (445) and federal (60) incarceration rates. Regionally, however, we can see that the use of incarceration varies dramatically. In the Northeast, the average rate of incarceration in 2008 was 306, in the Midwest it was 392, in the West it was 436, and in the South it was 552. Focusing on the extremes, we can see that southern states on average incarcerate almost 250 more people per 100,000 residents as compared with northeastern states. Put differently, the policy in the South, relative to the rest of the country, is to incarcerate substantially more people.

Equally dramatic variation occurs at the state level within each of the regions. In the Northeast, Maine has an incarceration rate of 151, whereas Connecticut has an incarceration rate of 407. So, in that one region, the variation reflects that across all of the regions. The range in incarceration rates is somewhat greater in the western states, running from a low of 232 in Utah to a high of 567 in Arizona. The Midwestern states exhibit even greater variation – the low and high incarceration rates are in Minnesota (179) and Missouri (509), respectively. Witness the greater variability in the South – whereas West Virginia has an incarceration rate of 331, Louisiana has an incarceration rate of 853. In short, considerable variation exists both across regions and within regions in the extent to which incarceration as a policy is used.

Finally, when we turn away from regional differences and focus exclusively on states, we can see that the variation in the use of incarceration as a policy is even greater among states than among or within regions.[22] In Figure 4.3, for example, observe that the use of incarceration varies from a low of 151 in Maine to a high of 853 in Louisiana. The difference in rates of incarceration is 702. Viewed somewhat differently, Louisiana has an incarceration rate 5.7 times greater than that of Maine's. Of course, these two states constitute *outliers* – that is, the extreme ends of a range of values. Even so, we can see that the incarceration rates among the remaining states vary greatly. Such variation has led one scholar to remark, "Over the past twenty years, the fifty American states have engaged in one of the great policy experiments of modern times."[23]

IDENTIFYING THE NEED FOR INCARCERATION. Returning to the question at hand – when do we need more incarceration? Here, let us first stop to consider the variation in the use of incarceration across states. To put such variation in perspective, imagine an antibiotic known to cure some disease. Then, imagine that the use of the antibiotic varies along the lines of the

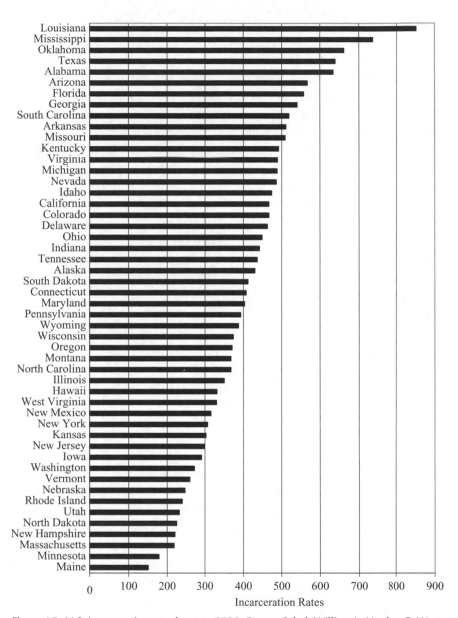

Figure 4.3. U.S. incarceration rates by state, 2008. *Source*: Sabol, William J., Heather C. West, and Matthew Cooper. 2009. *Prison Inmates, 2008*. Washington, D.C.: Bureau of Justice Statistics, p. 30.

variation in incarceration rates. We would of course anticipate, or perhaps hope, that there would be no variation because we know the antibiotic works and so it would seem to be a treatment that should be used whenever and wherever it was needed. Of course, it might be that the rate of the disease varies across places, and so that might create variation in treatment. However, after making an adjustment for this possibility, if we still saw dramatic differences in the treatment of the disease, we would be concerned.[24]

Consider the implications of this example for decisions about incarceration. If increasing the use of prisons "works" (by some criterion and as established by research), then there would seem to be little reason for variation in the use of it, save for any differences due to variation in the amount of the problem addressed by incarceration. From this perspective, the regional and state differences in the use of incarceration stand out as cause for concern. Why? Because, by and large, it cannot be accounted for by variation in the problem that many of us would think incarceration addresses – crime. Studies show that increases in crime either exert no effect or a modest effect on increases in incarceration rates. David Greenberg and Valerie West (2001) found, for example, that increases in violent crime and property crime were unassociated with increases in incarceration rates among states for the years 1971–1991.[25] Their study merits special attention because, in contrast with most prior research, they examined *changes* in crime to determine if they led to *changes* in incarceration. Put differently, their study provided one of the few direct assessments of whether crime is causally related to incarceration, and they found that appears not to be so related.

Let us view the matter from a different angle. In the medical example, we assumed that the medical establishment agreed that antibiotics effectively treat a particular disease. If, however, we assume that the medical establishment disagreed about the treatment's effectiveness, we would likely anticipate that some places would put greater faith in the treatment than others. In turn, we would anticipate variation in the use of antibiotics to treat the disease. Some doctors would think antibiotics work and so would use them, and some would be skeptical and thus refrain from using them.

Seen through this lens, variation among states in the use of incarceration perhaps should not be surprising, given that little consensus exists in the policy-maker or scholarly community about the effectiveness of incarceration. That may seem odd. How could incarceration not be an effective way to "treat" the problem of crime? Society takes criminals out of commission – we incapacitate them – and sends a message to would-be offenders that crime will get you in trouble. So clearly, in turn, crime should go down. In reality, though, studies find that incarceration contributes, at best, to modest reductions in crime, and the effect varies across types of crime. As Marie Gottschalk has written, "There is some relationship between the crime rate and the incarceration rate, but it is slight. Analysts using a variety of methodologies have found that the deterrent and incapacitation effects of incarceration in bringing down the crime rate are small, and that the offenses avoided through the greater use of prisons tend to be nonviolent rather than violent crimes."[26]

One of the more generous estimates of a crime-reducing effect of incarceration comes from work by William Spelman, whose analyses suggest that increased incarceration in the 1980s and 1990s contributed to roughly one-fourth of the drop in crime in the late 1990s.[27] That effect can be seen in two ways. On the one hand, the reduction, if real, translates into a significant improvement in public safety. Many state and local policy makers would be glad to take credit for a 25 percent reduction in crime that resulted from policies, like incarceration, that they may have initiated.[28] On the other hand, states must invest large amounts of resources to achieve that reduction. In the time period Spelman used in his analyses (1971–1997), the prison population grew fourfold, leading him to comment: "Even if imprisonment were an incredibly *inefficient* means of reducing crime – and there are strong arguments that it is exactly that – it could hardly have helped but have a substantial effect on the crime rate, given the enormous scale of the difference."[29] Viewed somewhat differently, investment in strategies other than prison might have produced comparable effects at less cost.

In short, if we focus on crime as a social problem that needs to be addressed, we find some evidence to suggest that this problem leads states to invest in prisons.[30] At the same time, Gottschalk, Spelman, and others have indicated that incarceration rates stem from many other causes. For example, Greenberg and West's study showed that states with more conservatives experienced higher rates of incarceration as well as increases in incarceration; states with greater increases in the religious fundamentalist population experienced greater increases in incarceration; and states with greater levels of and increases in unemployment experienced greater incarceration growth.[31] Such findings suggest that incarceration may address some other needs besides crime.

CRITERIA FOR DETERMINING THE NEED FOR INCARCERATION. The previously mentioned observations set the stage for more formally taking stock of some of the considerations that bear on evaluating the need for incarceration. First, a needs evaluation would attempt to make clear exactly what social problem incarceration addresses. The admittedly simple question in fact defies simple analysis. For example, incarceration can be viewed as help-ing to address two very different problems – society's desire for retribution when its laws are violated and society's desire for public safety. Many policy discussions about incarceration center on the idea of public safety, but ret-ribution stands as a critical part of any punishment policy.[32] Incarceration also can be viewed as a response to prison overcrowding. Ultimately, an effective policy response involves first targeting a clearly stated problem or set of problems. Focusing on only one aspect of the problem (e.g., a need to reduce crime) while ignoring another (e.g., societal demands for retribution) places any subsequent policy efforts on weak footing.

Second, a needs evaluation would attempt to quantify the scope of the problem. *How much crime exists, how much has it changed, where is it occurring, and what causes it?* Few states actually quantify the true amount of crime, but instead use proxy measures, such as arrests, even though the latter typically do not provide an accurate basis for estimating crime or changes in crime. For example, if states invest more heavily in law enforcement, more arrests will occur even if true crime declines.

The problem lies deeper than this measurement issue, however. The more fundamental question is, How much crime is bad enough to warrant a response? More specifically, how high do crime rates have to rise before society believes a response of some type, such as increased incarceration, should be imposed? Similarly, how much do crime rates have to increase before society deems that a response to be warranted? In contemplating these questions, we confront a stunning fact – states typically provide no explicit standards regarding the levels or changes in crime that warrant a response. The variation among states in their use of incarceration indicates, however, that they differ in the implicit, unarticulated criteria that they follow.

Much the same can be said for states' assessments of the public's need for retribution. Not all crime is the same, and so, by extension, demand for ret-ribution may vary depending on the types of crimes that occur in a state. In addition, retributive feelings may vary along social and demographic lines,[33] and so an accurate assessment of the state-level need for retribution would require taking such differences into account. Once, again, few states ever systematically take stock of public views toward crime, much less how these views change over time or what the specific sanctions are that the public thinks constitutes sufficiently retributive responses to particular crimes. The issue serves as pause for concern, if only because public opinion research shows that policy makers consistently overestimate the punitiveness of the public and underestimate their desire for and willingness to support rehabilitative measures.[34]

Overcrowding, too, entails consideration of similar questions. For example, how much overcrowding must occur before more prisons should be built? In answering that question, we would want to identify how much of a prison sentence inmates should serve. Inmate overcrowding can be relieved, for example, simply by having prisoners serve less time. The public tends to be shocked when they learn that inmates rarely serve their entire sentences. Nevertheless, it is true. For example, a Bureau of Justice Statistics study found that "violent offenders released from State prisons in 1992 served 48 percent of the sentence that they had received"[35] and that, among released prisoners, the "average sentence for a violent crime was 8 years, and the average time served was about 3.5 years, or just under half of their total maximum sentence."[36] The study also found that states varied greatly in the percent of sentence terms served by violent offenders, from a low of 21 percent (Ohio) to a high of 89 percent (Delaware).[37]

In the 1980s and 1990s, such differences prompted many states to enact so-called truth-in-sentencing laws aimed at making time served more closely mirror the length of sentences handed down at sentencing. Observe, however, that such efforts sidestep a basic question – how long should sentences for specific offenses be? The implications of not answering that question can be severe. To illustrate, a state might be incarcerating offenders for terms that are twice what the public feels is appropriate and yet be releasing prisoners once they have completed half of their assigned terms. In that case, the end result mirrors what the public wants in terms of the total length of sentence actually served. Even so, policy makers might focus instead on the fact that only half of the total assigned sentence length was served, view this as a problem, and then enact legislation aimed at requiring prisoners to serve their full terms. The end result? Prisoners serve lengthier prison terms than what the public wants.

View the matter from a slightly different perspective. Almost all prison bed-space forecasts make a highly problematic assumption – namely, that current bed-space use is the "right" amount for the level of crime faced in a particular state or jurisdiction.[38] That is, policy makers frequently assume that current bed-space usage constitutes the correct, or nearly correct, response for achieving some amount of crime reduction. Empirically based models then rely on current bed space use, along with estimates of future crime rates, to predict the need for future bed space. Observe that "need" never actually gets defined.

To illustrate, imagine a state where a thousand assaults occurred. Assume that all could be prosecuted and would likely result in conviction, but that only three hundred result in an arrest. Of course, from a purely legalistic perspective, virtually all of the assaults warrant punishment. Only three hundred are arrested, however; so, from the outset, one faces the problem that 700 of the assaulters (assuming no repeat offenders) will go unpunished. In virtually every state, crimes such as the 700 assaults occur that never come to the attention of law enforcement. The question, then, is when is that amount – what might be termed the dark figure of unpunished crime – too much? Jurisdictions do not typically answer the question, thus the need for legal punishment remains unknown. Even for the 300 arrests, states rarely define need, save that the most "severe," however operationalized, typically should be prioritized by prosecutors and the courts. Not all 300 will be given equal attention; indeed, some will be dismissed.

If one turns from purely legalistic to crime prevention definitions of need, questions arise about the amount of punishment needed to achieve some specific quantity of reduced crime in society at large. How many of the 300 arrested assaulters must be punished? What is, on the one hand, the amount of crime that "needs" to be reduced and, on the other hand, a reasonable amount of crime reduction to expect? Can a substantial reduction be had by punishing only a small percentage of the offenders, perhaps, for example, the most serious assaulters? Or is it necessary to sanction all of them? If so, by how much, and what about the 700 assaulters who went untouched? Not least, how much of a crime prevention effect will arise through specific and general deterrence mechanisms? That distinction is important because for some crimes, such as homicide, one can anticipate that certain sanctions, like the death penalty, will produce little by way of a general deterrent effect.[39] For other crimes, such as assault, it may be that a combination of specific and general deterrence collectively gives rise to an appreciable crime reduction.[40]

Against this backdrop, consider again the question of bed-space "need." How many prison beds are "needed" when there are 1,000 assaults? Certainly, one can anticipate that not all assaulters should be incarcerated. The question is, Which ones should be? Prosecutors might focus on the most serious cases, those in which substantial injury was involved, but that suggests a criterion of need – assaults in which only major injuries were sustained. Legislators have enacted laws that endorse greater punishment for weapons-related offenses, so perhaps "need" could be defined as assaults in which a weapon was used. In both cases, to establish the need for bed space, one first must identify how many assaults occurred that met the definition of "serious." Few jurisdictions or states in fact provide such operational definitions of need, or base their implicit or explicit definitions on the amount of crime reduction that can be expected from using specific quantities of incarceration for particular types of offenders.

Third, a needs evaluation would attempt to characterize the nature of the problem, including a description of its causes. If overall crime rates have dramatically risen but violent crime has declined, then, by extension, there would seem to be less of the kind of problem (violent crime) typically viewed as candidates for prison. Perhaps the public's preferences for punitiveness have changed. That would call attention to the importance of considering whether incarceration policies should be adjusted to reflect public sentiment. A careful analysis of overcrowding might lead to similar considerations. Overcrowding can stem from other factors, prison admissions in particular. Perhaps, for example, certain counties are quicker than others to incarcerate people for committing any kind of crime. Such counties could disproportionately contribute to state prison populations. At the same time, they might incarcerate the types of offenders that other counties and perhaps citizens at large view as better punished using other sanctions. Here, a needs evaluation, in the course of attempting to characterize the problem at hand and its causes, might find that the problem lies not with overcrowding but with overly aggressive use of incarceration by some counties. Of course, the opposite finding might emerge as well – to wit, other counties may be too lenient and not be sending appropriate cases for incarceration in state prisons. In this case, overcrowding estimates would actually be understating the true scope of the problem.

Fourth, a needs evaluation would attempt to ascertain not only the scope and nature of a problem as well as its causes but also whether a need exists for a proposed solution, such as incarceration. As the preceding example indicates, if policy makers want to address the problem of overcrowding, it may well be that increased incarceration constitutes the most appropriate, effective, and efficient response. An analysis might show that counties throughout a state are failing to use incarceration in appropriate cases because of concerns that the state will simply return new admissions back as quickly as possible. In this case, increased prison capacity may be warranted. However, in other cases, increased capacity may be unnecessary, ineffective, and inefficient. For example, if a few "rogue" counties overincarcerate, the appropriate response might be to intercede, not build more prison capacity.[41] Otherwise, a vicious cycle ensues in which increased capacity creates a greater demand to use incarceration in inappropriate cases.[42]

In addition to investigating such possibilities, a needs evaluation would want to investigate whether, among the options available to address a particular problem, incarceration constitutes the most appropriate and effective solution or, put differently, whether it constitutes the most needed option among those available. That is, it would assess the expected relative benefits of incarceration in achieving such goals as public safety, retribution, and reduced overcrowding relative to the expected benefits associated with other possible approaches. When making assessments about the expected benefits of incarceration, particular attention should be given to whether defensible assumptions have been made about anticipated incapacitation, specific deterrent, general deterrent, and rehabilitative effects.[43]

Fifth, a needs evaluation would attempt to assess the relative need for an increase in a solution, such as incarceration, to some problem (e.g., increased crime, public desire for retribution, overcrowding). This issue assumes considerable importance when we talk about incarceration because prisons constitute one of the most costly criminal justice investments society makes. Any balanced set of criminal justice system policies would, in the ideal case, build on a systematic assessment of needs across the entire system, not just those of the correctional system.

Sixth, a needs evaluation would attempt to weigh and balance the potential harms that may emerge from a policy. Potentially, the need to address some problem may outweigh the costs of some solution. Ideally, though, policy makers conduct such assessments in advance. Here, again, a discussion of incarceration highlights the importance of this consideration given that prisons may cause more harm than good. For example, they may divert or obligate resources that might be expended on other potentially more effective alternatives. Incarceration may increase recidivism and worsen reentry outcomes of released prisoners, disrupt families and communities and, by extension, create more crime.[44] Not least, according to some studies, mass incarceration may increase poverty.[45]

These considerations certainly do not exhaust all of the possibilities, but they illustrate some of those most critical to conducting a needs evaluation. At the same time, they illustrate a key axiom of needs evaluations – namely, such evaluations entail considerable conceptual work. Clear conceptualization is as critical if not more so than empirical analyses, especially when the latter occur untethered from an understanding of the complexities relating to a seemingly straightforward "problem." Many different and highly sophisticated approaches exist for forecasting the need for prison bed space, but none of them are a good substitute for clear conceptualization and description of a problem. For example, one commonly used approach to forecasting involves the use of complicated time-series analyses, and another approach involves equally complicated microsimulation efforts aimed at incorporating information about prison admissions and lengths of stay for different types of offenses and for different cohorts. However, both approaches depend heavily on assumptions about current and past practices. They do not typically address questions about whether such practices are or were suitably responsive, or under- or overresponsive, to the extent of actual crime or to public preferences for specific sanctions for particular types of offenses.[46] Such issues can more easily be identified by first proceeding with a conceptual analysis of the problem under study.

Sex Crime Laws

THE POLICY. Coinciding with the rise of mass incarceration has been a pronounced effort to address sex crimes.[47] One recent assessment indicated, for example, that in 2005 alone, state legislatures enacted more than one hundred sex offender laws.[48] No single type of law stands out. Rather, diversity rather than uniformity characterizes these laws, which include registries that make public the names and addresses of sex offenders, statutes that limit where convicted sex offenders can live, and "get tough" sentencing policies aimed at increasing incarceration of sex offenders.[49] Increasingly, too, though less common, have been state-level efforts to enact laws allowing for the civil commitment of sex offenders in mental health facilities after their criminal sentences have expired.[50] In a few states, chemical castration has been promoted as both a sanction and a treatment to address sex offending. In addition, DNA data banks are beginning to emerge as a way to help law enforcement identify and arrest suspects.[51]

Federal policy-making efforts spurred the development of many of the state-level efforts. For example, under the Jacob Wetterling Crimes against Children and Sexually Violent Offender Registration Act, enacted in 1994 – and subsequently amended by Megan's Law in 1996 – states are required to "create and maintain a sex offender registration and notification program or lose 10 percent of the Federal crime funds."[52] This federal effort was sparked by victimizations of two young children, one of whom was abducted in 1989 when he was eleven years old (Jacob Wetterling) and the other of whom was abducted in 1994 when she was seven years old (Megan Kanka). Other prominent cases involving young children include the sexual assault and murder of twelve-year-old Polly Klass in 1993 and of nine-year-old Jessica Lunsford in 2005.[53] Such cases continue to prompt new federal legislation targeting sex crimes. For example, in 2006, Congress enacted the Adam

Walsh Child Protection and Safety Act, named for a boy who was abducted and murdered in 1981. This act provided for "increased registration requirements for states [and creation of] a federal civil commitment program."[54]

The result, according to Lisa Sample and Timothy Bray, is that all states now have "registry, notification, and DNA laws" that "include persons convicted of a violent or nonviolent sex crime against any person."[55] Notably, these laws encompass a wide range of offenses and so create the potential to greatly expand the criminal justice system's caseloads. For example, nonviolent sex crimes can include "crimes such as possessing, viewing, or manufacturing child pornography; enticing a child; soliciting a minor; and other such offenses for which offenders must register upon conviction."[56] Similarly, many states require that commission of any of a diverse array of crimes result in a person being registered as a sex offender. These crimes include such acts as "voyeurism, public exposure, adultery, giving obscene material to a minor, displaying obscene material on a bumper sticker, and bestiality."[57]

IDENTIFYING THE NEED FOR SEX CRIME LAWS. From a needs evaluation perspective, the basic question is whether a need for these laws exists. Clearly, sex crimes occur and so constitute a social problem that should be addressed. Such an assessment is too simplistic, however. Consider, for example, that sex crimes have always occurred, or have so long as laws have made such acts criminal. Thus, the relevant question is whether states suddenly experienced a marked increase in sex crimes in the 1980s and 1990s sufficient to justify a sweeping set of new, "get tough" policies. The answer appears to be no. As one recent review emphasized, "there is little convincing evidence" that sex offending has increased.[58] Indeed, if anything, the available, if limited, evidence suggests that it remained level or even declined in recent decades. For example, from the late 1970s through 2008, rape and sexual assault rates, as measured by the National Crime Victimization Survey, steadily declined.[59] No doubt, the survey underreports the true amount of such crime, but it likely does so consistently from one year to the next.

Unfortunately, the survey does not compile national data on the wide range of acts considered to be sex crimes. As a result, no reliable or valid estimates of sex crime trends exist for the country as a whole or for specific states. One could speculate that sex crime trends as a whole run counter to that for rape and sexual assault. However, doing so would require not just speculation but also careful arguments that convincingly show why sex crime trends in general would run in the opposite direction of the trend for rape and sexual assault.

This situation is especially problematic from a needs evaluation perspective, given that the enactment of sex crime laws has proceeded from an assumption that sex offending has increased. What if, however, it has decreased? The logical implication would be that a prominent social problem had declined and so, if anything, merited less attention. Of course, some might argue that the various laws have produced the declines in sex offending. However, the downward trend in rape and sexual assault rates began well before many of these laws emerged and paralleled an overall decline in violent crime in general, not just sex crime.[60] An alternative view might be that, in the past, the country failed to take adequate steps to punish and control sex offenders. Thus, even if sex crime rates trended downward of their own accord, new forms of punishment and new restrictions might be seen as needed to correct for the too-lax approaches of the past. Here, however, we would want first to define the appropriate response as a benchmark for determining whether past practice was sufficient or not.

Many sex crimes unquestionably involve horrific acts, and so for that reason spark outrage among the public and policy makers. That alone likely contributes to calls for tough responses to sex crimes. In addition, recidivism statistics, as presented in media accounts, likely create additional alarm. A widely cited and credible federal study shows, for example, that sex offenders released from prison are four times more likely than nonsex offenders to be rearrested for a sex crime.[61] However, such studies frequently gloss over or miss the fact that sex offenders rarely recidivate and that, as a group, they contribute less to sex crime nationally than do nonsex offenders.

How can that be? In the federal study, which examined inmates released from prisons in fifteen states in 1994, there were 9,691 male sex offenders. Of this group, 517 were rearrested for a sex crime within three years of release from prison. Put differently, 5.3 percent of the released male sex offenders were rearrested for a sex crime within three years of release. Without question, some sex crimes did not result in an arrest, and the arrests that did occur included many serious offenses. At the same time, the low base rate of recidivism (5.3 percent) gives pause for thought.

Of course, nonsex offenders also commit sex crimes after release. The federal study found that of the 262,420 released nonsex offenders, 3,328, or 1.3 percent, were rearrested for a sex crime. This lower rate of sex-crime recidivism leads to the estimate that sex offenders are four times more likely than nonsex offenders to be rearrested for sex crimes (5.3 percent vs. 1.3 percent). Such a fact obscures, of course, the fact that both groups have low rates of sex crime recidivism. In addition, because the nonsex offender group is much larger (262,420 released inmates), it results in a far greater number of sex crime recidivists. In absolute terms, there were, in the fifteen-state study, 517 sex offenders who were rearrested for a sex crime whereas 3,328 nonsex offenders were rearrested for a sex crime. Put differently, nonsex offender recidivists comprised the overwhelming bulk – 87 percent – of all released prisoners who were rearrested for a sex crime, whereas sex offenders comprised only 13 percent.

The results of this study and those like it point to two broad sets of findings. On the one hand, they suggest that sex offenders are more likely to be rearrested for sex crimes. On the other hand, they indicate that sex crime recidivism occurs rarely and that the bulk of such recidivism stems from crimes committed by nonsex offenders. Moreover, when attention turns to recidivism in general, not recidivism only for sex crimes, studies show that sex offenders have lower recidivism rates compared to other types of offenders. For example, in the fifteen-state federal study, 43 percent of sex offenders (4,163 of 9,691) were rearrested for any crime within three years of release, compared to a rearrest rate of 68 percent among nonsex offenders (179,391 of 262,420).[62] Perhaps, then, sex offenders merit closer attention if we wish to address sex crime. However, in so doing, we might fail to address most sex crime as well as other types of crimes if we focused more on them rather than other offenders.

CRITERIA FOR DETERMINING THE NEED FOR SEX CRIME LAWS. In short, if need is defined as increased rates of sex crime, there would appear to be less, not more, need for ever-increasing numbers of laws aimed at sex offenders. Of course, need could be defined differently. Perhaps certain definitions, when coupled with empirical research, might indicate that such laws should exist and perhaps be expanded. For example, many different types of sex offenders exist, as reflected in part by the range of crimes classified as sex offenses (indecent exposure, accessing child pornography, rape), and maybe the rates of serious sex crimes have dramatically increased in some areas. If so, a need for a response would be indicated.

Efforts to describe the scope of and trends in different types of sex crimes would want to take into account that considerable disagreement among scholars exists concerning the most appropriate ways to classify sex offenders. The problem in arriving at consensus stems in part from the fact that relatively few studies have empirically tested different theories of sex crime or the relative recidivism rates of different types of sex offenders. Why? The low base rates of sex crime and recidivism require that studies have large study samples, as with the fifteen-state federal study discussed earlier. That raises study costs considerably, especially if new data, such as information about psychological characteristics of offenders, must be collected. The sum result? At present, we know little about the best way of classifying sex offenders or how to predict which offenders will go on to commit new sex crimes.[63] We know even less about the qualitative aspects of sex crimes. As one recent study emphasized, current actuarial risk assessment instruments "conceptualize violence risk solely in terms of probability of future violence, ignoring other facets of risk, such as the possible nature, severity, imminence, duration, or frequency of future violence."[64]

A needs evaluation also would consider the causes of any identified problem because such information would help in developing a policy response tailored to the specific causes of the problem. At present, there remains little empirical basis for claims that rates of sex crimes have increased or that sex crimes today are more serious than in the past. At the same time, many studies suggest that the primary drivers of today's sex offender policies include public concern about crime, which has resulted in part from highly publicized and sensationalized accounts of select tragic cases, and policy makers' efforts to demonstrate a clear record of being tough on crime.[65]

The policies seem to have emerged from incorrect assumptions not only about sex crime trends but also other facets of sex crime. For example, sex offenders can be treated in some instances, but many policy makers and members of the public believe otherwise.[66] In addition, accounts of sex crimes frequently treat all such crime as the same. Clearly, however, some crimes, such as indecent exposure, differ greatly in kind and severity from aggravated sexual assaults.

Assuming that a needs evaluation identified that increases in some types of sex crimes constituted a social problem meriting a new response, the question then would be what type of response to pursue. One option simply would be to expand current efforts. Law enforcement could be directed, for example, to expend more resources on any reports related to sex offending. Another option, the one pursued by most states in recent decades, is to implement many new types of laws. Ideally, however, a given law would be pursued only after establishing that a need existed specifically for it.

To illustrate, sex offender and community notification registries make some sense if they are likely to be accessed by residents in areas where sex offenders reside. They also make sense if most sex crimes involve situations where the victim does not know the offender. Neither claim, however, comports with research. For example, stranger victimizations tend to be rare. Instead, most sex crimes are committed by family members, friends, or acquaintances of victims. Notably, many sex crime laws have been prompted by horrific accounts of strangers who victimized children, yet "93 percent of offenses against children are committed by family members and acquaintances."[67] Such statistics arguably lead to the inference that sex offender registries may not be needed because most victims know who victimized them.

Another example involves residency restrictions, which limit where registered sex offenders can live. For example, such offenders may not be allowed to live within 1,000 to 2,000 feet of schools, bus stops, day-care centers, or other places where children congregate.[68] This type of a policy assumes, however, that most sex crimes involve children and that the crimes involving children occur in or near these places. That assumption may hold true in some places but in other places would not.[69] The more important point is that a needs evaluation would highlight if a policy aimed at limiting where sex offenders live should be pursued or whether perhaps a different type of policy should be created.

In assessing the need for specific policies, we ideally would have information about the relative need for them. Expanding the range of tough sentences for sex crimes may be needed in some states, but perhaps a greater need exists for a registry, residency restrictions, or treatment. Ideally, of course, states could implement every possible strategy. They operate, however, with limited resources and must make decisions about how to allocate them. To this end, their efforts can be greatly facilitated by needs evaluations that identify and measure a problem, that identify the most salient dimensions of the problem or those dimensions most amenable to policy influence, and that describe the relative need for different policies. In the case of sex crime, one critical type of need to consider is whether the public adequately understands important nuances concerning sex crimes. Some studies suggest, for example, that the public dramatically overstates the recidivism rates of sex offenders.[70]

Not least, needs evaluations of sex crime policies would take stock of the potential or likely harms associated with specific policies. Sex offender residency restrictions, for example, may inadvertently increase crime by forcing offenders to live with family members or to be homeless and they may also preclude offenders from obtaining employment.[71] The potential is far from academic. Jill Levenson and David D'Amora have noted that a variety of obstacles "leave many offenders no choice but to reside with family members, but when family members are located within restricted zones, sex offenders are left with literally nowhere to go."[72] They also have noted that the recent trend nationally "has been for cities and towns to expand residency restrictions to 2,500 feet [from schools, parks, playgrounds, etc.], essentially banning sex offenders from metropolitan areas."[73] Most jobs lie in metropolitan areas, and so residency restrictions can preclude sex offenders from finding work in those areas with the best prospects for gainful employment. The restrictions can also contribute to homelessness, which makes it more difficult to track and monitor sex offenders.[74]

Many sex offender policies are quite broad in their focus. Some benefits may accrue to the broad-based approach, but ideally a needs evaluation would provide a systematic assessment of different approaches and discussion of which seem most needed. Such an approach might reveal that a better investment would be in risk-based classification systems, which hold the potential for "resources to be used more efficiently to intensively monitor, treat, and restrict dangerous offenders while not disrupting the stability of lower risk offenders and their families."[75]

Here, consider that many policies proceed from incorrect assumptions about the relative risks of recidivism of different groups, assumptions that are easier to sustain in the absence of valid classification systems. Levenson and D'Amora have noted, for example, that "some recent policies target child abusers and exclude rapists, who, as a group, have higher recidivism rates, and are more likely than child molesters to target strangers and to cause severe physical injury to their victims."[76] In short, a greater need may exist for investing in better classification than in a new broad-based policy. Perhaps not. Perhaps better reentry planning for released inmates would emerge as especially critical. Or perhaps too much or too little treatment of sex offenders exists. Again, perhaps not. The point is that effective planning should include systematic and empirical assessment of the risks associated with addressing some needs and not others.

Are Current Criminal Justice Policies Needed?

Let us return to the question of whether the prominent policies that populate the criminal justice landscape today are needed. In this section, I begin with the focus in recent decades on "get tough" reforms and then turn to the two illustrations (mass incarceration and sex crime laws) and a number of other prominent criminal justice policies.

At the broadest level, a central question is whether the plethora of "get tough" reforms in recent decades was needed. It would appear not. Primarily, this assessment stems from the fact that states typically do not accurately estimate the true amount of crime nor do they explicitly articulate how much of it should be addressed. Unless one has a foundation for determining whether prior efforts were sufficient, no basis exists for knowing whether to increase or decrease them. Assume, for example, that a given state is spending more than it needs and then crime rates increase. Arguably, no additional funding should be invested because the state was overinvesting in crime-fighting efforts. Similarly, assume that a given state is spending more than it needs and crime rates decrease. It would make sense that crime reduction spending should be reduced.

Many observers might argue that funding for crime policies is never adequate. As long as any crime exists, the argument goes, resources should be dedicated to fighting it. That argument, however, assumes a definition of need. What, for example, is the proportion of crime that merits a response, and how much of it can be addressed with available funding? Answers to both questions require an assessment of the magnitude of the crime problem. Yet few jurisdictions or states compile independent self-report offending or victimization data on crime, and so have little idea how much crime occurs. (Law enforcement data invariably capture only a part of all crime, and so are of questionable use in assessing the scope of or trends in a crime problem because the data may reflect law enforcement practices as much as they do crime.[77])

The problem confronting criminal justice is broader, however, than one of not knowing how much crime of various types exists in particular states and localities or of defining when a level of or change in crime warrants a response. It also includes a failure to assess the range, scope, and nature of a wide range of problems within criminal justice. For example, to what extent do law enforcement officers follow appropriate protocols and laws for apprehending or questioning subjects or for using force?[78] To what extent do defendants receive adequate legal counsel? To what extent do prosecutors select and pursue cases in an appropriate manner? How well do judges run their courtrooms? Are probation or parole officer caseloads excessive?

When we turn our attention to the policies that states have enacted, similar questions emerge. The first illustration focused on mass incarceration. Here, the question is whether this policy has resulted from careful and studied analysis of crime patterns and trends, deliberation about actual versus ideal prison sanctioning and sentence lengths, assessment of the causes of crime and likely returns from incarceration, or the relative need for incarceration versus other policy responses to crime or such problems as prison overcrowding? It appears not. When one canvasses the literature on legislative decisions to expand prison system capacity, whether directly through increased funding for prison expansion or indirectly by enacting laws requiring lengthier sentences that in turn require more prison capacity, little evidence of such stock taking can be found. Put differently, little evidence exists to suggest that legislatures and correctional systems have systematically and carefully conducted needs evaluations for their incarceration invest-ments.[79]

Other prison system examples related to mass incarceration abound. Prison privatization has increased dramatically in recent years, and yet it frequently occurs in the absence of any clear information about whether public prisons are operating less efficiently than could be expected from private prisons. Viewed another way, there remains little evidence to date that private prisons operate cheaper than public prisons and do so while achieving comparable outcomes.[80]

Similarly, supermax prisons have emerged in almost every state over the past several decades, yet there is little evidence that states undertook needs evaluations to document whether they were needed.[81] The title of an article on the topic – "The Rise and Rise of Supermax: An American Solution in Search of a Problem?" – captures this view.[82] One common justification is that they serve to house the "worst of the worst" inmates. States typically do not, however, provide clear, measurable criteria for identifying such inmates; consequently, they cannot say how many supermax beds they need or, in turn, whether existing beds are too few, adequate, or too much.

Sentencing laws provide the central platform for increasing incarceration. Here, one of the most prominent changes in recent decades has been the emergence of sentencing guidelines. They have been justified as providing a way to eliminate unwarranted disparities in sentencing.[83] Judges, for exam-ple, were viewed as being too inconsistent in the sentences they gave, and the hope was that sentencing guidelines would result in "like" cases being treated in "like" manner. This argument depends fundamentally on establish-ing what "like" cases are and how much variability in sentencing such cases is "warranted." Notably, however, few states have empirically estimated the amount of variability in sentencing prior to enacting guidelines.[84]

Of course, tougher sentencing may emerge for purely politically expedi-ent reasons, such as to help a prosecutor, judge, or legislator get elected, or it may result from a myriad of social forces.[85] Even so, a needs evaluation would want to tackle such issues. And it would want to tackle the question of need on the most straightforward grounds available – to wit, what exactly is the need for the policy? How much crime of various types deemed to be worthy of incarceration exists? How much retribution, as measured in years of incarceration, is appropriate? Retribution is central to any punishment system. Even so, and as Andrew von Hirsch has highlighted, precious little empirical research has focused on the "quanta of punishments" that best reflect or put into effect specific theories of punishment, including retribu-tion, or the preferences of the public.[86]

Still other criminal justice policy examples exist. The chapter's second illustration focused on sex crime laws, which have proliferated and done so in the absence of any systematic, empirically based needs evaluations. These laws generally assume that recidivism is greater among sex offenders, that such offenders are less amenable to treatment and, more generally, that widely publicized cases reflect a pervasive problem. Each assumption is incorrect. As a result, states have little credible foundation on which to assert a need for tougher sanctioning of sex offenders.

Many other examples exist where prominent policies have been pursued in the absence of clear assessments of need. Drug sentencing and other "get tough" laws and programs aimed at stiffening penalties for drug-related offending have proliferated. Here, again, scant attention has been given to establishing the need for such laws. Certainly, drugs are implicated in much crime, but that is different from defining and quantifying the need for a law. In addition, the causal relationship between drugs and crime remains in question.[87] To the extent it is not causal, one might well argue that a need exists but that it is for treatment, not punishment.[88]

Mandatory arrest laws have proliferated because of a perceived need to address a critical problem – domestic violence. An important question, however, is whether a need for tougher law enforcement was needed more so than some other response. In answering this question, policy makers would want to consider such factors as the distribution of domestic violence and the possibility that it occurs more in some groups than in others and for different reasons.[89] Any significant variation would highlight the need for a nuanced approach to domestic violence rather than a single one-size-fits-all policy like a mandatory arrest law. Notably, lawmakers in the 1970s faced a range of possible policies for reducing domestic violence and an emphasis on arrest constituted but one of them. A systematic needs evaluation, which was not conducted, would have included consideration of other legal interventions (e.g., protective orders, mandated treatment), social service interventions (e.g., shelters for victims, advocacy services), and health care interventions (e.g., identification of domestic violence in medical settings and reporting of such violence to legal authorities or social service agencies).[90] Today, it remains unclear whether mandatory arrest laws are more or less needed than these other types of interventions.

In the juvenile justice system, almost all states have recently embraced a wide array of laws enabling youths to be transferred to the criminal justice system for processing and sanctioning.[91] Again, empirical evidence in support of the need for such laws is lacking. Few states, for example, have systematically evaluated how much punishment youths receive in their juvenile justice systems and how these youths likely would be punished in the adult system. An empirical analysis might well reveal, as some studies have, that youths would receive less severe sanctions.[92] Were that true, the need for transfer laws would be eliminated.

Such examples, while illustrative, appear to be representative of a general failure of federal, state, and local jurisdictions to identify the need for their policies. Thomas Blomberg and Gordon Waldo have argued as much, noting that "juvenile justice policy has rarely been guided or significantly influenced by research,"[93] an assessment equally relevant to criminal justice. The consequences of this failure are at once simple and critical – resources are likely to be expended on problems that may not warrant attention and other problems may go largely unaddressed.

Conclusion

Needs evaluations provide many benefits. They can help determine whether a problem exists and its scope and nature. They can assist in debates about whether to retain or eliminate a particular policy. More generally, they can provide guidance about which types of needs should be prioritized and which policy responses should be pursued. They also can identify the critical assumptions or research gaps that put discussions of particular "problems" on a shaky foundation. They help establish the relevant criteria for evaluating a policy's effectiveness. And, more generally, they can spur more informed and constructive discussions about social problems and how best to address them.

Ideally, needs evaluations occur prior to implementation of any policy. That simply stands to reason – why expend scarce resources on a nonexistent problem? Moreover, needs evaluations can inform the development of policies by pointing to critical areas of need that may be especially amenable to policy influence.

To achieve these benefits, needs evaluations must be informed by empirical information about the size of a problem as well as trends in the problem, its distribution socially and geographically, and its causes. They also should focus on the extent to which a need exists for different types of policy interventions. Specific social problems, including crime, frequently can be addressed in numerous ways. Which ones are the most needed may well depend on the specific nature of a problem as it exists in particular towns, cities, and states. It may be that existing efforts are sufficient or simply need to be expanded. But it also may be that new efforts should be undertaken. In either event, a needs evaluation should also identify the potential benefits and harms of the different options. Doing so allows policy makers to make more informed decisions about the relative trade-offs associated with different strategies for addressing crime or some problem within the criminal justice system.

Unfortunately, when one canvasses the criminal justice policy landscape, it becomes clear that many of the most prominent policies there – including mass incarceration and sex crime laws – lack any well-established foundation in an assessment of need. That does not mean the laws should not have been implemented or necessarily are or will be ineffective. However, it does greatly diminish their likely success. At the same time, it raises the specter that considerable amounts of resources have been and are being inefficiently used in a context where the costs, including the risk of more crime, are great.

Discussion Questions

What are the benefits of evaluating the need for a criminal justice policy? What are the problems of not evaluating the need for a criminal justice policy?

How do you conduct a needs evaluation?

How do you define the need for a given policy? For example, what level of a crime problem is needed before policy makers should respond? Does there simply have to be any amount of crime? If so, how should policy makers decide how to allocate funds to specific types of crimes? To specific types of policies?

What amount of increase in a problem (e.g., crime) is needed before policy makers should take action? Should specific policies be reduced or eliminated if a social problem decreases? For example, if crime decreases, should policy makers reduce criminal justice funding because of the reduced need?

Many types of problems exist in criminal justice, and crime is but one of them. Law enforcement officer, defense counsel, prosecutor, or correctional personnel may engage in misconduct. Courts may suffer from case overload. The public may hold incorrect views about the prevalence of crime or the conditions of confinement. What priority should be given to these and other types of problems? On the basis of what criteria?

5

Theory Evaluations

I N OUR EVERYDAY LIVES, MOST OF US FACE MANY PROBLEMS THAT WE WORK to solve successfully. In trying to address these problems, we consciously or unconsciously use theories to determine how to proceed. For example, we may take a shortcut to work because of a theory that says, "If you take this road, the total distance will be shorter and so you will get to work sooner." Of course, the theory may be incorrect or incomplete. Distance may influence total travel time, but so, too, might the number of traffic lights along the way. Accordingly, we might revise our theory to take both distance and the number of traffic stops into account. Even so, we could be overlooking some other factor, such as the varying lengths of some traffic lights depending on the time of day. The route we ultimately take may be affected by how we adjust for such possibilities. Of course, in the larger scheme of things, a change in the route we take constitutes but one of several possible strategies we could adopt to ensure that we make it to work on time. For example, we could leave earlier and so allow more time for our commute.

In short, theory describes how we believe the world works. It also describes the way in which a social policy is expected to achieve its goals. The theory may not be fully articulated. It may not even be articulated at all. In these cases, the policy rests on an implicit understanding of a problem and how it can be solved. Regardless of whether a theory is articulated, it nonetheless constitutes the foundation of any policy. For that reason, flaws in policy theory amount to cracks in a building's foundation – they undermine the policy and its effectiveness.

The problem lies in the fact that many policies may make sense at first glance but rest on weak theoretical foundations, which is a recipe for ineffectiveness. As Rossi and his colleagues have observed, "Given a recognized problem and need for intervention, it does not follow that any program, willy-nilly will be appropriate for the job."[1] Indeed, a policy guided by weak or faulty theory "will fail no matter how elegantly it is conceived or how well it is implemented."[2]

When applied to the world of criminal justice, theory evaluations can help answer the critical question of whether policies rest on defensible sets of assumptions about the nature of a particular problem (e.g., crime, prison overcrowding, inadequate defense representation). In turn, they also can help answer the related question of whether the policies can be or are likely to produce intended outcomes (e.g., reduced crime, less overcrowding, better defense representation).

This chapter describes theory evaluations and their importance in developing criminal justice policies and in assessing policy implementation and impacts. It then provides two case studies – one focused on supermax prisons and the other on faith-based prisoner reentry programs – aimed at illustrating theory evaluations and their benefits. Building on these discussions, the chapter turns to the question of whether criminal justice policies in the United States are well grounded theoretically.

What Is a Theory Evaluation?

Theory Evaluation: Step 2 in the Hierarchy

Once the need for a social policy intervention is established, the second step in the evaluation hierarchy is to conduct a theory evaluation. The term *theory* sometimes brings to mind some complicated account of a particular phenomenon. To some, it may connote an approach to explanation that only social scientists can use or understand. Although some merit for these impressions exists, the fact remains that a theory ultimately is nothing more than an attempt to explain how the social or physical world works.[3] For example, if a study shows that X (punishment) causes Y (reduced crime), a theory would attempt to explain why. Deterrence arguments suggest that the explanation centers on fear – punishment creates fear in those who have been punished and those who witness it, and this fear in turn induces people to avoid behaviors that might lead to a similar sanction. Other explanations can be posited (e.g., punishment might educate the public about society's laws). In the end, empirical research can help us to determine which explanation has greater validity.

In evaluation research, policy theory serves much the same purpose as theory does in the social sciences. Specifically, it helps explain how some specific policy-related activities or services are expected to cause some intended outcome. Put differently, it identifies the causal logic underlying a policy, such as how some factor, X, causes an outcome, Y. Deterrence theory, for example, provides a basis for anticipating why punishment should lead to reduced crime.

Virtually any social policy rests on some theory, whether articulated or not. It may be faulty, incomplete, or overly simple, but it exists. Ideally, however, the theory is explicit and credible. Otherwise, the policy likely will be ineffective and waste scarce resources.

Evaluating the credibility of policy theory thus constitutes a critical step in the evaluation hierarchy. The main task consists of describing the nature and character of the policy, including its essential activities and how these activities should lead to some end outcome, such as reduced crime, improved case processing, greater prison order, or the like. Rossi and his colleagues have described the process as one of identifying whether a credible policy theory or causal logic (or what sometimes is referred to as a *policy model*[4]) exists that convincingly shows that policy-related activities will likely contribute to intended outcomes.[5]

Needs Evaluations and Theory Evaluations

Before we examine theory evaluations in detail, a brief discussion of the relationship between needs and theory evaluations is warranted. The logical sequence in evaluating policies consists first of identifying whether a social problem exists that needs to be addressed and then determining whether the policy designed to target that problem rests on a credible theoretical foundation. In many cases, however, the two types of evaluation can and should overlap.

Recall, for example, that a needs evaluation involves not only the description of a problem but also its causes. In so doing, a needs evaluation ideally is guided by theory that points us toward probable causal forces. To illustrate, many criminological theories tell us about the types of factors that might contribute to a crime problem in some community. A needs evaluation could use these theories to inform an assessment of what particular factors seem to be driving local crime rates. It also could explore possible contributing factors not contemplated by criminological theories but that nonetheless may be relevant to understanding the causes of the problem. Among other things, a needs evaluation would want to examine the distribution of the problem in social and geographic space. This effort in turn would provide information that could be useful for understanding the causes of the problem. If, for example, increased crime occurred only in one part of town, we might reasonably infer that the causes of the crime increase do not necessarily involve citywide conditions but rather those specific to the particular area. Such information could be used to ensure that a policy targeted its energies toward the specific contours of the problem, not to citywide crime.

That observation leads to the critical axiom that policy theory should build on the information gleaned from needs evaluations. In particular, it should build on "a thorough understanding of the social problem the [policy] is intended to address and the service needs of the target population."[6] To proceed otherwise is to risk allocating resources toward areas or populations where no problem exists or that fail to address the characteristics of the areas or populations that contribute to the problem.

In short, needs evaluations and theory evaluations should be integrated. On the one hand, by identifying the causes of a problem, a needs evaluation creates the foundation for creating a range of more theoretically informed policy responses. On the other hand, a theory evaluation can be used to examine how well the responses accord with the identified problem and with prior theory and research, and which responses may merit the most attention. As but one example, consider a legal drug that policy makers believe is widely used in an inappropriate and harmful manner. One initial response might be to make the drug illegal. However, that assumes that users would be deterred. If that assumption finds support from a needs evaluation or in existing theory and research, perhaps criminalizing use of the drug makes sense. Otherwise, it may not make sense. Even if it does, it may be that some other policy response makes more sense (e.g., educational campaigns, drug counseling or treatment).

Theoretical or Causal Logic

An effective policy typically rests on a sound theoretical or causal logic. Quite reasonably, then, we might anticipate that theory evaluations are used to develop and assess policies. Frequently, however, one finds that policies lack any clear statement or evaluation of the underlying theory or causal logic. Policy evaluations do occur. However, they typically consist of implementation or impact evaluations. Theory evaluations are, however, important in their own right. If a policy does not embody a set of expectations, assumptions, practices, or protocols that reasonably accord with theory, research, or the social reality of the agents or targets of change, it will not likely be effective.[7]

Consider, for example, a policy aimed at reducing truancy. A community might be concerned about increased rates of truancy and the possibility that this problem has contributed to higher delinquency rates. A local lawmaker notes that many students care deeply about being able to drive, and so she promotes the following policy – if a student is truant, his or her driver's license will be revoked for one year. Local officials agree that the idea has merit and create a policy implementing it. Subsequently, they find that truancy rates remain unchanged. Why? Researchers conduct a study and discover that few truants had driver's licenses. In cases like this one, we would logically anticipate that the policy should have had no effect because it had no teeth. Had a theory evaluation been conducted prior to implementing the policy, it might well have identified that the policy rested on a critical and perhaps questionable assumption about the overlap between truancy and having a driver's license. In turn, it might have led policy makers to investigate more carefully and empirically whether the policy's logic was credible.[8]

Although no single agreed-upon approach exists for describing a policy, the basic ingredients involve three dimensions: the organizational plan, the service utilization plan, and the impact theory.[9] The *organizational plan* refers to how a policy will be implemented. It describes the agents responsible for implementing the policy; the targets of the policy; the types and numbers of personnel and their respective responsibilities; the facilities or locations where the policy is implemented or delivered; and the services, activities, or actions the policy provides. For example, if the policy were a drug court, the organization plan would describe, among other things, which court or courts would serve as the venue for the drug court operations, how many judges and other personnel would be assigned to the court, the responsibilities of each courtroom practitioner, and the number and types of members in an advisory board to the court.

The *service utilization plan* describes how specific aspects of the policy will be implemented. It involves reference to such dimensions as how frequently clients will be contacted or treated, the duration of participation in or exposure to the policy, and the protocols that must be followed in executing different activities or providing certain services. Extending the drug court example, it might include a description of how rapidly offenders must be processed through the court, how frequently they should meet with community supervision officers and check in with the sentencing judge, the frequency and type of drug treatment, and the amount and range of rehabilitative services that offenders should receive or use.

More detailed descriptions of how to describe policies and programs, including organizational and utilization plans, can be found in many sources.[10] Here, our primary focus will be on impact theory – that is, how the policy's design can be expected to cause intended outcomes – because this theory ultimately embodies the essence of a policy and determines whether it will be effective.[11]

CAUSAL LOGIC DIMENSIONS. In describing a policy's causal logic, it can be useful to differentiate the following dimensions: targets, inputs, outputs, short-term outcomes, longer-term or end outcomes, and conditioning factors.[12] Targets constitute those individuals, groups, or areas upon which the policy focuses or that benefit from it. Inputs consist of the resources, such as funds, staffing, and other supports, that collectively enable the policy to exist. Outputs refer to the actions, products, or services that define the policy. Stated differently, they constitute the "completed products of internal activity."[13]

Short-term or intermediate-term (sometimes termed *proximal*) outcomes are the relatively immediate changes (e.g., learning prosocial values) expected to result from the outputs (e.g., counseling) and that are expected to create an ultimate, or end, outcome (e.g., less recidivism). They can include service quality because typically this dimension matters to the public.[14] For example, we typically view speedy or timely processing of criminal court cases as an essential element of what it means to have a fair and just system. Longer-term or end (sometimes termed *distal*) outcomes refer to the ultimate, or final, changes thought to result from the outputs and/or the short-term or intermediate-term outcomes.[15]

Conditioning factors consist of characteristics of the policy environment – the policy, or target groups or areas that directly, indirectly, or in interaction with other factors, affect activities, outputs, or outcomes. The central idea here is that a particular activity, like drug treatment, may have different effects for different populations (e.g., long-term drug addicts versus occasional drug users). A theory evaluation would aim to identify potential conditioning effects to guide subsequent assessments of the implementation and impacts of a policy.

POLICY GOALS AND OUTCOMES. A logic model essentially consists of an effort to show how these different dimensions (e.g., outputs and outcomes) relate to each other. Policy goals, and the outcomes associated with these goals, bear special emphasis. Three considerations should be addressed. First, all relevant goals should be included in the theory evaluation. A fundamental tenet of evaluation research is that all goals, not just a select one or two, should be identified and factored into any summative assessment of the worth of a policy.[16] If we focus on one goal only (e.g., reduced recidivism) and not another (e.g., increased employment), we do an injustice to the policy, in much the same way that a supervisor would be doing us an injustice if they rated our performance on only one of many different sets of activities for which we are responsible. The fact that multiple policy goals may exist frequently is overlooked when evaluators jump straight to conducting impact evaluations. The use of theory evaluations can avoid this problem by identifying all policy-related goals, along with relevant outcome measures, and how the policy is expected to achieve them.

Second, the temporal sequencing of goals should be identified. Some policy goals (e.g., increased public safety), as measured by specific outcomes (e.g., reduced recidivism), may not emerge for some time. At the same time, other goals (e.g., improved transitions back into society, as measured by obtaining housing and employment) may occur relatively quickly. This temporal sequencing of outcomes necessitates a distinction between shorter-term or intermediate-term policy effects and longer-term (or end) outcomes or impacts. Without this information, we may use inappropriate follow-up periods in impact evaluations and thus fail to identify accurately how well a policy achieves its goals.

Third, where appropriate, logic models should distinguish between in-program and after-program outcomes. This distinction is important because some outcomes may occur prior to and after participation in a program. To illustrate, a drug treatment program might provide drug awareness classes. However, well before participants have completed the program, they could have learned key facts and ideas upon which the curriculum is focused and, as a result, reduce their drug use.[17]

AN ILLUSTRATION – ACTION. To illustrate these concepts and how they can be linked together in developing a causal logic model, let us turn to Figure 5.1, which provides an example of a causal logic model for a policy aimed at reducing agricultural crime, including theft of livestock, crops, chemicals and pesticides, and large and small equipment.[18] The policy – named the Agricultural Crime, Technology, and Operations Network, or ACTION – was implemented in California's Central Valley area and relied on a small number of personnel across different agencies, including law enforcement and prosecutors' offices, to undertake a number of activities aimed ultimately at decreasing agricultural crime.[19]

As can be seen in the left side of the figure, the program targeted several groups – offenders, farmers, law enforcement agencies, and prosecutors. Each of these groups played a part in ACTION. The resources, or inputs, included the staff at ACTION as well as personnel at several law enforcement agencies and district attorneys' offices. ACTION's main efforts

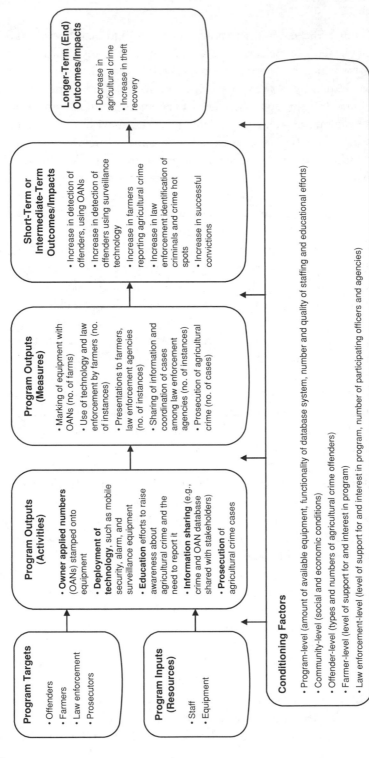

Figure 5.1. Agricultural Crime, Technology, Information, and Operations Network (ACTION) causal logic model.

Program Targets
- Offenders
- Farmers
- Law enforcement
- Prosecutors

Program Inputs (Resources)
- Staff
- Equipment

Program Outputs (Activities)
- **Owner applied numbers** (OANs) stamped onto equipment
- **Deployment of technology**, such as mobile security, alarm, and surveillance equipment
- **Education** efforts to raise awareness about agricultural crime and the need to report it
- **Information sharing** (e.g., crime and OAN database shared with stakeholders)
- **Prosecution** of agricultural crime cases

Program Outputs (Measures)
- Marking of equipment with OANs (no. of farms)
- Use of technology and law enforcement by farmers (no. of instances)
- Presentations to farmers, law enforcement agencies (no. of instances)
- Sharing of information and coordination of cases among law enforcement agencies (no. of instances)
- Prosecution of agricultural crime (no. of cases)

Short-Term or Intermediate-Term Outcomes/Impacts
- Increase in detection of offenders, using OANs
- Increase in detection of offenders using surveillance technology
- Increase in farmers reporting agricultural crime
- Increase in law enforcement identification of criminals and crime hot spots
- Increase in successful convictions

Longer-Term (End) Outcomes/Impacts
- Decrease in agricultural crime
- Increase in theft recovery

Conditioning Factors
- Program-level (amount of available equipment, functionality of database system, number and quality of staffing and educational efforts)
- Community-level (social and economic conditions)
- Offender-level (types and numbers of agricultural crime offenders)
- Farmer-level (level of support for and interest in program)
- Law enforcement-level (level of support for and interest in program, number of participating officers and agencies)

centered on five activities, or outputs: (1) stamping owner-applied numbers (OANs) on equipment; (2) deploying surveillance equipment to farmers' properties in cases where theft occurred or was anticipated to occur; (3) educating farmers, law enforcement officers, and prosecutors about the nature and importance of agricultural crime; (4) encouraging different stakeholders, especially farmers, law enforcement agencies, and prosecutors' offices, to share information within and across counties; and (5) aggressive prosecution of cases involving agricultural crime.

Assuming that ACTION generated these outputs or measures of these outputs (as shown in the first two columns, respectively), a number of short-term to intermediate-term impacts could be expected. These include: increased detection of offenders, which could occur if they tried to sell stolen equipment marked with OANs or if surveillance equipment recorded their illegal activities; increased instances of farmers reporting crime to law enforcement; increased targeting of criminals and crime hot spots by law enforcement; and increased numbers of successful convictions. Such changes, in turn, could be expected to cause several longer-term, or end, outcomes, including a decrease in agricultural crime and an increase in the recovery of stolen property.

As inspection of the bottom of the figure highlights, several conditioning factors were anticipated to influence the implementation of the policy and the production of outputs and outcomes. For example, the logic model anticipates that the quality of county-level implementation might vary depending on such factors as the number of law enforcement officers and prosecutors available to participate in the initiative. Similarly, it contemplates the possibility that the policy's effects might vary depending on the types and numbers of offenders engaged in agricultural crime in some counties or on the social and economic conditions in them. To illustrate, perhaps aggressive prosecutorial activity might create deterrent effects in areas with relatively high amounts of crime but little by way of a deterrent effect in low-crime or high-poverty areas.

A theory evaluation would highlight these and other dimensions, and it would focus particular attention on the causal logic. In this case, ACTION's policy theory consisted of the view that several mechanisms would combine to reduce agricultural crime and increase recovery of stolen property. The three main mechanisms included (1) increased guardianship of crime targets (through the use of video monitoring and better surveillance of farm property), (2) decreased opportunities for theft (through increased surveillance and changes in the location or physical surroundings of livestock, chemicals, and equipment), and (3) increased deterrence and recovery of

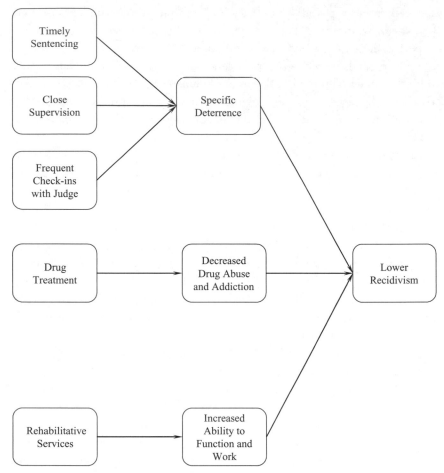

Figure 5.2. Drug court causal logic model.

property (through OANs, arrests, and prosecutions). The theory evaluation of ACTION indicated that it rested on a credible set of assumptions about the nature and distribution of agricultural crime and the likely effectiveness of the central causal mechanisms.[20]

ANOTHER ILLUSTRATION – DRUG COURTS. A causal logic model does not have to be this detailed. A simplified one might focus exclusively on the theoretical logic and not the targets or resources, for example. Figure 5.2 depicts one such logic model focused on drug courts. Many different logic models exist for these courts, reflecting in part the fact that not all of them operate the same way or with the same set of features.[21] Nonetheless, a relatively generic presentation of a drug court model includes the dimensions detailed in the figure.

The theoretical logic consists of at least three assumptions. First, timely sentencing, close supervision of offenders, and frequent check-ins with the court will deter offenders from committing more crime. Second, drug treatment will reduce drug abuse and addiction and in turn decrease recidivism. Third, a variety of rehabilitative services (e.g., counseling, family therapy, life skills training) will increase the ability of offenders to function and to find work, in turn decreasing the likelihood that they will recidivate.

The logic has much to recommend it, including research on deterrence and drug treatment. As such, it might be defensible to proceed with implementing drug courts. Even after implementation, however, theory evaluations remain important because they can guide efforts to evaluate why certain impacts emerge. For example, if we evaluate a specific drug court and identify no impact on recidivism, we would know to investigate whether each theoretically relevant dimension was well implemented. Similarly, if we identify a reduction in recidivism, we know to explore whether it stems from deterrence, treatment, some combination of the two, or the influence of judges who specialize in illegal drug cases.[22]

SPECIFYING THE TYPE OF CAUSAL RELATIONSHIP. In describing policy theory, it can help to state explicitly the type of causal relationship anticipated. Different types of such relationships exist. For example, they may be linear or nonlinear. A *linear* effect would mean that for each additional "unit" of the policy (e.g., for each additional prosecution), some specific quantity of effect can be anticipated (e.g., two fewer crimes). A *nonlinear* effect would mean that the effects of a unit change might vary depending on the level of dosage. For example, in a given county, the effect of going from no convictions to one conviction might create a much greater deterrent effect than the effect of going from 100 convictions to 101 convictions.

Figure 5.3 depicts one example of a nonlinear effect. The figure plots the effects of increases in strain, using an index where 0 equals "low strain" and 100 equals "high strain," on the frequency of offending. Strain constitutes one of the central factors that criminological theory says may produce criminal behavior.[23] As inspection of the figure shows, moving from low levels of strain to higher levels of strain leads to increased offending, but the effect varies as we move toward the higher levels of strain. Observe, for example, the variation in the delta (Δ), or change, values along the curved line. These values depict the increase in offending due to an increase of 10 in the strain

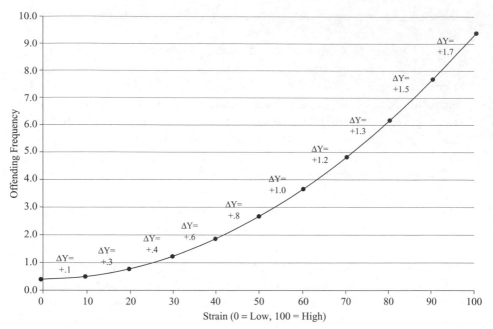

Figure 5.3. Nonlinear effect of strain on offending.

index. Starting at the left, we see that going from zero to ten in the strain index produces an increase of .1 more crimes. By contrast, an increase from eleven to twenty in the strain index produces .3 more crimes. Clearly, a ten-unit increase exerts a different effect on offending, although the difference does not seem especially large. The situation looks much different, however, as we proceed toward the higher levels of strain. An increase from seventy-one to eighty on the strain index, for example, is associated with 1.3 more crimes, and an increase from ninety-one to one hundred is associated with 1.7 more crimes.

Consider the policy implications of this nonlinearity. If we did not test for it in an impact evaluation, we would conclude that a policy aimed at reducing strain among individuals produces the same effect regardless of the individuals' baseline levels of strain. The figure suggests that such an inference would likely be incorrect. Instead, it points to the possibility that much greater reductions in offending would occur if the policy focused primarily on high-strain individuals. For example, if the policy could lower, by ten points, the strain of individuals with a score of one hundred, 1.7 crimes might be averted per individual. If the policy focused on individuals with strain scores of ten, however, only .1 crimes per individual might be averted with an identical reduction in strain. If we did not design a policy to consider these potential differences, we might apply it willy-nilly to, say, all prisoners, even though substantially greater returns might be gained by focusing on those with the highest amount of strain.

Creating complexity for the sake of it clearly defies reason. All else being equal, simpler explanations are to be preferred. At the same time, the world frequently operates in a complicated way, and the failure to take that into account when evaluating policies can lead us to identify null effects, or relatively small effects, in situations where large effects exist. The previous example illustrates that possibility and comes from research that documents nonlinear effects of strain on criminal behavior.[24] Unfortunately, because social scientists are trained to seek the simplest explanations, such nonlinearities frequently go unidentified. However, a number of prominent criminologists, including Charles Tittle and Robert Agnew, have convincingly argued, and in some instances shown, that many of the major causes of crime exert nonlinear effects.[25]

It therefore stands to reason that many crime-focused policies have nonlinear effects. For example, community policing programs became increasingly popular in the 1990s, but it makes little sense to anticipate an appreciable effect of such a program unless it passes a critical threshold of implementation.[26] (Threshold effects are one type of nonlinear relationship.) Similarly, some sentencing studies suggest that lengthy terms of incarceration may not create an appreciably larger reduction in recidivism beyond what could be gained by relatively short prison terms. For example, in a recidivism study by Ian O'Donnell and his colleagues, the authors found evidence of diminishing returns associated with lengthier sentences. Specifically, they found that inmates "who served less than three months were significantly more likely to be reimprisoned following release than those who served longer," but that there were "no such significant differences in reimprisonment between those who served three to six months, six to twelve months, or more than twelve months."[27] More generally, the policy literature and studies in medicine clearly establish that, as a general matter, interventions may have differential effects depending on such factors as dosage and the characteristics of the populations being served.[28]

Theory evaluations can sensitize researchers to these types of possibilities and lead them to investigate important ways in which policies may exert effects in nonobvious ways. Perhaps, for example, a policy greatly reduces offending among women but not men. A study that failed to investigate this possibility might well find that a prison program produced no effect on recidivism, especially because the samples would likely consist overwhelmingly of men, who greatly outnumber women in prisons.

How to Conduct a Theory Evaluation

The question arises of how one goes about identifying policy theory. As with much of evaluation research, no single or best way exists. Instead, different strategies can be used. In some instances, the process is straight-forward. For example, Carol Weiss has noted that sometimes documentation exists that explicitly describes a policy's theoretical foundation.[29] She has described such descriptions as articulated program theory to distinguish them from those cases where an implicit program theory exists, one where no clear or fully articulated account of the theory has been recorded. Frequently, evaluators encounter the latter situation and so must elicit the policy theory. In such instances, "the evaluator's objective is to depict the '[policy] as intended,' that is, the actual expectations held by decision makers about what the [policy] is supposed to do and what effects are expected to follow."[30]

How can this step – the description of a policy's theory or logic – be undertaken? One strategy consists of interviewing key decision makers and asking them to describe their understanding of the policy. The questions should center on their views concerning the policy's inputs (e.g., resources and staffing); outputs (e.g., core activities); and short-, intermediate-, and longer-term outcomes or goals. Different decision makers may vary in their views of these dimensions, and so the evaluator must work not only to elicit the range of views that exist but also to get the decision makers to come together to develop a consensus, if possible, about the characteristics of the policy. For example, in talking to the director of a faith-based prisoner reentry program, an evaluator might learn that the program's main goal is to promote greater spirituality among inmates. In conversations with funders or program staff, however, the evaluator might learn that the program has several equally important goals, including fostering not only greater spirituality but also improved life skills, successful employment experiences, prosocial relationships with others, and the like.[31] Discussions with both the director and the staff would ensure that these additional goals were identified. They also would underscore the need to develop an understanding about which, if any, goals should be weighted more heavily and also how specific program activities are expected to contribute to each of the goals.

Another strategy involves reviewing policy documentation or using site visits. Programs frequently have reports that describe their main activities and sometimes their goals. Similarly, statutory language or legislative briefings may describe the purpose and logic of specific laws. Existing studies, too, may provide accounts of various aspects of policies. They may also provide detailed descriptions of the theoretical underpinnings of related initiatives. For example, many specialized courts exist. A detailed theoretical account of one type (e.g., drug court) might well be relevant to or fit well with another (e.g., teen or mental health court). Evaluators might also conduct site visits to observe an existing program or the circumstances or conditions under which a proposed one would be implemented. Not least, the clients targeted or served by policies may offer insights into the activities and goals of the policies and how the two may be linked.

Regardless of the sources used, the ultimate goal consists of describing as completely as possible the assumed causal means-end relationships among all the different facets of a policy (e.g., resources, staffing, services, activities, and how they relate to outcomes). Failure to fully specify these relationships risks providing an incomplete description of the policy, how it is supposed to work, and, by extension, the standards that should be used for assessing policy implementation and impacts.

Whether the policy is in development or already exists, the evaluator may find that a series of "successive approximations" must be undertaken before a fully developed theory can be identified.[32] The evaluator might need, for example, to send descriptions of the policy theory to key stakeholders, obtain their feedback, and then revise the theory and resend it to all the stakeholders for additional comments. Evaluation ultimately involves careful consideration of the views and concerns of key stakeholders. Accordingly, this process constitutes a critical step not only in eliciting policy theory but also in ensuring that the stakeholders perceive the evaluation to be legitimate.

Criteria for Evaluating the Credibility of Policy Theory

Once a policy theory has been identified, we want to evaluate its credibility. Here, again, evaluation research as a field has not identified a single best approach. Instead, several strategies can be pursued.[33] In using them, evaluators rarely will be able to assess every aspect of a theory, but typically they will be able to test many of the critical assumptions upon which the theory rests.[34]

One approach is to examine whether a policy theory targets a social problem that actually exists. For this step, recourse to a needs evaluation is critical. By contrasting the policy theory with the needs evaluation results, the evaluator can identify whether the theory relates to the specific contours of the social problem. If it does not, problems likely will emerge and the policy likely will be ineffective.[35] To illustrate, a needs evaluation might document that pesticide theft in a particular area of one county is on the rise. Examination of the policy theory might show that the core activities focus on all parts of the county and consist of efforts to ensure that livestock and large equipment cannot easily be seen from roads. This broad-based focus would be inappropriate and likely ineffective given that the problem centers in one part of the county. In addition, the strategies, while perhaps useful for preventing livestock and large equipment theft, would probably do little to prevent farm workers from stealing pesticide.

A second approach evaluators can use is to assess the logic and plausibility of a policy's theory. This step can be undertaken by reviewing any prior needs evaluation, policy documents, decision-maker and stakeholder comments, and existing theory and research, and also by soliciting insights from a panel of experts. In assessing policy logic and plausibility, Rossi and his colleagues have advocated using a series of questions:[36]

- Are the goals and objectives well defined? For example, are they described in specific and measurable terms (e.g., increased public safety through reduced violent crime rates)?
- Are the goals and objectives feasible? For example, can the conditions targeted by the policy actually be changed? Are the outcomes ones that could be appreciably affected by the policy? A policy might aim to reduce crime rates and yet target only a small number of offenders each year, and so would be unlikely to affect overall crime rates much.
- Is the change process presumed in the theory plausible? For example, do the policies' activities (e.g., drug treatment) logically relate to specific changes in the target population (e.g., reduced drug use and drug-related offending)?
- Are the procedures for identifying members of the target population, delivering services to them, and sustaining the services well defined and sufficient? For example, will the target population (e.g., drug users) be likely to access program services (e.g., drug treatment) at designated times?
- Are the constituent components, activities, and functions well defined and sufficient? For example, if a prisoner reentry program is supposed to increase the ability of released inmates to find housing, are there personnel or activities actually allocated to achieving this goal?
- Are the resources (e.g., funding, personnel, material, equipment, facilities) allocated for various activities adequate? For example, do sufficient numbers of probation officers exist to provide the targeted levels of supervision to offenders?

Ideally, the answers to each of the previous questions are affirmative; otherwise, problems will arise. For example, if the policy's goals are too vague, it becomes difficult not only to know what criteria to use in evaluating it but also to know what measures should be used. Saying that a drug court exists to promote public safety is too vague. A drug court, for example, is unlikely to affect overall crime rates in metropolitan areas. A more precise and measurable description would be to say that a drug court exists to reduce recidivism and drug abuse among convicted offenders. Similar specificity is required in responding to the other questions. Otherwise, the policy theory will rest on a weak foundation and, in turn, the policy will be more likely to fail.

Of all the questions, one of the most important centers on the plausibility of the theoretical logic. Many policies entail a complicated cause-and-effect sequence, with one change (e.g., job training) leading to another (e.g., securing a job) and still another (e.g., less offending). Any weak link in this causal chain can undermine the effectiveness of a policy. For this reason, evaluators should critically examine each part of the causal sequence to determine if it rests on sound theory, logic, or research.

A third way evaluations can examine the credibility of policy theory is by investigating whether social science theory or research exists to support all or parts of the policy, especially its critical assumptions.[37] For example, evaluations of similar policies, or of policies that rest on similar assumptions, may exist. Information from them may provide insight into whether the policy's central assumptions are defensible. To illustrate, sex offender legislation might stipulate that registered sex offenders may not reside within one thousand feet of a school. Studies of similar legislation that use different distances (e.g., 1,500 or 2,000 feet) would help evaluators determine whether this residency restriction is likely to reduce sexual victimization.[38] Any of the critical sequences in a policy's cause-and-effect chain can be evaluated in this way. Ideally, all causal claims can be backed by credible theoretical or empirical studies. Through examination of each claim, evaluators can provide a summary evaluation of a policy theory's credibility and also identify any especially "weak links" in the theory's logic.[39]

Finally, preliminary observations of a policy or of the conditions or populations it targets can inform assessment of policy theory. This approach could include interviews with program leadership, personnel, or clients as well as observations of the program in action to determine if critical assumptions are supported.[40] For example, visits to and observations of a faith-based prison program might reveal that few participants take part in the religious activities offered by it and instead opt primarily for the secular services. That situation in turn would suggest that a premise of the program – that inmates want religious programming – is incorrect.[41] Similarly, interviews with program staff may reveal that insufficient resources exist to provide many of the intended services.

Why Are Theory Evaluations Important?

Theory evaluations can produce several important benefits. First, they can clarify the purposes of policies, including their goals and objectives. For example, what need does a given policy address and what outcomes will be produced? Although it would seem that most policies have clearly stated goals and objectives, they frequently do not.[42]

Second, theory evaluations can guide the development and theoretical foundation of existing or proposed policies so that the policies have a better chance of producing intended outcomes. For example, they may focus on whether proposed activities could be implemented that would target the most critical causes of a problem and whether extant theory and research supports the view that these activities will produce the desired outcomes. Similarly, existing policies may be examined with an eye toward making changes that place it on a stronger, theory- and research-based foundation. As noted in Chapter 4, social problems typically result from a diverse range of factors. It would be inefficient and likely ineffective to target all of them at once. A theory evaluation can help guide policy makers toward those factors that most contribute to the problem and that are most amenable to policy influence.

Evaluability assessments, which involve preliminary theory evaluations, serve a similar purpose.[43] They consist of (1) description of a policy's causal logic, including specification of the program goals; (2) analysis of how well the policy and its operations, activities, and services are described and thus how evaluable the policy is; and (3) investigation of the extent to which different stakeholders have an interest in an evaluation.[44] These assessments can identify whether a policy can be evaluated at all. They also can serve as preliminary theory evaluations because they attempt to identify the nature of the policy and how its activities relate to different outcomes. In so doing, they contribute to the development of a clearer and more explicit causal logic. One result can be that officials and administrators revise a policy so that it rests on a more solid and credible foundation.

Third, theory evaluations can identify activities and services relevant to assessing policy implementation. Causal logic mapping, for example, helps us to see what activities and services collectively comprise the policy and that therefore should be implemented. As such, theory evaluations can be invaluable to performance monitoring efforts aimed at holding the agencies and organizations responsible for policy implementation accountable.

Fourth, theory evaluations can identify dimensions that may influence whether a policy is found to be effective. A theory evaluation could establish, for example, whether poor implementation of an especially critical policy activity would be likely to undermine the policy's effectiveness. To illustrate, a theory evaluation of a drug court might find that provision of drug treatment and intensive supervision constitute necessary ingredients for any intended outcomes to emerge.[45] In so doing, it would underscore the need to couple an impact evaluation with a process evaluation that documents whether treatment and supervision occurred in sufficient doses. Were treatment, supervision, or both missing, we could anticipate that the drug court would be found to be ineffective. Similarly, we would know to view more skeptically a null finding of drug court effectiveness until evaluations of well-implemented drug courts emerged. More generally, theory evaluations can illuminate the "black box" of a policy – that is, the activities and services that constitute it – and how these may contribute to why the intended outcomes were or were not identified in an impact evaluation.

Fifth, and not least, theory evaluations can be used to identify unintended harms that may result from a policy and thus that, at a minimum, may merit study. In some cases, the harms may be insufficient to raise concerns about a policy; in others, the harms may raise doubts about it. For example, suppose that a legislature wants to impose a new law restricting where sex offenders can reside or to expand an existing residency restriction law. A theory evaluation might highlight that some studies not only have failed to identify a beneficial effect of such laws but also that, at least in some cases, they may have contributed to increased offending and homelessness.[46] Such information can be used to modify legislation or various policies in ways that would help avoid adverse outcomes and maximize intended, beneficial outcomes.

Case Studies: *Supermax Prisons* and *Faith-Based Reentry Programs*

We turn now to two case studies – one focused on supermax prisons and the other on faith-based reentry programs – to illustrate theory evaluations and their importance and to explore how well grounded these policies are in theory and research. Each case study begins with a description of the policy and then focuses on the theory that guides it. In the subsequent section, we step back and focus on the broader question of whether these policies, and others like them, rest on solid theoretical grounds.

Supermax Prisons[47]

THE POLICY. Incarceration in supermax prisons entails single-cell, twenty-three-hour-per-day confinement for an indefinite period of time with almost no services or visitation. The security measures in them greatly exceed those used in maximum-security prisons. For example, supermaxes typically rely heavily on technology to minimize contact with inmates and to monitor them. Proponents of supermaxes emphasize the idea that supermax confinement is needed to manage the "worst of the worst" inmates and to prevent or reduce violence; critics argue that such confinement is painful and demeaning, harmful, and expensive.[48]

Research on this unique type of housing remains minimal despite the rapid growth in such facilities nationally.[49] Twenty-five years ago, the only supermax facility in the United States was one in Marion, Illinois, operated by the federal prison system.[50] By 1996, thirty-four states had one or more supermaxes, holding 19,630 inmates, or roughly 2 percent of all prison inmates.[51] By 2004, forty-four states had supermax prisons, collectively housing approximately 25,000 inmates.[52] Today, supermax prisons constitute a common feature of the corrections landscape and yet have gone largely unexamined. The limited research to date is remarkable given the substantial costs of these prisons and the fact that they have been lightning rods for controversy, including domestic and international criticisms that they are inhumane and unconstitutional.[53]

THE THEORY OF SUPERMAX INCARCERATION. Few detailed attempts to explicate the theoretical foundation of these prisons exist, and those that do have focused solely on one goal critical goal of supermaxes – increasing systemwide prison order.[54] The notion of increasing order by targeting the most disruptive inmates is an approach generally consonant with what some scholars have characterized as the new penology's emphasis on managing risk.[55] However, that description leaves open the question of whether supermaxes can be expected, on theoretical grounds, to improve systemwide order. Jesenia Pizarro and Vanja Stenius's theoretical analyses suggest that they do not and cannot. For example, the authors have argued that general deterrence constitutes a weak causal mechanism: "It is unlikely that supermax facilities serve as a [general] deterrent because of the certainty of punishment, [given that] placement in these facilities is relatively rare

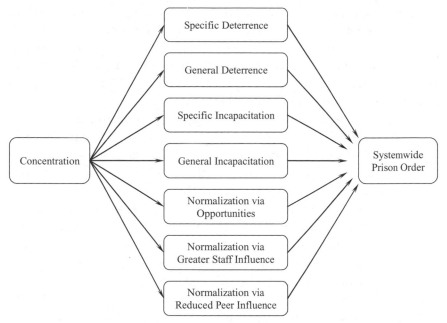

Figure 5.4. Different causal pathways through which supermax housing might produce greater systemwide prison order. *Source*: Mears and Reisig (2006:39, fig. 1). Used with permission from Sage Publications.

and often based on administrative decisions using risk factors over which inmates have little control."[56]

A colleague and I extended that argument by systematically examining the different theoretical mechanisms by which supermax prisons might improve systemwide order and found that these facilities have little merit on logical or empirical grounds.[57] Figure 5.4 details the different mechanisms. As inspection of the figure shows, the basic theoretical premise consists of the view that concentrating the most disruptive and violent inmates in one place should lead to seven causal pathways that contribute eventually to increased systemwide order. The pathways include (1) specific deterrence (i.e., inmates placed in supermax housing should, upon release into general population housing, be afraid to commit further disruption or violence); (2) general deterrence (i.e., general population inmates should be afraid to be placed in supermax housing); (3) specific incapacitation (i.e., the most disruptive and violent inmates are prevented, by dint of placement in supermax housing, from being disruptive or violent); (4) general incapacitation (i.e., the most disruptive and violent inmates are prevented, by dint of placement in supermax housing, from causing others to be disruptive or violent);

(5) normalization of the prison environment by freeing up staff time to provide more and better programming opportunities for inmates; (6) normalization of the prison environment by allowing staff to focus their energies on controlling and helping a greater number of the general population inmates; and (7) normalization of the prison environment by reducing the negative peer influence of the most disruptive inmates.

In each instance, the pathways rest on unreasonably strong assumptions, many of which run counter to theory or research. For example, specific deterrence appears to be an unlikely mechanism through which supermaxes produce systemwide order, given that supermax inmates, putatively the "worst of the worst," may be among the least likely to be influenced by severe sanctions and that evidence for a consistently strong deterrent effect of sanctions has not been found.[58] Among other things, such inmates typically have demonstrated repeatedly a disregard for others or for a host of other sanctions. Moreover, unless such inmates contribute to most disorder – an assumption that conflicts with research[59] – any specific deterrent effect as well as any incapacitative effect would exert a negligible impact on aggregate amounts of disorder. In addition, the assumption that supermaxes "normalize" the general prison system environment appears tenuous. Why? Removing disruptive inmates would not necessarily or even likely free staff to offer programs to or focus more attention on the remaining inmates, especially in periods, such as the past three decades, when incarceration levels have risen continuously and when the amount of programming services has declined.[60]

Additional theoretical analyses suggest that supermax prisons may, if anything, increase disorder. Pizarro and Stenius have argued that disorder may worsen via "experiential effects," wherein the failure to follow through with threats to place inmates in supermax confinement increases misconduct, and via inmate perceptions that such confinement is illegitimate and unfair.[61] Similarly, the "rage hypothesis" suggests that supermax inmates, upon release to general prison facilities, will be so angry that they attack staff and other inmates.[62] Consider, for example, the state of mind of an inmate interviewed by Lorna Rhodes who had been confined in a control unit: "If I'm being good and they don't give me nothing, I can't take that. . . . I just went off, spitting, urinating, tearing up my cell. . . . If they feel like I'm gonna be a badass, why not be one?"[63]

More generally, as scholars have emphasized, supermax prisons do little to address the structural conditions that research has shown contributes to disorder.[64] Policies like supermax prisons, which target specific types of individuals, cannot "magically . . . unlock the problem of order for a prison system as a whole."[65] For example, such prisons do not target maladaptive systemwide inmate social norms or the general deprivations that most inmates face.[66] Indeed, they could be argued to contribute to the problems that arise when inmates perceive prison systems to be operating in an unjust manner.[67] Moreover, they do not in any obvious way contribute to improved managerial efficiency or effectiveness.[68]

Supermax prisons have been associated with other goals, such as reducing prison violence and escapes and improving public safety, and similar theoretical assessments have yet to be rendered that examine the credibility of the causal logic for how supermaxes contribute to these goals. Some preliminary appraisals suggest that analogous problems exist, however.[69] For example, given that the certainty of placement in a supermax is low, few would-be offenders in the general population can be expected to refrain from criminal activity, after release to society, through a general deterrence process. Also, inmates in supermax confinement receive little to no programming or services over several years and then may be released outright into society with no supervision. In such cases, individuals might well be expected to have higher rates of recidivism than if they had received services.[70]

Some might argue that supermax prisons constitute an effective crisis management tool, a view that comports with the initial justification undertaken at the Marion facility[71] and in many states (e.g., Texas[72]) and countries (e.g., the Netherlands[73]). Nevertheless, solutions to crises represent unlikely solutions to noncrisis situations.[74] To illustrate, if an individual comes down with an infection, a doctor might prescribe an antibiotic as a short-term "crisis" management solution. However, use of the antibiotic on a regular basis would not be indicated and would not address such factors as exercise, nutrition, and the like, which may contribute to illness. Similarly, supermax facilities may enable prison systems to gain control when riots or extreme amounts of violence or disruptions occur, but that would not mean that they necessarily nor even likely are effective over the long term for managing inmates.

OBSERVATIONS AND IMPLICATIONS. The supermax prison theoretical logic rests on strong assumptions that, upon close inspection, appear to be overstated or incorrect. At the same time, some theoretical and empirical research exists to suggest that supermax facilities may cause harm, such as increased disorder and violence as well as increased recidivism.[75] Prison wardens, who arguably have special insights into the matter, have suggested that these possibilities exist.[76] Even so, research may find these assessments to be overly pessimistic. Perhaps, for example, supermaxes do deter general population inmates from disorder and violence. One of the only rigorous studies to examine the issue found that some supermax prisons decreased systemwide violence; however, the authors cautioned that the effect was not consistent, may not generalize to other states, and could have emerged from methodological shortcomings associated with the research design.[77]

Even if studies find that supermax prisons improve systemwide order, a theory evaluation can provide policy-relevant insights. For example, the complexity of the supermax theoretical logic indicates that improvements likely could be had by bolstering attention to such critical dimensions as (1) ensuring that general population inmates perceive supermax incarceration to be a likely consequence of specific types of misconduct and (2) accurately identifying those inmates who contribute disproportionately to disorder and violence. In addition, a theory evaluation might find that supermax incarceration could create harms, such as increased mental illness and recidivism. In turn, it would highlight for policy makers and officials that they might want to take steps to reduce the likelihood of these specific adverse effects on inmates, staff, or the system as a whole.

A final observation – a thorough theory evaluation of supermax prisons would focus on whether a clearly defined problem exists and what causes it. Supermax prisons unequivocally focus on order and violence in prisons. However, few states compile consistent or valid measures of these two constructs, so establishing need is challenging.[78] In addition, even fewer states monitor how order and violence are linked, or not, to specific factors. Thus, not only is it unclear whether a problem exists, but it also is unclear what causes it and, by extension, how best to respond.

To illustrate this last point, assume that prison disorder has increased greatly in several states. It would help to know what factors caused the increase so that a credible, effective intervention could be implemented. Such an assessment might lead states to find that a few "bad apple" inmates cause the vast bulk of problems in their prison systems. However, if research on prisoner misconduct is any indication, states might well find that a range of other factors, including poor management strategies, contribute to disorder and violence in their prison systems more so than a few "bad apples."[79]

A theory evaluation would also highlight the possibility that, depending on the causes of the disorder and violence, policies other than supermaxes might be warranted. Consider, for example, the findings from a meta-analysis of thirty-three studies, which found that "'appropriate' programs [i.e., those that targeted criminogenic needs or any management style that manipulated variables known to predict prison misconducts] reduced prison misconducts by approximately 17 percent."[80] The study's findings underscore the possibility that effective alternatives to supermaxes may exist. A national survey of prison wardens echoed this view. It identified a range of alternative approaches, including staff training and provision or rehabilitative services, which wardens felt would be effective in achieving the goals targeted by supermaxes.[81]

Faith-Based Reentry Programs[82]

THE POLICY. Faith-based prisoner reentry programs, like faith-based efforts in general, have become increasingly popular in recent years. They have actually been present in one form or another since the first penitentiaries – with their not-so-surprising emphasis on penitence – were founded, but their popularity has increased.[83] Proponents argue that these programs reduce recidivism and improve such post release outcomes as employment, housing, and family reunification. To date, however, minimal evidence exists to support that claim.[84] The lack of evidence does not mean that faith-based reentry programs are not or cannot be effective. Future studies may identify significant, positive effects due to these programs or ways in which the programs can be modified to produce such effects. The lack of evidence also does not mean that faith-based reentry programs constitute a bad idea. These programs, especially those built on volunteer efforts, may free up scarce correctional system resources and thus be justified even if no direct effect on recidivism or other post release outcomes is identified. In addition, they may improve in-prison behavior and also "counteract the tendency of prisons to dehumanize people and help prisoners prevent a further decline in their humanity."[85]

THE THEORY OF FAITH-BASED REENTRY PROGRAMS. Juxtaposed against such considerations is the basic question of whether faith-based reentry programs have coherent theoretical rationales. The short answer, according to scholars, appears to be no.[86] The longer and more complicated answer is that several factors make it difficult to discern a clear theoretical or causal logic. A focus on some of these factors can serve to justify this claim and to illustrate the salience of theory evaluations to the development and assessment of criminal justice policy.

First, no consistently used definition of a faith-based reentry program exists, which in turn makes it difficult to identify a clear causal logic. A diversity of programs comes under the faith-based umbrella even when programs share little to no characteristics with one another.[87] For example, faith-based prison programs – frequently characterized as ubiquitous in American correctional systems – have been described as including prayer groups, personal development and parenting classes, meditation groups and marriage classes, the provision of separate housing for certain faiths or faith-based programming, peer mentors, revivals, life skills, Bible study, anger management, and many others.[88] In some cases, faith or religion is not even the focus of the program. For instance, in one study of prison chaplains, the researchers found that 40 percent "did not select religion as the best method of treatment" and instead felt that "secular methods are better suited to bringing about inmate change."[89]

The variation extends beyond differences in service provision, however; it also includes differences in the providers. *Faith-based* can include traditional social service providers, such as mission shelters, and interfaith organizations that may be "loosely bound to the authority of a given denomination."[90] Notably, this confusion extends well beyond the realm of criminal justice. For example, some organizations that do not consider themselves to be faith-based have been listed as such by the White House Office of Faith-Based and Community Initiatives,[91] which, notably, provides no operational definition of a faith-based program.[92]

Such variation highlights that many problems arise when we focus on the basic question of identifying the features of a program that make it faith-based. Is it delivery of services by a faith organization or within a prison facility comprised of faith-oriented inmates? What if the programming consists primarily of secular activities and services? Does programming that emphasizes spirituality count if it is untethered to any particular religion?

The questions are far from academic. Rather, they speak directly to any effort to articulate a causal logic that says that specific activities or services lead to specific changes through specific mechanisms. For example, if a faith-based program consists of an initiative largely run by a faith-based organization but that provides primarily secular services, any resulting causal logic would not likely center around faith or religion but rather around these services. By contrast, if a faith-based program consists of a wide range of both secular and faith-oriented activities and services, presumably any causal logic would need to take into account how the two sets of activities and services, either separately or conjointly, contribute to change.

This situation characterizes one of the more widely publicized faith-based reentry programs, the InnerChange Freedom Initiative administered by Prison Fellowship Ministries.[93] In cases involving such programs, a clear description of the theoretical logic is essential for any evaluation of program effectiveness. Assume, for example, that a study finds the program to be effective in reducing recidivism. A theory evaluation would highlight that any of a large set of programming efforts, secular and faith-oriented, could have produced the effect, thus underscoring the importance of isolating the extent to which the effect stems from faith, some other characteristics of the program, or both.

A second factor that complicates the identification of a clear faith-based reentry program theory is that many faith-based programs provide no clear statement of what they do or how their actions produce changes in participants. Several possibilities can easily be envisioned. For example, perhaps efforts to enhance an individual's spirituality or faith lead participants to develop a deeper moral compass or greater self-esteem. Perhaps an increase in spirituality or faith helps individuals develop stronger social ties with others. Or perhaps it creates a fear of divine retribution. Other mechanisms can be identified as well. For example, Christian Smith (2003) has argued that no fewer than nine indirect pathways between religion and offending can be hypothesized. Specifically, he identified three dimensions that include three factors each: (1) moral order (moral directives, spiritual experiences, and role models), (2) learned competencies (community and leadership skills, coping skills, and cultural capital), and (3) social and organizational ties (social capital, network closure, and extracommunity skills). In each instance, the suggested logic is that religion changes each of these dimensions and that these changes in turn lead to improved outcomes, such as reduced offending.

Still other mechanisms are possible. One particular type, a threshold effect, bears mention. Here, the notion is that an effect of faith may arise only after a sufficient "dose" of faith has been achieved. This type of effect may be especially relevant in discussing faith-based programs. For example, there are many accounts of individuals in the criminal justice system, as well as outside of it, who experience epiphanies, moments in which they come to view faith or the presence of a higher power as critical to their lives or in which an existential shift in perspective leads them to view the world and their role in it differently.[94] Some faith-based programs may be structured to promote such moments in the belief that any lasting effect can only be realized through profound inner change. Whether the belief is true, the logic implies that it is insufficient simply to be exposed to faith programming. Rather, a requisite level or amount of such programming must occur before inner change occurs that can produce improved outcomes.

The essential point is that specification of the mechanisms matters if we are to assess the credibility of the program theory and also to assess program implementation and impacts. For example, a program's causal logic may focus on the role of religion in fostering stronger ties to family and community. If so, an impact evaluation would want to assess whether participants indeed develop stronger social ties in the short term and whether these contribute to reduced offending in the longer term. In developing a program, the causal logic would lead us to focus on providing opportunities (e.g., through prison visitation) for such ties to be created or activated.

A third complicating factor is that criminological research provides little grounds for anticipating strong effects of faith-based programs. Across a range of studies, using diverse if perhaps inadequate measures of faith, religiosity, and spirituality, no strong or unequivocal relationship between these measures and criminal behavior exists.[95] Research has tended to focus on general population samples, and so it remains unclear to what extent these findings generalize to correctional system populations.[96] On logical grounds, it may seem self-evident that, say, religion and crime should be associated. Presumably, for example, religiosity leads to a stronger morality, and in turn, less offending. However, many people commit crime even though they may well share the same strength of moral feeling that noncriminals have. More relevant perhaps is the conspicuous gap in the literature concerning change – specifically, few studies examine whether increases in faith, religiosity, or spirituality contribute to decreases in offending.[97] This gap stands out because faith-based reentry programs focus on such change and assume that it should give rise to reduced offending. Regardless, were a program to draw on criminological theory and research, it would typically find support for either no effect or a relatively small effect of faith-oriented activities and services.

Fourth, on theoretical grounds it is at least conceivable that faith-based programs might increase recidivism.[98] For example, twelve-step programs, which sometimes are characterized as faith-based, typically begin with the premise that God or a higher power ultimately is responsible for an individual's behavior. Acceptance of this belief might lead some inmates to take less rather than more responsibility for their actions. Their interpretation might be incorrect, but it nonetheless might contribute to increased recidivism. A labeling theory perspective would anticipate such an effect – inmates may be labeled by others, or come to label themselves, as lacking in self-control, and this labeling process in turn may lead them to adopt or embrace a low self-control or morally weak identity.[99] Other possibilities exist as well. For example, failure to attain a certain level of faith or religiosity might create strain that participants otherwise would not have experienced, and this strain in turn might contribute to recidivism.[100]

Additional considerations would be relevant for a theory evaluation of faith-based reentry programs. For example, an evaluator would want to describe clearly the inmate population targeted by a particular program.

Inmates cannot legally be coerced into faith-based initiatives, and so only inmates with an interest in them could be considered. In addition, for security or other reasons, participation might be restricted to lower-custody inmates. Should such restrictions be imposed, they would lead to the need to specify how the effects of the program might differ from one that included inmates of all security levels. The effort to characterize the type of inmates targeted for the program would be critical not only in developing a more credible basis for anticipating program impacts but also for specifying a reasonable level of impact. Unfortunately, relatively little scholarship provides a clear foundation for making such determinations.

OBSERVATIONS AND IMPLICATIONS. Although faith-based prisoner reentry programs hold considerable appeal to many people, and although they seem intuitively to be efforts that would reduce offending, a number of considerations collectively suggest that these programs – or at least the faith element in them – may not have much if any effect in reducing recidivism. Of course, that assessment could be incorrect. Even so, it remains the case that few such programs articulate clear theoretical rationales, which in turn likely undermines their effectiveness and efforts to improve program operations and impacts. It also leads to inappropriate generalizations, where results from one faith-based program are anticipated to hold for another, even though they may share few common features.

Are Current Criminal Justice Policies Well Grounded in Theory?

As the illustrations and several examples in this chapter highlight, it would appear that many criminal justice policies in the United States lack well-developed theoretical or causal logics that convincingly – and with reference to existing theory, research, and practice – show how specific policy-related efforts should or will lead to intended outcomes. Next, I elaborate on this observation in three ways. First, I discuss the role of criminological theory in policy. Second, I discuss the illustrations and other examples of prominent criminal justice policies. Third, I discuss the frequent adoption of, and the problem with, silver bullet approaches to solving criminal justice problems.

Criminological Theory

As a social science discipline, criminology provides a wealth of information on the causes of crime as well as on such issues as the causes and effects of sentencing and of different approaches to law enforcement and to managing prisons. Some theories have garnered considerable empirical support and have been around for decades. Surprisingly, however, criminal justice policies frequently make no mention of this work.

Recent meta-analytic work on intervention programs underscores this point. Meta-analyses involve quantitative methodologies that assess the findings of a large number of studies. In the field of criminology, meta-analyses have become increasingly common and consistently point to a central finding – programs that target criminogenic factors are more effective in reducing recidivism than those that do not.[101] Programs that fail to target criminogenic factors produce less positive results, no effects, or sometimes worsen behavior. The meta-analyses demonstrate that, contrary to the conclusion of the famous Martinson[102] report that said that rehabilitation programs do not work, effective interventions exist. At the same time, they reveal that many interventions neglect to draw on established crime theories and the types of criminogenic factors identified by research.

This situation may stem from the reluctance of scholars to tease out the policy implications of their theories.[103] Or it may simply result from a lack of policy maker or practitioner familiarity with criminological theory and research. Regardless, it is odd. On the one hand, an entire discipline exists that concerns itself with understanding crime and the practice of criminal justice; on the other hand, policy makers and criminal justice officials seek to develop strategies for reducing crime and improving the criminal justice system, and yet appear to proceed as if criminology never existed. Wherever the fault for that gap between theory and policy lies, the implication remains the same – the effectiveness of many criminal justice policies is undermined.

Weak Theoretical Foundations of Prominent Criminal Justice Policies

When we turn from the general question of the link (or lack of one) between criminological theory and policy to the theoretical foundation of particular criminal justice policies, we find again a less-than-ideal situation. Consider the two case studies from this chapter – supermax prisons and faith-based reentry programs.

Supermax prisons seem to make intuitive sense, at least at first. Some inmates clearly cause a lot of harm and trouble and so what could be more logical than housing the especially violent and disruptive ones in special facilities? By confining them in isolation, prison systems incapacitate them. They also induce a specific deterrent effect and a general deterrent effect.

Not least, they normalize the prison system environment in different ways, and so free up officers and the "good" inmates to exert more influence.

Notably, however, these arguments frequently go unarticulated. Proponents instead typically justify supermaxes simply on the notion that such housing exists to house the "worst of the worst." No theoretical logic is given. Even when causal arguments are articulated, they suffer from a number of strong assumptions, which, if found to be incorrect, would undermine the likelihood of a significant effect on systemwide order and safety. For example, are the inmates who go to supermaxes the types who likely are deterrable? Some criminological theories would argue no. Self-control theory argues that individuals with low self-control commit more crime.[104] By implication, individuals who lack self-control likely will commit crime no matter where they are housed or what happens to them. A general deterrent effect assumes that other inmates fear placement in supermax housing. However, many inmates may not fear such placement, especially if they "do the math" and determine that the odds of placement in supermax housing are slim. Not least, an emphasis on the theoretical arguments that support supermax housing ignore two critical considerations. First, on theoretical grounds, we could anticipate that supermaxes might actually increase disorder and violence. They might, for example, undermine inmate perceptions of prison authority as valid or legitimate. Second, the central premise of supermax prisons ignores a large theoretical literature that underscores the idea that prison order and safety stems primarily from environmental conditions, including how administrators run a prison system, not from the behavior of a few problematic inmates.

Studies may one day support the optimistic view that the theoretical pathways work as many policy makers and prison officials think. The point, however, is that theoretical work ideally would have been conducted prior to investing in supermax prisons both to determine if the investment was reasonable and to determine if these prisons could be modified in certain ways so as to be more effective. For example, perhaps certain nonviolent inmates instigate much violence and disorder but do not commit it themselves.[105] A more effective use of supermax prisons might be to incarcerate these inmates, not just the extremely violent ones.

A similar situation confronts us when we look at faith-based reentry programs. It seems self-evident that criminals must lack a moral foundation and that helping them find their moral compass through a deeper religiosity or spirituality will contribute to improved behavior. As with supermax prisons, the theoretical logic has considerable initial intuitive appeal – it just makes sense. Nonetheless, a number of problems quickly emerge after careful consideration. The logic assumes that criminals suffer from moral, religious, or spiritual deficits. However, they may not. Many criminals know that what they have done is wrong, but they proceed to do it anyway. Many of them may be deeply religious but commit crimes regardless. At the same time, few criminological theories argue or imply that religion should exert an effect. Indeed, some, such as labeling theory, could be construed as predicting negative effects of some faith-based reentry programs. For example, if as some twelve-step programs promote, a faith-based initiative leads some inmates to believe that they are powerless over certain behaviors (e.g., use of alcohol or illegal drugs) or that a higher power controls their behavior, they might be led to feel that they cannot control their criminal behavior. That inference on their part might be incorrect, and perhaps few inmates would make that leap, but it stands as a theoretically logical implication of such programs.

More broadly, faith-based programs frequently do not present a clear theoretical rationale that describes how critical program-related activities will lead to specific changes in individuals. Complicating that situation is the lack of consistency in defining a faith-based program. Another complicating factor lies in the fact that many faith-based reentry programs emphasize activities and services central to many secular ones. As a result, we know little about why a faith-based program would, on theoretical grounds, lead to improved behavior, whether in prison or outside of it, over and above what would occur after exposure to the secular activities or services. To be clear, faith-based programs, like supermax prisons, may be a good idea on many counts and they may lead to many beneficial outcomes. However, well-developed theoretical rationales would increase the likelihood of that occurring.

If we turn to the case studies from the previous chapter, we again find poorly developed policy theories. The large-scale investment in mass incarceration suggests that we should find the opposite – a well-developed, credible theory of policy impact. To be certain, as a general matter, one can argue that tougher penalties should induce specific and general deterrent effects. However, the deterrence literature suggests, at best, that under ideal conditions, a modest deterrent effect can be obtained, and any such effect hinges greatly on the specific characteristics of the offenders and on such factors as the timeliness, certainty, and severity of punishment.[106] Assuming that speedy, certain, and severe punishment occurs is risky and could be incorrect. Caseload-processing delays, for example, may increase during periods of increased incarceration, thus potentially delaying the time to and the certainty of punishment.[107]

Other questions about mass incarceration arise as well when viewed through the prism of a theory evaluation. To illustrate, if we assume that the mass incarceration in recent decades achieved large reductions in crime, we still would face the question of whether similar reductions would likely continue. On theoretical grounds, strong cases can be made for and against that possibility, but research remains largely quiet on the matter. Reviewing research on the crime reduction associated with prison expansion in the 1980s and 1990s, James Lynch and William Sabol have observed that "not enough is known about the magnitude of the relationship [between incarceration and crime rates] to determine whether the reduction [in crime caused by incarceration] is large enough to warrant continued expansion of prison capacity."[108]

If we take a less sanguine view of the matter, the possibility of potential harms resulting from mass incarceration should be considered. On this front, a large body of theoretical and empirical studies suggests that incarceration may not only not produce much of a reduction in crime, if any; it also may cause social harms, such as increases in crime and disruptions to the lives and labor outcomes of families and communities.[109]

An entirely different tack would be to emphasize the role of mass incarceration in satisfying the public's desire for retribution and, specifically, for retribution through incarcerative means. Here, policy makers have been guided by an implicit causal logic that says, in simplified form, that (1) the public wants tougher punishments, (2) they want more punishment than they want rehabilitation, and (3) increased incarceration levels register in the public consciousness. This logic suffers from several significant shortcomings. Yes, public opinion polls in the 1980s and 1990s frequently indicated that the public wanted tough punishments, but they also showed that the public supported rehabilitation and a more nuanced approach to managing different types of offenders.[110] As important, studies have shown that policy makers consistently overstate the punitiveness of the public.[111] Whether any of a range of tougher policies registers in the public consciousness after they have been enacted remains largely unknown. However, some basis for skepticism comes from studies that show that the public knows little about criminal justice policies and the specific sanctions that offenders receive.[112]

Investigation of the causal logic of many sex offender laws highlights a range of similar problems. Many of these laws call for the creation of sex offender registries, which victims or the public purportedly will use to track where sex offenders reside. That logic rests on the questionable assumption that victims and offenders will access registries on a regular basis and that they will take precautions, implemented on a presumably equally regular basis, to protect themselves from potential assaults. What precautions exactly could be taken? Few people can readily move from one residence to another or change their commuting route, so creating greater distance from sex offenders would not be a viable option for them. Just as problematic is the assumption that victims do not know their offenders. In this vein, and noting that the vast majority of women who are raped know the offender, Richard Wright has aptly asked, "How useful is the information contained in sex offender registries where the victim knows and has an ongoing relationship with the perpetrator?"[113] On the face of it, of course, the information would seem to be of little apparent use.

Sex offender legislation illustrates as well an incorrect theoretical assumption underlying many policies; namely, the notion that a particular law will affect all groups equally. Consider widely publicized sexual crimes involving children. Frequently, the accounts depict a crime committed by a stranger rather than the far more typical scenario – molestation or abuse of a child by a family member, relative, or someone known to them. The problem, as Jill Levenson and David D'Amora have observed, lies in the fact that it is precisely these atypical cases that "are the ones most likely to provoke legislation that is then broadly applied to all sexual offenders. Such policies are unlikely to deter the majority of sex crimes that are perpetrated by familiar assailants against victims who are often family members or close acquaintances."[114]

Moving from the case studies, consider still other examples, such as Scared Straight prison programs and boot camps, both of which have been enormously popular. Visitation programs assume that would-be youthful offenders who learn about prison from the inside will be deterred from future offending – put differently, they will be scared straight. Boot camps operate under a similar logic. Although such programs have intuitive appeal, the logic is questionable. Certainly, a large body of work has focused on deterrence, but its implications for visitation programs remain unclear. Among other things, visitation programs and boot camps typically emphasize the severity, rather than the certainty and swiftness, of punishment, thus neglecting two other components of deterrence theory. They also do little to address other factors known to cause crime. At the same time, one could anticipate, on theoretical grounds, that such policies could create more harm than not. Boot camps, for example, may create a greater dependence on external sources of motivation and control. When these sources depart, as occurs when someone graduates from boot camp, the potential emerges for individuals to be more vulnerable to antisocial influences, especially if they return to crime-ridden communities. Notably, rigorous evaluations have found that

Scared Straight and boot camp programs either have no effect or are harmful.[115]

Another example of a policy involving a dubious causal logic involves drug sentencing laws. These laws often target drug dealers. However, as Mark Kleiman has argued, "the logic of replacement – deterring or incapacitating one dealer opens up a market niche for another dealer – suggests that deterrence and incapacitation have limited capacity to shrink the drug markets."[116] That ultimately is an empirical issue, yet little evidence exists that "incarceration levels are important determinants of drug prices," and so, "if incarceration cannot substantially raise prices or limit their physical availability, then it cannot reduce drug consumption, which means that it cannot reduce the side-effects of drug consumption in terms of . . . crimes."[117] An equally problematic issue is that the causal role of drugs in offending needs to be elaborated, and the possibility remains that drug use and criminal behavior result from similar underlying factors.[118]

The problem in these cases lies not simply with a failure to draw on theory. Rather, one frequently encounters a failure to show clearly that a policy's theory can be implemented in a manner that would contribute to a desired outcome. Consider, again, supermax prisons. The policy theory assumes that placing violent and disruptive inmates in one place where they experience twenty-three-hour-per-day single-cell confinement with few services produces a deterrent effect among general population inmates. However, because so few inmates get placed in supermax incarceration, the prospect of a general deterrent effect appears dubious.[119] Put differently, to achieve the intended outcome, it might be that far greater supermax capacity would be needed.

Many other examples exist, and ultimately an empirical study would be needed to assess what percentage of all crime policies are guided by a solid theoretical logic consistent with extant research. Nonetheless, the examples here are of prominent policies. And although many examples of effective policies, as well as principles of effective intervention, can be cited,[120] far more appear to exist that are ineffective and that rest on questionable theoretical foundations.[121]

The Problems with Silver Bullet Policy Strategies

The emphasis by policy makers on silver bullet crime policies bears brief discussion, if only because of the ubiquity of such "solutions" and because they so frequently rest on flawed theory and logic.[122] The aphorism "bad cases make for bad laws" is relevant here. Criminal justice policy abounds with examples where new, sweeping reforms or all-encompassing laws are enacted based on widely publicized crimes that do not reflect the vast majority of offenses or problems in criminal justice. The case studies in the previous chapter and this one illustrate the point. Supermax housing, for example, frequently has been motivated by especially violent outbursts at specific prisons, and many sex crime laws have emerged immediately after extremely violent and widely publicized offenses. Regardless of the factors that contribute to the political penchant for silver bullet solutions, it is important to be clear about exactly why such solutions are likely to be ineffective and may even be harmful.

As discussed in Chapter 2, a silver bullet solution is premised on several critical assumptions. First, a particular problem, such as drug use, is assumed to cause criminal behavior and to do so to a large extent. Second, the problem is assumed to be widespread so that any efforts to focus on it will necessarily produce large-scale impacts. Third, effective solutions to the problem are assumed to exist. Fourth, these solutions are assumed to appreciably prevent or reduce crime. The "theory," then, consists of a series of assumptions about a problem and its solution.

These assumptions create high bars to meet that do not accord with reality. Consider the first assumption concerning causal factors. Many putatively criminogenic factors – including those commonly cited by policy makers, such as drugs,[123] mental illness,[124] family dysfunction,[125] and immigration[126] – are not necessarily or strongly associated with crime. They certainly have not been identified by research as the primary or sole causes of crime. Indeed, few criminological studies definitively show that a particular factor causes crime; rather, they establish correlations between a range of factors and a range of crimes. In many instances, the correlations, as with mental illness and immigration, are weak or nonexistent.[127] Some criminogenic factors are, in fact, widespread, but frequently the prevalence is overstated, as occurs when studies equate "drug use" with "drug problems."[128] Not least, although effective interventions undoubtedly exist and have been documented, all too often the effectiveness is a statistical artifact. That is, a study identifies a statistically significant effect of treatment but the effect may be nominal in magnitude or it may be overstated because the study did not sufficiently control for potential selection effects.[129]

Juxtaposed against these challenges lies a critical consideration – namely, research increasingly suggests that multifaceted policies that target multiple causes of crimes using principles of effective intervention produce greater reductions in crime than those that target fewer crimes and that do not rely on these principles.[130] Accordingly, such research underscores that silver bullet solutions cannot substantially reduce crime or reduce the myriad problems targeted by criminal justice policies.

Conclusion

Theory evaluations have multiple benefits. They can clarify the purposes and design of a particular policy. They can aid in guiding the development of new policies or the refinement of existing ones. They can identify specific activities and services relevant to assessing policy implementation, as well as those that may influence a particular policy's effectiveness. In addition, they can point to theoretical logics that would yield potentially greater policy impacts as well as ones that might suggest the need for concern about unintended harms.

For such benefits to be realized, theory evaluations ideally should occur in conjunction with or soon after needs evaluations and prior to policy implementation. For existing policies, theory evaluations can still be conducted and yield multiple beneficial outcomes. As but one example, a theory evaluation might demonstrate that a program would likely produce greater impacts if it focused on a particular type of individual or population or if it targeted certain areas. The reason for combining needs evaluations and theory evaluations is that the former provide critical information about the size, distribution, and character of the social problem to be addressed as well as the causes of that problem. Such information can be used to generate policy theories with more direct links to the specific nuances of the particular problem.

The central task of a theory evaluation consists of describing and assessing the credibility of a policy's causal logic – that is, how particular activities or services (i.e., outputs) will produce specific short- and long-term changes in various behaviors or outcomes. The credibility of the policy theory or logic depends on such considerations as how well the policy's activities or services fit with the specific nature and circumstances of the observed problem at hand, whether a clear theoretical logic has been or can easily be articulated, whether social scientific theories exist that support the policy, the extent to which any articulated logic is plausible, and evidence that empirical research supports critical assumptions underlying the policy.

Unfortunately, as the illustrations of supermax prisons and faith-based reentry programs and the other examples showed, it appears that many of the country's most prominent criminal justice policies rest on weak theoretical foundations. In addition, many silver bullet solutions exist in criminal justice, but these typically lack a credible theoretical platform and frequently make incorrect assumptions about particular problems, their causes, and the policy responses most likely to be effective. That assessment, if correct, points to the need for more theory evaluations and for the integration of such evaluations into policy formation and assessment.

Discussion Questions

What are the benefits of evaluating the theory of a criminal justice policy? What are the problems associated with not evaluating policy theory?

How do you conduct a theory evaluation? What criteria should be used to assess a policy theory's credibility?

Should criminal justice policies only draw on criminological theory and research? If so, why? If not, why not?

Is it appropriate for criminal justice policies to be developed based on policy makers' or others' personal views about the causes of crime or of the problems in the criminal justice system?

If so, what are the risks of allowing personal views to guide policy? If not, what are the risks of not following intuition or of allowing personal views and experiences to guide policy?

Why do you think criminal justice policies frequently lack clear or defensible theoretical foundations?

6

Implementation Evaluations

I MAGINE TAKING A CAR IN AND BEING TOLD THAT THE TIRES HAVE WORN thin and need to be replaced. You pay for the new tires; they put them on; and then, on the ride home, the car shakes and rattles. Worse yet, as you pull up to an intersection, you hear a strange "thunk." You get out and discover that one of the tires has fallen off. The repair shop, it turns out, replaced the tires but did so in a shoddy way.

A different example – imagine that you hire contractor to build a new house to your specifications and within a specific budget and time line. What if the contractor used the wrong materials, added an extra room where you did not want it, left rooms half-painted, forgot to include a garage, and took two years longer than had been stipulated to complete the project? Unless you are among that rare group of individuals with the ability to let life's troubles roll off your back, you presumably would be upset. You also likely would be put in a difficult situation financially. Here, as with the car repair scenario, there was a clear failure to fully or appropriately execute an agreed-upon plan.

Framed in evaluation research terms, an implementation problem arose in both instances. The mechanic poorly implemented the correct approach for replacing car tires and the contractor failed to comply with a promise to follow a specific blueprint, to use specific materials, and to stay within a specified budget and time line. Poor implementation typically means that protocols or ideal processes have not been followed. By extension, it also means that desired outcomes (e.g., good gas mileage) may not be achieved and that adverse consequences (e.g., car accidents) may occur.

A similar problem – where actual implementation falls short of the ideal – can emerge with almost any criminal justice policy. For example, prosecutors may fail to use a new sentencing law or they may use it in unintended ways. A drug court may aim to provide ten or more drug treatment sessions to

131

participants but provide only two or three. Perhaps it provides low-quality treatment in locations that participants find difficult to access. In these cases, disjunctures between ideal and actual practice define poor performance and undermine the effectiveness that a drug court or other policies might have. A community policing initiative that fails to take steps to generate community participation will not likely reduce crime. A public defender's office that fails to meet with clients will not likely provide adequate defense representation. And so on.

Implementation, or "process," evaluations examine the activities associated with specific policies and practices and the extent to which the amount and quality of implementation accords with the ideals set forth in protocols, standards, or policy descriptions. They have several benefits. They can be used to improve policy design and, of course, implementation. If undertaken regularly (e.g., annually or semiannually), they can be used as part of performance monitoring and efforts to increase accountability. Not least, they can inform the interpretation of impact evaluations.

This chapter describes implementation evaluations and their importance in developing, improving, and judging the performance of criminal justice policies. It then provides illustrations of the logic and uses of implementation evaluations by focusing on two case studies – policies for transferring juvenile offenders to adult court and laws mandating arrests in cases involving domestic violence. The chapter concludes by exploring the question of whether prominent criminal justice policies in the United States are well implemented.

What Is an Implementation Evaluation?

Implementation Evaluation: Step 3 in the Hierarchy

The third step of the evaluation hierarchy, an implementation evaluation, ideally proceeds after the need for a policy has been established and its theoretical foundation has been developed, tested, and refined. The basic goal of an implementation evaluation consists of documenting whether a policy delivers the appropriate amount and types of operations, decisions, services, and activities to intended targets in a high-quality manner. In short, it establishes whether a policy has been implemented as intended.[1] It does not establish whether a policy produces intended outcomes – that step constitutes the next logical one after first establishing that quality implementation has occurred.

Implementation evaluations sometimes are referred to as *process* evaluations.[2] The idea is that a policy involves a range of processes that result in the delivery of some product or output. In this book, I refer to implementation rather than process because I believe that it more directly captures the central idea of this type of evaluation. Each of the terms is equally valid, however, and so should be viewed as equivalent.

Two related but distinct dimensions can be the focus of an implementation evaluation. The first is the *delivery of services or activities* associated with a policy and, in particular, whether they reach or are accessed or used by the intended target population. Services and activities in the criminal justice context should be viewed broadly to include a wide spectrum of possibilities. These include various types of treatment, training, crime-prevention activities, arrests, sanctions, community supervision, and any of a host of other efforts associated with different parts of the criminal justice system. The second type of focus is a policy's *operations*, that is, the mode and quality of service delivery and of the activities undertaken.[3]

Many implementation evaluations examine both dimensions, which reflects the fact that we typically expect a policy not only to provide some service to intended targets but also to do so in an appropriate, efficient, and effective manner. This expectation holds regardless of whether policies are programs (e.g., halfway houses, drug treatment facilities), laws (e.g., "three-strikes-and-you're-out" statutes), new practices or initiatives (e.g., community policing, specialized courts), or the daily decisions that comprise the everyday practice of criminal justice (e.g., assigning court cases, deciding where to allocate law enforcement efforts). In each case, a group is targeted for some type of service and a prescribed or expected protocol, rule, or standard exists for delivering it. We expect, for example, a drug treatment program to offer some type of treatment. But we also expect the treatment to be of a certain quality, for it to be administered in accordance with established protocols, and for it to be delivered to all participants in a comparable manner regardless of, say, their racial or ethnic origin. Similarly, we expect law enforcement officers not only to arrest potential criminals. We also want them to do so in legally appropriate ways.

An implementation evaluation focused on service delivery, access, or use would likely examine a range of related questions.[4] To illustrate, how many individuals or communities are receiving intended services? For example, how many communities are receiving community policing services? What percentage of all intended targets (e.g., high-crime communities) are receiving intended services? To what extent are the services of the appropriate type, amount, or quality? Are some nonintended targets (e.g., low-crime communities) receiving services, and, if so, how many?

When the focus is on policy operations, the implementation evaluation questions differ somewhat in that they focus on the agencies and agents responsible for taking specific actions. To illustrate, are policy-critical activities being undertaken by the appropriate personnel or agency? For example, are prison admissions staff conducting risk assessments of new inmates and following protocol during the assessments and when making classification decisions? Are the allocated resources and staffing sufficient to implement all expected activities and services in the amount and quality envisioned? Does staff responsible for implementing the policy have adequate training and do they cooperate with one another? Is the implementation comparable across different sites or locales? Is it consistent with legal, ethical, or professional requirements or by mandates from governmental or funding organizations?

EXAMPLES OF IMPLEMENTATION EVALUATION APPROACHES AND DIMENSIONS. Consider the example of the ACTION program described in the previous chapter. This program consisted of several sets of activities, or outputs, collectively aimed at reducing agricultural crime and increasing the recovery of stolen farm property (e.g., tractors, livestock, pesticides) (see Figure 5.1). One activity included marking farmer equipment with unique identifying numbers, called owner-applied numbers (OANs). Several ACTION staff members were designated to provide this service to any farmers who requested it. An implementation evaluation of ACTION focused on service delivery and program operations might ask several questions. How many farmers – the intended targets – contacted the program, and what percentage of them in turn received OAN-marking assistance? It might also examine the extent to which farmers were satisfied with the experience and perceived the ACTION staff to be professional and courteous. Did the staff, for example, mark all relevant equipment? The evaluation might also assess the extent to which the targeted population was being reached. In the evaluation my colleagues and I undertook, this focus turned out to be critical because it led us to identify that the program provided services to only a small fraction of the targeted population (farmers). At the same time, it also showed that, from an operational perspective, program staffing was insufficient for reaching many more farmers. The ACTION staff were actually quite busy and efficient. The problem was that the scale of operations could not match the amount of need, which in turn underscored the importance of developing a more precise description of what the program could reasonably offer.

This observation highlights a critical axiom – each type of evaluation can inform other types of evaluation efforts. In developing the design of a policy, for example, a theory evaluation ideally would help identify whether certain expectations are too vaguely stated. If it did not, an implementation evaluation, like the one of ACTION, would provide an important platform from which to improve policy design. Such improvements in turn can produce more realistic criteria for evaluating the level and quality of policy implementation and impacts.

In the drug court illustration from the previous chapter, we can see a parallel set of questions and issues that should be addressed in an implementation evaluation. The causal logic model, for example, identified that frequent check-ins with judges constituted a critical feature of drug courts (see Figure 5.2). An implementation evaluation would examine, among other things, whether staff scheduled regular check-ins with judges (an operational focus) and how frequently participants showed up (a service utilization focus). It might also investigate participant perceptions of the process by which they were notified of court check-ins and their satisfaction with or experiences of them. A well-done implementation evaluation of a drug court not only would investigate such dimensions but also would likely identify a range of important policy design considerations. For example, it might show that the designated number of check-ins could not be accommodated given judicial caseloads and thus that a more realistic target should be set or that check-ins should be spaced farther apart from one another.

Let us turn to a more in-depth example – prison systems – to highlight the range of service delivery and operational measures that can be relevant to evaluating policy implementation and, as will be discussed later, to performance monitoring. If we wanted to assess the implementation of ideal prison system practice, what would we measure? Observe that our focus is not on a single policy or program per se but rather on how well an entire prison system operates. States vary in how they run their prison systems. The rules, protocols, and laws under which they administer their systems also vary. These differences in turn can make identification of relevant measures of implementation, or performance, difficult.

Fortunately, however, national standards exist that govern many dimensions of prison system activities (or outputs). In addition, a considerable amount of work on the topic of prison performance has been conducted. Thus, even though few systematic empirical evaluations of prison system

TABLE 6.1. Prison implementation/performance domains and subdomains

Domains	Subdomains
1. Security	Security procedures, drug use, significant incidents, community exposure, freedom of movement, staffing adequacy
2. Safety	Safety of inmates, safety of staff, dangerousness of inmates, safety of environment, staffing adequacy
3. Order	Inmate misconduct, staff use of force, perceived control, strictness of enforcement
4. Care	Stress and illness, health care delivered, dental care, counseling, staffing for programs and services
5. Activity	Involvement in and evaluation of work and industry, education and training, recreation, and religious services
6. Justice	Staff fairness, limited use of force, grievances (number and type), grievance process, discipline process, legal resources and access, justice delays
7. Conditions	Space in living areas, social density and privacy, internal freedom of movement, facilities and maintenance, sanitation, noise, food, commissary, visitation, community access
8. Management	Job satisfaction, stress and burnout, staff turnover, staff and management relations, staff experience, education, training, salary and overtime, staffing efficiency

Source: Adapted from Logan (1993:34–35) and Mears and Butts (2008:270).

operations exist,[5] many sources provide the conceptual mapping of the criteria by which to evaluate prison system performance. Martha Burt, for example, has identified many performance dimensions, including security (e.g., escape rates), living and safety conditions (e.g., victimization, prison atmosphere, overcrowding, sanitation), inmate physical and mental health, and program and services impacts (e.g., improvements in basic life skills, education, and vocational training).[6]

More recently, Charles Logan systematically compiled a list of domains, summarized in Table 6.1, which could serve to measure any prison system's performance. The table presents eight dimensions, or domains, along which correctional facilities and systems might measure their performance, including security, safety, order, care, inmate activity, justice, conditions, and management.[7]

Each domain is an abstract concept, one ideally measured using indicators for a range of specific subdomains. To illustrate, security might be measured using such subdomains as security procedures, drug use, significant incidents, community exposure, freedom of movement, and staffing adequacy.

Each subdomain, like each domain, is itself an abstract concept requiring specific empirical indicators. For example, indicators of security procedures might include such measures as the proportion of staff who, during a given six-month period, observed staff ignoring disturbances, or the frequency of shakedowns or body searches.[8] These and other indicators could rely on staff and inmate surveys and institutional records, such as incident logs, disciplinary logs and files, grievance logs and files, inmate employment records, education records, health clinic logs, psychologist logs, and personnel records. Regularly scheduled focus groups and interviews, as well as observational data, could also be collected.

DIMENSIONS THAT SHOULD BE EXAMINED. It is not necessary to conduct an implementation evaluation of all the domains and subdomains in Table 6.1. Rather, emphasis should be given to those that most directly relate to an agency's priority goals, recognizing that many aspects of performance (e.g., providing adequate health care) are critical even if they do not relate to such overarching goals as justice or public safety. Indeed, the relevance of specific indicators of performance will depend greatly on specific agency goals or philosophies. For example, from some perspectives (e.g., rights-based theory), justice is a process, "an ongoing property of criminal sanctioning as it occurs" rather than the achievement of a specific outcome (e.g., less crime).[9] As with any evaluation of a program or policy, indicators of justice system performance ideally should reflect relevant goals and give greater weight to those considered to be most important. Goals as diverse as justice, retribution, and public safety are likely to be prominent in any evaluation of prison systems, but they may carry different weight in one era or state than another.

As these examples illustrate, an implementation evaluation serves to illuminate what sometimes is referred to as the policy "black box." It enables policy makers, funders, administrators, staff, and the public to see more clearly a policy's inner workings – how all the pieces (e.g., resources, staffing, various activities) come together, and how, if at all, they lead to the production of intended outputs.[10] The resulting information can serve many purposes, which will be discussed later in the chapter.

TYPES OF IMPLEMENTATION EVALUATIONS. Considerable variation exists in how some researchers characterize implementation evaluations. For example, Arnold Love has distinguished five types: (1) formative, which refers to the "use of evaluation to improve a program during the development phase"; (2) process, which "examines how well the services delivered match those that were planned"; (3) descriptive, which "provides extensive details about programs so their implementation can be compared across sites or replicated elsewhere"; (4) performance monitoring, which "connotes an ongoing system of measurement and feedback of program operations and results"; and (5) implementation analysis, which examines "what happened to a policy after it [has] been formulated and during its implementation in real-world settings."[11]

The distinctions are useful but, as Love avers, not always clear or consistently followed by evaluators. For example, in the aforementioned schema, a process evaluation looks similar to an implementation analysis. In addition, different classifications can be found in other evaluation texts. Ultimately, no single categorization is best; each has its uses and limitations. I have focused here on the underlying foundation of implementation evaluations in general and as found in most texts – namely, the dual emphasis on measuring the type, level, and quality of policy services and operations.[12]

Performance Monitoring and Implementation Evaluations

One important variant of an implementation evaluation – performance monitoring – warrants special discussion because of its increasingly prominent role nationally and among many states in efforts to promote government accountability and evidence-based practice. Performance monitoring essentially constitutes an ongoing implementation evaluation. Specifically, it consists of monitoring "measures of program, agency, or system performance at regular time intervals and report them to managers and other specified audiences on an ongoing basis."[13] Performance measures can cover virtually any dimension associated with a policy. Typically, they refer to whether specific outputs were delivered as intended and whether intended outcomes occurred.

Although an implementation evaluation is important, among other things, for providing a one time assessment about the extent to which a policy does what it is supposed to do, the fact that it covers only one period of time limits its usefulness. Imagine, for example, that an implementation evaluation shows that a particular drug court has provided only half the judicial check-ins (i.e., opportunities to meet with the judge) that should have occurred. It may be that this figure was different the year before or after the evaluation. For this reason, we would not want to generalize from a one time evaluation to arrive at a statement of agency performance. In addition, we would want to be cautious about explaining performance levels. For example, perhaps check-ins vary in proportion to court caseload or to turnover in court personnel. We would be unlikely to learn about such a pattern from a one-time evaluation.

By contrast, imagine that we monitor drug court judicial check-ins on an annual or semiannual basis and, concomitantly, that we monitor court caseloads, personnel changes, and various other dimensions that might influence the court's operations (e.g., the types of offenders referred to the court, the amount and quality of drug treatment). We then can easily compile information about trends relating to many different dimensions of drug court operations and to the delivery of services, activities, and sanctions (i.e., outputs). The monitoring ideally would involve step-by-step descriptions of implementation. For example, how many offenders eligible for the drug court are referred to it? Of those referred, what percentage receives drug abuse assessments? Of those identified as having a substance problem, what percentage continues on with the drug court and what percentage are referred back for traditional court processing? Of those sanctioned within the drug court, what percentage receives or participates in all required drug treatment sessions, counseling, court check-ins, and so on? In each instance, are there variations in the processing and experiences of different groups of offenders by age, sex, race, ethnicity, or other social or demographic characteristics? Monitoring efforts can identify trends along these different steps or dimensions and, in turn, provide critical information for judging the court's performance and for identifying potential problems and possible solutions to those problems.

This example illustrates the critical importance of performance monitoring for improving and assessing criminal justice policies. It also illustrates why many states, cities, and counties have mandated that government agencies implement performance-monitoring systems.[14] They have recognized that without such information, they cannot demonstrate that promised services or activities have occurred or make adjustments in a timely manner when inefficiencies arise. In short, they have recognized that performance monitoring – what amounts to a continuous implementation evaluation – constitutes the linchpin of efforts to promote accountability and effectiveness.

Criteria for Assessing Policy Performance

A common problem with many criminal justice policies lies in the fact that no performance criteria exist. For example, what should be the total number of cases handled by a prosecutor, what percentage of his or her cases should result in convictions, and what should be the amount and level of effort expended screening cases so that weak ones are weeded out?[15] How frequently should probation officers meet with offenders on their caseloads and what should be covered at these meetings? How many vocational training sessions should a prisoner reentry program offer? In each instance, even if criteria have been established, they may not be the most appropriate ones.

This situation bodes ill for any rational assessment of policy implementation or the performance of organizations and agencies responsible for it. Put simply, to assess how well any policy is implemented, or, alternatively, how well it performs, we need criteria or standards.[16] Otherwise, we lack a basis for determining whether some level of activity constitutes good – that is, expected, appropriate, efficient, or effective – practice. Perhaps we find that 30 percent of all drug court participants drop out of a drug court. It seems less than ideal to have participants dropping out of a program willy-nilly. At the same time, drug courts deal with difficult populations.[17] It may be, therefore, that 30 percent constitutes a credible dropout rate relative to other drug courts, whose dropout rates may easily exceed 40 or 50 percent.[18]

The point cannot be emphasized too much. Consider the implicit policy that states follow – from some unknown amount of actual crime, a certain number of arrests are made, from those arrests a certain percentage eventually end up in prosecutions, and from those prosecutions some percentage end up going to prison. At each stage, the percentages vary greatly across states. In addition, states incarcerate offenders for different percentages of the sentences that they were given. As mentioned earlier, for example, one national study in the 1990s identified that violent offenders in some states served roughly one-fifth of their sentence term, whereas in other states they serve almost 90 percent of their term.[19] Sometimes policy makers see these percentages and proclaim that they are too low. Yet, as the state-level variation indicates, no national consensus exists about the "proper" percentage. States themselves rarely state what the percentage should be. As a result, no clear basis exists for asserting that a percentage of time served is too low, too high, or just right. That situation in turn creates room for arbitrary judgments about the courts or the prison system as well as for arbitrary determinations that prison expansion "needs" to occur to address the low percentages of time served.

Performance criteria can be generated from many different sources and in different ways. Needs and theory evaluations, for example, typically provide details about the goals, objectives, and activities associated with a particular policy. A theory evaluation, in particular, may describe the specific types, amounts, and quality of activity that should be undertaken, and the types and levels of outcomes that should result. In turn, these descriptions can be used to judge whether the performance is adequate or appropriate. One important source can be the standards articulated by professional associations (e.g., American Bar Association, American Correctional Association). Still other sources can include: "norms from other programs; legal requirements; ethical or moral values [such as] social justice [or] equity; past performance; targets set by program managers; expert opinion; preintervention baseline levels for the target population; conditions expected in the absence of the program (counterfactual); cost or relative cost."[20]

In practice, performance criteria frequently develop on an ad hoc basis. Evaluators may be called to undertake an evaluation, for example, and policy administrators may guess at what they believe the standard for outputs or outcomes should be. Such an approach may be appropriate to "get the ball rolling," so long as administrators and evaluators revise the standards, as needed, based on such considerations as the performance of similar policies in other places or changes that might increase or decrease the level or quality of performance. The risk of failing to make adjustments parallels that associated with having no criteria – namely, unrealistic, inappropriate, or arbitrary standards may be imposed that result in unduly favorable or unfavorable assessments of performance as well as missed opportunities to improve policy accountability and effectiveness.

How to Conduct an Implementation Evaluation

Many different strategies exist for conducting implementation evaluations and for undertaking performance monitoring.[21] Indeed, almost every approach described in social science research methodology texts can be used. For example, data might be generated from administrative records, survey questionnaires distributed to officials, practitioners, clients (e.g., prisoners), interviews, focus groups, site visits, observations, and document reviews. In short, implementation evaluations and monitoring require no special expertise beyond that required for conducting research in general.

The more critical step in conducting an implementation evaluation is conceptual: if, for example, a theory evaluation has not yet been conducted, it would be important to do so. If done well, such an evaluation would identify the types and levels of activities and the processes that collectively comprise a particular policy. The importance of this step lies in the fact that, without a clear articulation of a policy's theory or design, we will not know what to measure. Alternatively, we may err by measuring only a small subset of relevant activities and so fail to provide a comprehensive assessment of implementation. By contrast, a theory evaluation provides a road map for knowing which activities or processes to measure and guidance about which ones merit especially close attention. For example, frequent offender check-ins with judges constitutes a central feature of drug courts. An implementation evaluation that failed to measure this activity would risk creating a highly incomplete profile of a drug court's performance.

A second conceptual step consists of clarifying precisely why an implementation evaluation is being sought or undertaken. As will be discussed in the next section, implementation evaluations can be used to achieve several goals, including improvement of policy design and implementation, providing accountability, and illuminating why impact evaluations find no or smaller-than-expected policy effects. Although the goals relate to another, they also involve distinct endeavors. These in turn have implications for the scope and costs of an evaluation, the types of information collected, and how and to whom the evaluation results are communicated.

To illustrate, a program director for a new halfway house may request a formative implementation evaluation aimed at identifying services or activities that should be prioritized and those that may merit less attention. The director's goal here may be to maximize the few resources he or she has by targeting them toward services that not only may yield the greatest gains but also can feasibly be provided by staff and would be used by the clients. In this instance, the evaluator might focus less attention on providing highly accurate estimates of the different services and more attention on tapping into the perceptions of staff and clients about these services. By contrast, an evaluator tasked with helping to develop a performance measurement and monitoring system for a well-established program might expend more energy on creating data collection and analysis protocols that would allow the director to track critical program activities and services.

Attempts to clarify the precise purpose or goal of an implementation evaluation can be complicated by the fact that different stakeholders may have divergent views about the need for or focus of an implementation evaluation. In addition, their views may differ from those of the agency providing the evaluation funding. It would not be uncommon, for example, for program staff to report that their director wants an evaluation of the program's activities and then for a subsequent discussion with the director to reveal that he or she wants an impact evaluation. Even if agreement exists that an implementation evaluation of some sort should be undertaken, disagreement may arise as to which dimensions of program performance should be examined.

Evaluators, too, may complicate matters. Because of their experience and preliminary assessment of the situation – including the policy, the diverse stakeholders, the available data, time lines, available resources, and other such factors – they may feel that a particular approach should be undertaken. Perhaps, for example, the stakeholders want to invest in a performance-monitoring system. However, the precise contours of the policy may be unclear, suggesting the need for an intensive and careful theory evaluation followed by a formative evaluation. Once the policy design is clear and operational problems have been addressed, the evaluators may feel that investing in a performance-monitoring effort would make more sense.

A third conceptual step involves carefully determining which precise dimensions of (1) policy delivery, access, or use, and (2) policy operations (i.e., mode and quality of policy-related activities and services) should be measured. For example, an implementation evaluation of a sex offender registry might examine the extent to which the general public accesses the registry web site or the percentage of the targeted population that received mailings notifying them of the registry. Such information would help us to gauge the extent to which the public is using the registry. An implementation evaluation might also, or instead, focus on the frequency with which the registry is updated and the accuracy of the information in it. That is, how well is the policy – the sex offender registry – being "delivered" to the general public?

Ultimately, for an implementation evaluation to prove useful, the most relevant dimensions of performance must be identified and valid measures must be collected. Selection of them, therefore, should proceed carefully and, as with selection of criteria for assessing performance, be informed by existing information about the policy, evaluations of similar efforts, consultation with key stakeholders, and realistic assessments of the data and resource constraints under which the evaluation will operate. As Theodore Poister has emphasized, "Developing a measurement system is both an art and a science, and it often involves weighing trade-offs among competing criteria."[22]

These three issues – clarifying policy design, the goals of an implementation evaluation, selection of the dimensions and measures of performance – underscore the importance of clear conceptualization for improving and assessing policy. Explicit conceptualization of a policy and relevant dimensions of performance can help avoid the problem of placing undue emphasis on certain findings and help to promote a balanced assessment of the full range of activities, services, or treatments that should be examined.

Consider a study that shows that a state's supermax prisons house mentally ill inmates.[23] The concern lies in the fact that such housing typically
should not – per the protocols, rules, and laws governing most supermaxes –
be used with such inmates and that it may aggravate a prisoner's mental
illness.[24] In implementation terms, the study shows that some intended targets are not being incarcerated in supermax facilities while some targets
inappropriate for such incarceration nonetheless experience it. However,
this finding should not dictate whether supermax prisons remain as a policy. Why? As with any other policy, the criteria for appropriate supermax
implementation include multiple dimensions, many of which may be relevant to assessing performance. Imagine, for example, in a state where some
mentally ill inmates end up in supermax confinement, it nonetheless be the
case that typically only the most violent and disruptive (non–mentally ill)
inmates get placed in such confinement. Overall, a balanced review of the
facts would likely lead to the view that the prison system has performed well
but that clearly improvements are needed to prevent placement of mentally
ill inmates in supermaxes.

Given a clear conceptualization of a policy, evaluation goals, relevant activities, services, and performance dimensions, evaluators then can proceed to
determine what types of measures can be created from existing data or can
readily be created or collected. At this stage, the challenge lies in balancing
what is ideal with what is possible. With many crime policies, for example,
we would like to know the true amount of offending. Unfortunately, most
states, counties, cities, and municipalities lack such information and typically, they cannot afford to undertake comprehensive crime surveys. As a
result, they rely on administrative records, such as data on arrests or calls
to the police, which can be readily compiled and used as potentially valid
proxy measures of crime. In some situations, funding allows for creation
of more reliable or valid measures of specific activities or services. Here,
however, the challenge remains one of maximizing resources to provide the
most complete and valid information of critical areas of implementation.

Once data have been collected, the basic task consists of providing a
summary presentation of empirical information about policy activities, services, and operations. In general, the goal in so doing is to document the
extent to which policy implementation accords with expectations set down
by statute, policy, protocol, standards, funders, or any other source. For
example, what percentage of a target population received intended services?
Beyond that, the goals of the evaluation as well as the nature of the policy clearly dictate what exactly will be presented. For example, a formative
evaluation aims expressly to provide feedback about areas of policy design

or implementation that merit attention. It thus should include a description of what, say, interviews and focus groups with policy practitioners or clients reveal about impediments to implementation, problems with inadequate or uneven implementation, and opportunities for changes that might substantially improve performance. Similarly, if a policy, such as community policing, is enacted across multiple sites, an implementation evaluation might provide a site-by-site comparison of various measures of activities and services. Doing so would allow evaluators to identify discrepancies in implementation, possible reasons for the discrepancies, and how these might affect achievement of long-term outcomes.[25]

Why Are Implementation Evaluations Important?

Implementations evaluations can be used for at least three purposes.[26] First, they can help improve policy design and implementation. When used in this way, they typically are referred to as *formative evaluations* because they help to form the structure, focus, and design of a policy, to identify the appropriate criteria for assessing performance, and to provide guidance about how to improve implementation.[27] Policy directors, administrators, or funders may be especially interested in this use because they have a vested interest in ensuring that a policy gets off to a good start. Also, funders may want to support the development of pilot initiatives that may become a model for similar efforts in other places. In such instances, it almost is inevitable that a number of design and implementation problems will arise that should be addressed before assessing impacts or exporting the policy to other areas.

Second, implementation evaluations can facilitate performance-monitoring efforts and help to hold organizations and agencies accountable. When used in this way, implementation evaluations typically are referred to as *summative evaluations* because they provide a summary judgment of a policy's performance and worth.[28] However, they also serve as a way of providing continuous feedback to organizations about their implementation, what might be impeding performance, and what might improve it. Policy sponsors and funders typically will be interested in the use of implementation evaluations, or ongoing performance monitoring, to promote accountability. Legislators, for example, frequently request information about the extent to which agencies comply with their mandates, the reasons for poor implementation, and how best to improve it.

Third, and not least, implementation evaluations can help inform interpretation of impact evaluations and any identified (or null) effects. To illustrate, consider a situation in which an impact evaluation of a prisoner reentry program identifies no impact. That is, after comparing recidivism outcomes of program participants with another group of similar ex-prisoners, the evaluators find no difference – both groups exhibit the same level and types of reoffending. We might be tempted to conclude that the program does not work or that it is ineffective. Such an inference would be problematic for at least three reasons: (1) the program may not have been implemented at all or only partially; (2) the wrong types of activities may have been undertaken or the wrong types of services may have been provided; and (3) the implementation may have varied dramatically across sites or populations.[29] Any one of these implementation failures, discussed next, would likely undermine any chance of the program being effective.

It may seem odd that a program would provide few if any services, but in fact incomplete implementation plagues many criminal justice policies and, indeed, social policies more generally.[30] Implementation failure may well constitute the primary contributor to policy ineffectiveness.[31] Consider sentencing laws. Legislatures enact such laws on a regular basis, yet many of these laws may never be used. In a study of a juvenile justice sentencing law in Texas, for example, I discovered that many prosecutors were unaware that the law existed or, if they knew about it, had never used it even when the opportunity to do so presented itself.[32]

It also may seem odd that a program might provide the wrong services or activities or be applied to the wrong populations. Here, again, many such cases exist. As previously discussed, for example, supermax prisons in some states have been found to hold nuisance inmates – such as individuals who irritate officers and inmates and who commit minor infractions – even though, by design, such prisons have been viewed as places for holding only the most violent inmates.[33]

Less odd is the notion that a policy may be implemented in different ways across multiple sites or with a variety of populations. Prosecutors, for example, clearly differ in their willingness to invoke certain laws. And some directors operate their program differently than similar or even "identical" programs run by other programs. Whether expected or not, the end result is that policy effectiveness is undermined.

Documenting implementation failures can help ensure that we do not too quickly characterize a policy as ineffective. Just as important, it can highlight when identified effects understate the benefits that might accrue with better implementation. For example, a prisoner reentry program might be found to reduce recidivism by 5 percent. It may be, however, that several critical activities, such as job training or helping prisoners to secure housing, received relatively little attention compared to such activities as educating prisoners about the reentry process and preparing them for the challenges that they will face. In this case, we could anticipate that the program might achieve larger reductions in recidivism if the other critical activities were fully implemented.

Not least, implementation evaluations can illuminate the black box of policy operations and practices to identify the factors or combination of factors that may have produced any identified impact. For example, an evaluation of a reentry program may reveal that the largest reductions in recidivism occurred among prisoners who received a combination of several services rather than just one or two. Such information can highlight how policy impacts might be increased and also whether some services or activities can be eliminated without harming the policy's overall effectiveness.

Case Studies: *Juvenile Transfer* and *Domestic Violence Mandatory Arrest Laws*

Two case studies, one focused on policies for transferring juveniles to adult court and the other focused on domestic violence mandatory arrest laws, can serve to illustrate the central idea of implementation evaluations. I describe the policies and, in each instance, discuss evaluation research on their implementation and considerations that bear on such research. In the next section, I then discuss whether these and other prominent criminal justice policies typically are or have been well implemented.

Juvenile Transfer

THE POLICY. "Get tough" approaches in juvenile justice emerged during the 1990s as a response to escalating violent juvenile crime, especially homicide. Between 1984 and 1993, for example, the juvenile arrest rate for murder increased from five to fourteen arrests per 100,000 juveniles.[34] At the same time, reports about the rise of juvenile "super predators" and a coming demographic "time bomb" intimated that even greater levels of violence could be anticipated.[35] No one at the time predicted that juvenile violent crime rates would drop, as they did, almost as fast they rose.

The passage of waiver or transfer laws, enacted by almost every state, represented the most striking of the "get tough" reforms. Other reforms included sentencing guidelines and graduated sanctions models; greater information sharing within and among juvenile justice systems, law enforcement, schools, and child and social service agencies; and reduced confidentiality of court records.[36] To a greater extent than these, however, transfer symbolized the no-nonsense approach that policy makers took to address juvenile crime. Their goal was to promote greater accountability and punishment in juvenile justice.[37] Indeed, many states made punishment a priority in defining the mission of juvenile justice, a focus antithetical to the traditional emphasis of promoting rehabilitation and the "best interests" of young offenders.[38]

To expand the options for transferring youth to the adult system, legislatures created a diverse and sometimes bewildering array of transfer statutes.[39] Broadly, these statutes fall into three categories: *judicial transfer*, *prosecutorial discretion*, and *statutory exclusion*.[40] A range of factors can determine when and how each of these transfer provisions can be implemented, including the type of offense, a youth's prior record, and minimum-age criteria. In general, most states allow for at least one or more of these different transfer options.

Judicial transfer has existed since the inception of the juvenile court. Judges have always been allowed to waive – either at their own discretion or at the request of prosecutors – certain cases to adult court through transfer. However, the opportunities for doing so have been greatly expanded through such mechanisms as allowing judges to transfer younger juveniles and youth charged with less serious offenses. Today, three types of judicial transfer exist. The first, discretionary judicial transfer, gives judges the authority to determine whether a given case should be transferred to the adult justice system. Mandatory judicial transfer, by contrast, requires the transfer of certain cases, assuming certain conditions are met. Finally, presumptive judicial transfer anticipates that cases will be judicially waived unless a compelling argument can be presented for not doing so.

Prosecutorial discretion describes approaches, such as direct file, that give prosecutors the authority to determine whether a youth will be tried in juvenile or adult court. Under direct-file provisions, prosecutors can choose the jurisdiction they believe will be most responsive to their handling of a particular case.

Statutory exclusion provisions require that entire categories of offenses be tried in adult court, thus removing the transfer decision from judges and prosecutors. However, prosecutors determine what charges are officially filed and thus determine whether a case in fact is excludable.[41] As Barry Feld has written: "Because offense categories are necessarily crude and imprecise indicators of the 'real' seriousness of any particular offense, prosecutors inevitably exercise enormous sentencing discretion when they decide whether to charge a youth with an excluded offense."[42] Statutory exclusion laws do not, therefore, remove discretion from prosecutors; if anything, they increase it.

In addition to creating laws allowing these three mechanisms of transfer, many states have enacted reverse transfer and "once an adult, always an adult" provisions. Under reverse transfer, an offense begins in adult court, but specific mechanisms allow the case to be transferred back to the juvenile justice system. "Once an adult, always an adult" provisions apply to juveniles already tried or convicted as adults and involve the permanent termination of juvenile court jurisdiction.

IMPLEMENTATION OF TRANSFER LAWS. The contours of specific transfer statutes can vary dramatically. Accordingly, implementation evaluations should take into account the unique dimensions of each statute. Even so, we can identify several core dimensions that most implementation studies would want to assess in an effort to gauge the extent to which transfer laws are used as intended – that is, with fidelity to the letter and spirit of the law.

First, an implementation evaluation would want to identify the number of transfer-eligible and ineligible cases and, in each instance, the percentage of cases transferred. Notably, despite the plethora of transfer statutes, there exist no national estimates of transfer-eligible cases or the extent to which transfer occurs.[43] At present, for example, we have no national data on transfers that result from prosecutorial decision making or statutory exclusion. We fare no better at the state level. Although some states can report the number of some types of transfer, especially judicial transfers, they typically lack the data required to report on other types of transfer that can be sought under state law.[44]

Second, an evaluation would want to determine whether prosecutors and judges use statutorily defined factors for determining who to transfer. If, for example, a statute says that a fifteen-year-old juvenile who commits capital murder may be transferred to adult court but that a fourteen-year-old juvenile who does so cannot, do prosecutors ever mistakenly seek transfer with a juvenile who falls below the legally allowable age threshold or who has not committed capital murder? More generally, what percentage of transfer cases involves transfer-ineligible youth? Assuming that some ineligible cases get transferred, what is the cause? For example, how frequently do defense counsel file motions, when appropriate, to impede the transfer of inappropriate cases?

It may seem unlikely that the juvenile court personnel would fail to implement statutes as intended or when appropriate, but many accounts highlight precisely that possibility. Consider an account from Edward Humes, who spent one year observing the juvenile court in Los Angeles. A sixteen-year-old male, Geri, was plea-bargained to a twelve-year sentence in the adult justice system for attempted murder. However, per Section 1731.5 of the California Welfare and Institutions Code, his public defender could have asked the judge to sentence Geri to a sentence in the juvenile justice system, which would have entailed a substantially shorter term of incarceration. When Humes investigated the matter, the defender reported, "I didn't even know that law existed."[45]

Third, evaluators would want to identify the factors that could give rise to implementation failures. To illustrate, probation officers may rely exclusively on police arrest reports rather than trial testimony when writing presentence reports for judges. In so doing, the officers may indicate that the youth was convicted of a more serious crime, such as armed robbery, rather than a misdemeanor, such as simple assault. Such discrepancies can arise, as Humes has noted, because prosecutors frequently will charge an offender with a lesser charge than that described in an arrest report.[46] These types of mistakes can go unchecked and have a ripple effect on all subsequent handling of a youth. This process can occur to many cases in no small part because many juvenile court practitioners have little familiarity or experience with juvenile law. Here, again, Humes' observation of the Los Angeles juvenile court is instructive. He reported that "the least experienced prosecutors, sometimes only one year out of law school, end up staffing Juvenile Court, trying murder cases."[47] In addition, and as other accounts of the juvenile court have shown, many judges, prosecutors, and public defenders view work in the juvenile court as "a low-prestige assignment, even a punishment."[48]

Fourth, a comprehensive implementation evaluation might investigate in detail precisely how transfer laws are used. For example, discretion stands as a fundamental tenet of many transfer laws – prosecutors and judges typically can choose whether to transfer youth. Although no systematic or comprehensive national studies have been conducted, many scholars have found that states and counties vary greatly in their use of judicial transfer.[49] In some counties, prosecutors may refrain from using transfer or similar "get tough" laws, whereas in others they may use it in every eligible case.[50] Variability has been found along other dimensions as well. For example, studies show that the "majority of youth[s] who enter the adult court are not there for serious, violent crimes" even though the impetus for transfer laws stemmed largely from concern about such offenses.[51] They also show that transfer laws disproportionately affect minorities.[52] Perhaps because of the limitations in using court data, few studies examine a range of other dimensions, such as a juvenile's family situation (e.g., education, income) or the characteristics of the community from which he or she comes (e.g., poverty, unemployment), that might be associated with transfer.

Fifth, an evaluation would explore why variation occurs in the use of transfer or the targeting of certain populations for transfer. To illustrate, at the state level, we might find that black youths disproportionately are transferred to adult court. That, in turn, might lead to a concern about equity or fairness. However, closer inspection of the data might reveal that the state-level disproportionality results primarily from intensive use of transfer in one metropolitan county that has a large minority population. In this instance, it may be that no racial or ethnic disproportionality in the use of transfer occurs in other counties. This information then might direct us to focus our attention not on the state as a whole but on the one county that transfers large numbers of black youth. Additional investigation of the causes of variation might uncover other such factors. For example, it may be that probation officers play a greater role in facilitating or impeding transfers in some areas (e.g., rural and suburban communities) than in others (e.g., urban locales).[53]

Sixth, implementation evaluators ideally would investigate unintended uses of and potential problems with transfer laws. For example, a central argument for transfer is that it allows for tougher punishment of juveniles who commit certain types of crimes, but that may not always happen. Indeed, transferred youths sometimes may receive less severe sanctions than they would have received in juvenile court. Others may receive more severe sanctions than young adults who have committed similar crimes.[54]

Juvenile sentencing occurs within a systems context, and so it may be that countervailing forces can offset any intended change. Howard Snyder and his colleagues, for example, found that Pennsylvania's statutory exclusion law failed to increase the numbers of youth processed in adult court because the court "decertified" many of the cases (i.e., sent them back to juvenile court) and prosecutors declined to pursue many of them; in addition, roughly half of those that did get pursued resulted in dismissal.[55]

There also is the possibility that prosecutors use transfer laws not to send youth to adult court – the clear intended use of transfer laws – but to gain leverage in plea-bargaining negotiations. To illustrate, a prosecutor might threaten to invoke a transfer statute to motivate a youth into accepting a plea bargain to a juvenile court sanction. Given the widespread use of plea-bargaining in juvenile court, we would be justified in anticipating that such a use would be likely. Notably, however, the issue has received little attention. The reason lies in part in the fact that evidence of plea-bargaining would require going beyond official records data and collecting case file data or conducting interviews or surveys of youth and court practitioners.[56]

Other considerations would warrant investigation as well. Perhaps, for example, and as some studies have found, transferred youth experience lengthy delays in the processing of their cases and more victimization because of placement in adult jails.[57] Perhaps, too, the process in adult court is perceived by transferred youth to be less fair, more adversarial, and unconcerned with their well-being, which, in turn, may result in increased recidivism.[58] Not least, critical steps, such as assessing the competency of youth to stand trial, may not be undertaken in many transfer proceedings or the assessments may not be conducted in an appropriate manner by a trained professional. This issue is of critical importance to transfer because studies have shown that younger adolescents typically are more likely to be "seriously impaired" in their understanding of the court process and to be found "incompetent to stand trial."[59]

OBSERVATIONS AND IMPLICATIONS. The discussion to this point illustrates some of the important dimensions that an implementation evaluation of transfer laws would consider. It also underscores, again, the critical role that the evaluation hierarchy plays in developing the conceptual framework for assessing a policy. For example, in evaluating the implementation of a transfer law, it would help to know what exactly the law aimed to achieve and the precise conditions under which it is supposed to be invoked. It may be that lawmakers anticipate and expect that prosecutors will use transfer laws primarily to plea-bargain youth to tougher juvenile justice sanctions than they otherwise would be able to obtain without these laws. If so, this use would not constitute poor implementation; to the contrary, it would suggest that the law is being used as intended.

The case study illustrates as well that efforts to evaluate implementation require considerable attention to data. In transfer studies, researchers typically rely on court records data. The approach makes sense – the data exist and cost little to access and analyze. Even so, such data may provide relatively little relevant information about such critical issues as plea-bargaining, the extent to which transfer is disproportionately used among youths from socially and economically deprived families or communities, and how youths experience the process of transfer. No simple answer exists for how to proceed in these situations. Ultimately, policy makers, funders, and justice system administrators must decide which types of information are most critical for assessing implementation and accountability, and, in turn, whether investment should be made to collect data from additional sources.

Not least, the case study illustrates how studies of implementation can inform impact evaluations. For example, a number of studies suggest that transfer has no effect on recidivism or that it increases it.[60] Such possibilities could be anticipated by some studies on the process and experience of transfer – if youths experience adult court as less fair, if they are more likely to be victimized in the adult system, and if they receive fewer services and less treatment, we might well expect that transfer would increase recidivism. Similarly, existing studies highlight the importance of assessing the impacts of transfer in ways that go beyond a comparison of transferred versus nontransferred youth. To the extent that prosecutors use transfer laws to obtain plea-bargained juvenile court sanctions, for example, one would want to assess whether outcomes among youths sanctioned in this way vary from similar youths who were not subject to transfer-related plea bargains.

Domestic Violence Mandatory Arrest Laws

THE POLICY. Historically, domestic violence has been viewed primarily as a family matter, one emerging from the "normal stress and interpersonal conflict" within families; it thus merited no formal criminal justice intervention.[61] That situation changed dramatically in the 1970s, when the "criminal justice system came under attack for being too lax with the perpetrators of domestic violence."[62] A number of factors contributed to this change, and not least was the increased recognition that domestic violence is widespread. For example, in a national survey conducted in 1995–1996 in the United States, 22.1 percent of women and 7.4 percent of men reported having ever experienced intimate partner violence.[63] Estimates of domestic violence vary depending on the definitions, measures, and data used; regardless, a diverse body of research consistently shows that such violence occurs frequently and does so across a diverse range of social and demographic groups.[64] In addition, it shows that domestic violence can contribute to long-lasting trauma, disrupted friendships and family relationships, injury, and death.[65]

Such considerations gave rise to the Minneapolis Domestic Violence Experiment.[66] In this study, the experimental condition consisted of mandating arrest of the offender in cases where a domestic violence call for service occurred. Researchers randomly assigned cases to this response and to two others: separating the abuser from the victim and advising couples of alternative avenues to resolve the conflict (e.g., mediation). They found that recidivism among the arrested abusers was substantially lower than for the other groups. Results of the study – one of the most famous in

criminology – appeared prominently in many media accounts, and soon thereafter many jurisdictions and states enacted "mandatory arrest" policies.[67]

The widespread adoption of mandatory arrest laws occurred despite
researchers' concerns about the possibility that the results were not gener-
alizable. In fact, this concern appeared justified given subsequent research.
Some studies conducted in other sites found no effect of mandatory arrest
laws on recidivism; others found that such laws had an effect only for some
groups, such as those who were married or had a job or home; still others
found that the laws might increase recidivism.[68] Today, the jury is still out
on whether mandatory arrest laws effectively reduce domestic violence and,
by extension, the precise conditions that must exist to create reductions.

IMPLEMENTATION OF MANDATORY ARREST LAWS. The different estimated impacts of mandatory arrest laws could easily stem from inadequate
or inconsistent implementation. Many studies highlight that a wide range of
activities occur under the rubric of "mandatory arrest." In the Minneapolis
experiment, for example, "officers had advance knowledge of the response
they were supposed to make and therefore could reclassify a domestic violence case if they did not wish to make the assigned response."[69] This type of
diversion might conceivably increase or decrease the effect associated with
an evaluation of a mandatory arrest law by changing the composition of the
pool of cases considered to be "mandatory arrests." A related implementation issue that arose in the experiment was that "officers sometimes gave a
'treatment' that they were not supposed to [which] happened to 17 percent
of cases."[70] The Minneapolis experiment researchers dropped these cases
from their study, leaving open the question of whether the results might
have differed were the cases included.

Variation in implementation is not specific to the Minneapolis experiment.
Many mandatory arrest laws, for example, do not call for dual arrests – that
is, arrest of the abuser and of the victim – and guidelines sometimes explicitly discourage such practices. Presumptively, then, we might anticipate that
only abusers would be arrested. However, as Drew Humphries has noted,
"Despite guidelines to the contrary, reports show that police officers do
arrest both parties in domestic violence incidents" and that, in one study,
dual arrests occurred in one-third of such incidents, whether due to poor officer training or some other factor.[71] Dual arrests thus may occur frequently,
suggesting poor implementation and raising concerns. For example, these
arrests can create more, not fewer, problems for victims. The fact of an
arrest can be used "to impeach the testimony of victims in felony trials"; in

addition, an arrest can "trigger actions against a victim in areas of child custody, housing, and employment" and contribute to deportation of immigrant women involved in a dual arrest.[72]

Differential implementation can occur along many other dimensions and create unintended consequences. Consider, for example, that in one of the replication studies of the Minneapolis Domestic Violence Experiment, the researchers found that "domestic violence recidivism *increased* for arrested black men but decreased for arrested white men."[73] Put differently, it is possible that mandatory arrest laws create positive effects for whites and negative effects for blacks. That obviously raises concerns because it means the laws may harm blacks. However, at least some of the time, differences in arrests could result from an implementation-related consideration – racial differences in the willingness to call the police.[74] For example, victimized whites who contact the police for assistance may subsequently be less willing than their black counterparts to contact the police. As a result, recidivism, as measured by rearrest, would appear lower among whites when, in reality, the true rates of revictimization could be comparable among both groups.

Consider yet another dimension of implementation. In a situation in which law enforcement officers consistently implement mandatory arrest laws, a prominent barrier to full or complete implementation may emerge – prosecutor willingness to take action. Prosecutors may screen out cases where the victim expresses no willingness to support the formal sanctioning of the abuser, reasoning that such cases are less "winnable" and will consume scarce resources.[75] The result? Mandatory arrest may result in more domestic violence arrests but have little effect on prosecutorial practices, thus reducing the likelihood of a specific deterrent effect on domestic violence recidivism.[76]

Similar problems play out with mandatory, or "no drop," prosecutorial policies in which prosecutors "file cases regardless of victim support for proceeding."[77] The logic underlying such policies parallels that of mandatory arrest laws: the hope is that a greater number of victims can be protected. However, the effectiveness of no drop policies hinges in no small part on the ability of prosecutors to obtain convictions, which may not be appreciably advanced by forcing victims to participate in proceedings or by pursuing a conviction without victim support. In a study of Brooklyn's no-drop policy, for example, prosecutors filed on 99 percent of domestic violence cases, but 95 percent of those "cases were dropped in 90 days because the failure at changing victim decisions and the reluctance of the prosecutor to prosecute without victim support."[78]

OBSERVATIONS AND IMPLICATIONS. The implications of inconsistent implementation of mandatory arrest laws are profound. As the preceding discussion highlights, inconsistency could account for the conflicting results from impact evaluations. Weak or poor implementation, in particular, might reasonably be anticipated to reduce and even eliminate any potential specific deterrent effect of mandatory arrest laws. It also could lead to unintended effects, such as decreased victim satisfaction and increased victimization by abusers. The studies of domestic violence mandatory arrest laws thus highlight an important evaluation research axiom – implementation and impact evaluations should occur together to allow researchers to identify differential effects of policies and the reasons for them.

Implementation evaluations of mandatory arrest laws can help us to identify why they are poorly implemented and thus why they may fail to produce expected impacts. For example, officers may implement mandatory arrest laws differently in contexts where they know that prosecutors will drop most of the cases versus those where they know that few such cases will be dropped. Similarly, in areas where prosecutors file cases regardless of victims' wishes, victims may be more reluctant to contact the police when domestic violence occurs. The relevance? Many prosecutions result not from law enforcement actions, such as arrests, but from victims directly contacting prosecutors. Indeed, studies show that, in some cases, the bulk of domestic prosecutions stem from victims calling prosecutors.[79] Implementation evaluations enable us to detect such possibilities and how they may undermine policy effectiveness.

Efforts to evaluate the implementation of mandatory arrest laws have benefits not only for helping us to understand the results of impact evaluations, but also for pointing to ways in which implementation could be improved. The problem of dual arrests, for example, could be identified in the course of conducting an implementation evaluation of mandatory arrest laws. Attention then could be turned to identifying the cause of the problem (e.g., a lack of training) and how to solve it. Similarly, such efforts could be used to identify whether victims support mandatory arrest laws, explore the experiences of victims, and investigate the potential for these laws to cause harm to victims.[80] They also could be used to determine whether the laws are more likely to be used with certain populations (e.g., poor, black) than with others (e.g., wealthy, white) and whether any identified differences stem either from a differential willingness to call the police in cases of domestic violence or from some other reason.[81] Variation along any of these dimensions would help us to determine if the policy or the implementation of it need to be modified to reach certain populations more effectively.

A focus on implementation also can lead us backwards to a seemingly simple question: how do we know when a need specifically exists for mandatory arrest or prosecution laws? Answering the question is actually complicated. As Joel Garner and Christopher Maxwell have emphasized, "There are no accepted standards for what would constitute an appropriate amount of prosecution or conviction for any offense."[82] Enactment of mandatory arrest and prosecution laws implies that too few arrests and convictions occur. What, though, would constitute an appropriate amount of arrests or prosecutions?

Consider a study by Robert Davis and his colleagues of the Milwaukee District Attorney's Office. Despite a 1987 Wisconsin law mandating arrest in domestic violence cases, as of 1994, only about 30 percent of such arrests resulted in prosecution. The situation led the district attorney "to realize that Milwaukee was prosecuting a smaller proportion of arrests than other Wisconsin cities"; in response, his office "decided to substantially increase the proportion of arrests prosecuted."[83] However, the percentage of domestic violence arrests that should be prosecuted was never clearly established.

Certainly, it would be unreasonable to expect that all of them be prosecuted – not all arrests involve acts that meet the legal criteria for a crime or can be successfully prosecuted. The better alternative is to develop clear criteria for the kinds of cases that can and should be prosecuted, assess how many such cases currently are prosecuted and why some are not, and then, based on that assessment, determine how to proceed. The failure to do so can lead not only to the adoption of unnecessary policies that make questionable theoretical assumptions but also to policies that almost invariably will be poorly implemented and so fail to achieve their goals.

Are Current Criminal Justice Policies Implemented Well?

The previous chapters suggested that the need for many of the most prominent criminal justice policies today has not been well established and that the theories underlying these policies have not been well developed. A similar theme emerges when we examine the implementation of these policies – that is, many of them have been poorly implemented or are likely to suffer from considerable implementation problems.

Case Study Illustrations and Other Policies

The two case studies illustrate the problem of poor policy implementation. Despite the widespread adoption of numerous types of laws for transferring youths to adult courts, little remains known about the extent to which these laws get invoked. Little also is known about the extent to which the intended types of youths – that is, those who fit the legal requirements for transfer or who fit with the spirit of the law – get transferred. Similarly, little is known about whether youths who do not fit the intended profile are transferred to adult court. Other basic implementation dimensions remain largely unexamined. How frequently do prosecutors use the threat of transfer in plea negotiations? How do the experiences of transferred youths compare to those of nontransferred youths? How often do transfers result from poor defense representation? What factors impede or facilitate not only the use of transfer but also the appropriate use of it and the differential use of transfer among different groups of young offenders? Although a large body of transfer studies exists, few systematically address these questions. More generally, few if any jurisdictions in the country investigate these questions by monitoring the processing of transfer-eligible and transfer-ineligible youths. As a result, they have little ability to improve the design or implementation of transfer laws, to hold courts accountable, or to understand why their laws have any effects if any.

A comparable situation exists with domestic violence mandatory arrest laws and also with no drop prosecution policies. Law enforcement officers and prosecutors may not invoke these laws when they should or could and they may differentially invoke such laws for certain populations or in certain contexts. Some groups, such as minorities or immigrants, may be less likely than others to contact the police in cases involving domestic violence, which in turn impedes the ability of officers or prosecutors to invoke the laws. In addition, domestic violence victims' attitudes and behaviors may influence the processing of cases even when arrest or prosecution is mandatory. For example, victims may refrain from contacting law enforcement or refuse to cooperate with prosecutors. Not least, victims may experience less satisfaction with the criminal justice system under a mandatory rather than discretionary approach to handling domestic violence cases. Information about these issues could provide a foundation for improving policy design and implementation and, in turn, the chances of reducing revictimization and minimizing additional harm or wasted resources. Unfortunately, few jurisdictions systematically monitor how mandatory arrest or prosecution laws are used or have clear, well-grounded criteria for determining the appropriate amount of arrest, prosecution, or conviction of domestic violence cases.[84]

The transfer and mandatory arrest case studies highlight a critical implementation challenge relevant to many other criminal justice policies. Specifically, they underscore the importance of systems-level coordination. For example, if prosecutors wish to successfully transfer youth to adult court or to convict domestic violence abusers, they typically must rely on the decisions of law enforcement officers. Indeed, how officers proceed with cases, how they write their reports, and also how probation officers in turn describe cases – these factors can all directly influence the ability of prosecutors to proceed as they would like with criminal cases.

Domestic violence interventions, in particular, highlight the need for coordinated actions on the part of multiple individuals and agencies. In recent years, considerable attention has been focused on special domestic violence courts that aim "to improve the provision of comprehensive services to victims of domestic violence (DV), increase victim safety, and hold offenders more accountable."[85] Studies of such efforts have shown, however, that successful implementation of these courts requires attention to a wide range of details. These include case-flow changes, service and treatment capacities of partner agencies, data-sharing capacities and barriers among these agencies, and service and treatment provider unwillingness to participate due to concerns about confidentiality to name but a few.[86] Full and quality implementation along so many dimensions cannot be realistically expected to occur without extremely careful and deliberate planning. It also cannot occur without systematic monitoring of court activities and the feedback, problem identification, and problem solving that such monitoring allows.

Transfer and domestic violence mandatory arrest laws are far from the only examples of criminal justice policies that suffer from implementation problems and from relatively little systematic empirical valuation of their implementation. One way of capturing the extent of the problem is by focusing on the long-standing issue of justice by geography, wherein specific laws are applied with different intensity in particular cities or counties.[87] Such variation raises questions about fairness. Just as important, however, it highlights that consistent criminal justice policy implementation across different areas cannot be safely assumed and, indeed, is unlikely. The result? We cannot safely assume that large-scale (e.g., national or state level) policies will have positive impacts, much less large ones. For example, how effective, at least on a state level, can a law aimed at harshly punishing sex offenders be if some counties ignore the law, others only partially use it, and still others selectively use it only for particular sex crimes?[88] Replace *sex* with *juvenile*, *first-time felony, drug*, or any other type of crime, and the same question arises.

Poor, incomplete, or inconsistent implementation arises as much with programs, treatments, rules, and practices of various types as it does with laws. For example, many programs may operate smoothly and in conformity with expectations, but their counterparts in other areas may be poorly run. In these cases, even the most well-established interventions, including those considered to be best practices, will likely fail. Consider a prison system – typically, one set of guidelines and rules will exist for how each facility should be run. However, adherence to these guidelines and rules will likely vary greatly from one facility to the next. Without regular implementation evaluations or a performance-monitoring system, such variations run unchecked and thus undermine efforts to promote accountability. They also substantially reduce the possibility of effectively achieving intended outcomes.

When we look at the many decisions that occur in the criminal justice system, we can see that many aspects of this system operate largely as "black boxes" that is, as areas where little is known about what decisions are made, how they are made, how they are applied to different groups or in different areas, and, by extension, how decision making comports with expected practice.[89] For example, practitioners and scholars increasingly agree that juveniles referred to court intake or offenders arrested and taken in for booking should be screened for possible mental health, drug, or other problems, and that in cases where a potential concern exists more in-depth assessment should occur.[90] However, apart from studies of selected states or jurisdictions that consist of one time snapshots, most criminal justice systems lack any systematic or ongoing measurement or monitoring of screening and assessment practices. Many studies that have examined the issue document not only variability in these practices across jurisdictions but also considerable evidence of poor implementation. In a study a colleague and I undertook, for example, we found that many juvenile probation departments in Texas completed a state-mandated screening instrument in a perfunctory manner and also varied in the way in which they used the resulting information.[91] The result was a situation in which information of questionable validity was collected and then used in ways inconsistent with the law or appropriate practice.

If we move slightly earlier in the criminal justice process – to law enforcement decision making – we see a similar "black box" phenomenon. We know little, for example, about the quality of officer decision making within and across law enforcement agencies. Certainly, studies of individual agencies exist, but by and large, the day-to-day decisions of officers across the country occur largely within a black box. By extension, then, the extent to which these decisions comport with the ideals set forth in their training remains largely unknown.[92] Police interrogation constitutes one prominent example. As Richard Leo, in a comprehensive investigation of the topic, has emphasized, "Despite the importance of police interrogation to scholars, policy makers, the public, and criminal justice officials, in many ways we know very little about it."[93] Similarly, despite the widespread concern about racial profiling, scant evidence exists documenting the extent of it or why it occurs.[94]

Consider, in addition, the decision to arrest. What actually influences arrest patterns among law enforcement officers or law enforcement agencies? We might assume that the decisions directly result from calls to the police or patrols. In reality, however, many other factors come into play. In one study, Edith Linn examined factors that influenced officers' decisions to make arrests and found that a variety of considerations were influential.[95] For example, officers might make more arrests to increase their overtime and thus be paid more, whereas others might avoid making arrests in certain contexts because doing so could help avoid logistical conflicts related to childcare or personal appointments. Other studies have highlighted the importance of a related question, What influences citizens' views of the police? Research shows, for example, that "how the police treat people generally, and how they treat minorities in particular, appears to have a more profound impact on citizens' attitudes about the police and their willingness to cooperate than do police decisions to stop or arrest them."[96] The critical policy implementation question is how widespread such patterns are. To date, we have too little research to venture even an educated guess. Much the same can be said of the prevalence of police wrongdoing, in part because of a "code of silence" that "permeates many police line cultures" but also because of the limited research on the issue.[97]

Criminal justice decision making in general, not just among law enforcement agencies, occurs largely within a black box.[98] For example, we know little about prosecutorial decision making or plea-bargaining practices. Many sentencing studies exist, but most lack any information about how prosecutors arrived at their decisions. Plea-bargaining, in particular, remains understudied, yet it is characterized as the means by which 95 percent or more of all criminal cases get decided.[99] Existing scholarship on the topic has focused primarily on legal or philosophical issues related to plea bargaining rather than on empirical studies of how the process unfolds, how that process varies across different populations and areas, or how participants viewed the process.

One widely publicized example of how much criminal justice processing occurs within a black box is exoneration, which involves cases in which innocent people have been falsely convicted.[100] Few studies have empirically investigated the topic, but those that have emphasize that much more wrongful conviction occurs than ever comes to light. That situation stems from the fact that only the most extreme cases, involving the most serious crimes (e.g., murder or rape) or toughest sentences (e.g., the death penalty), receive attention. The state of knowledge is akin, as Bruce Smith has aptly characterized it, to what our understanding of automobile safety would be if "the only car accidents we knew about were exploding Ford Pintos and major highway pileups – no fender benders, no routine crashes at intersections, no drunk drivers who run off the road."[101] More specifically, a little is known about false convictions involving rape and murder; less is known about cases where police officers framed an individual; and "nothing is known about innocent defendants who plead guilty or are convicted of routine property or drug offenses, or even of less extreme crimes of violence."[102] Not only is the prevalence of such cases unknown, but, as Smith has emphasized, we also lack information about the extent to which false convictions in these cases stem from such factors as incorrect eyewitness testimony, coercive interrogations, perjury, or simple bureaucratic errors.[103]

Policy Implementation and Evaluation of It: The Broader Problem

Many scholars have highlighted the considerable disjunctures between intended criminal justice policy activities and those actually implemented. In fact, the literature documenting criminal justice policy implementation failures is vast.[104] The problem is a simple one – to be effective, a policy must be implemented in the way it was intended to be carried out.

That well-established axiom is unproblematic for areas in which implementation is simple and fidelity to a policy's design can be assumed. Few crime policies, however, enjoy that status. Indeed, it is a truism to say that the "law on the books" rarely resembles the "law in practice."[105] (Implementation problems associated with criminal justice policy evaluations also are common.[106]) Consider the study by Davis and his colleagues in which a Milwaukee prosecutor enacted a policy of increasing domestic violence case filings, regardless of victim desires. The researchers found that the policy contributed to delays in case processing, reduced convictions, and decreased victim satisfaction.[107] These outcomes stemmed primarily from the fact that staffing increases were not commensurate with the increased caseloads that the policy created. Such implementation problems can have ripple effects. For example, if prosecutors have little ability to successfully convict domestic violence cases, "police officers may devote less attention to collecting needed evidence or attempting to gain victim participation if they know that the case will be inevitably prosecuted – yet largely dismissed."[108]

One reason for the disjuncture between ideal and actual practice lies in the fact that criminal justice policies, as illustrated in the Milwaukee example, frequently entail relatively complex designs that require the coordination and cooperation of different stakeholders and a steady supply of resources. In addition, the policies frequently are developed more quickly than is reasonable, resulting in poor policy design. In such situations, implementation evaluations warrant special consideration because they can help identify ways to improve both the design and the implementation of the policy. In turn, they can improve accountability and, ultimately, the chances that a policy will effectively produce intended outcomes.

To underscore the importance of implementation evaluations to criminal justice policy effectiveness, consider the fact that evaluations of pilot initiatives typically identify larger effects on outcomes.[109] Such initiatives frequently involve considerable attention to implementation and to making adjustments where needed. By contrast, long-standing programs may go unevaluated and lapse into inattention to critical activities, services, or protocols. A vicious cycle then ensues – without information about implementation problems, needed corrections are unlikely to occur, and the poor state of implementation comes to be viewed as typical and acceptable practice even though it may depart dramatically not only from what is ideal but also from what is possible.

This vicious cycle occurs within a larger one in which new sets of policies emerge that push the old ones out of the way or get added on top of them. Legislatures exist in no small part to create new laws; at the very least, they feel pressured to develop such laws to demonstrate their responsiveness to the public's desire to do something about crime.[110] And state and local agencies frequently feel pressured to demonstrate that they are at the cutting edge, that they are pioneers, and that they are proactively addressing crime. Thus, they create or adopt new policies. In the meantime, most of the prior and poorly implemented policies remain.

A situation emerges, then, in which an ever-expanding set of crime-fighting initiatives, each competing with the others for scarce resources, receives an ever-diminishing amount of research attention, if any is given at all. As David Farabee, summarizing studies on the use of evaluations in criminal justice, has remarked, "[T]he actual operation of any given correctional program is rarely subjected to . . . evaluation."[111] That should not surprise us – federal, state, and local funding for criminal justice research is often trivial relative to the range of policies that exist. Consider the minimal staffing in most justice system research divisions and the fact that the staff frequently must spend most of their time providing highly descriptive empirical descriptions of system operations. Moreover, despite calls for more governmental accountability, research, a source of accountability, frequently receives little support. In 2003, for example, Texas eliminated the Criminal Justice Policy Council, which for more than twenty years had served as an independent criminal justice policy evaluation agency.[112]

Conclusion

As the third step in the evaluation hierarchy, implementation evaluations can produce multiple benefits: they can aid in the design of a policy and help ensure that it is implemented as intended, they can facilitate accountability, and they can inform impact evaluations. More generally, implementation evaluations can provide the foundation for policies to have a fighting chance of effectively and efficiently producing intended outcomes (e.g., reduced crime, increased processing of criminal cases with fewer errors, improved prison system order, greater citizen or victim satisfaction with the criminal justice system). Performance monitoring, which is akin to an ongoing implementation evaluation, can provide similar benefits.

At bottom, an implementation evaluation aims to measure critical policy-related operations, decisions, activities, services, treatments, and other dimensions that collectively constitute the policy. Broadly, it can focus on the delivery of a policy (e.g., whether intended targets received intended services) or on its operations (e.g., how well program staff provided a service). To this end, it can use any number of data sources, methodologies, and research designs.

As with other types of evaluation, the most critical tasks for an implementation evaluation are conceptual in nature – identifying why exactly the evaluation is being conducted and determining the dimensions of a policy that most merit attention. For example, an evaluation aimed at helping to improve a policy's design might dictate a different research design than an evaluation aimed at judging whether the policy has been well implemented or at demonstrating accountability. Here, a central task consists of working closely with policy makers, administrators, funders, staff, and other stakeholders to create consensus about the precise goals of the evaluation and whether the focus will be on policy delivery, operations, or both.

A related conceptual task consists of identifying the activities, services, and the like that should be examined. A well-conducted theory evaluation can prove invaluable to such an effort. It should identify all relevant components or activities (i.e., outputs) associated with a policy and the types of measures that should be used for quantifying them. It also should provide guidance on the criteria that should be used for gauging performance, whether the focus is on outputs or on outcomes. Regardless of whether a theory evaluation has previously been conducted, any effort to devise an appropriate set of implementation or performance standards typically requires a review of similar policies, consultation with policy makers, officials, and practitioners.

We cannot safely assume that criminal justice policies on the whole are well implemented. Certainly, one can find examples where quality implementation occurred. It is harder, however, to find examples of policies that have consistently been well implemented over time and across different areas. Stated more forcefully, as the case study illustrations and different examples highlight, poor or unmeasured implementation appears to constitute the norm, not the exception. Indeed, as a large literature attests, it seems fair to characterize most criminal justice policies as occurring within a black box, one that obscures many failures to implement laws as they were designed. The result is ineffectiveness and inefficiency and a situation that allows for abuse.

The blame for this situation does not lie, by and large, with criminal justice officials and practitioners. They work under difficult conditions and most genuinely want to make a difference. Rather, poor criminal justice policy implementation and its attendant consequences likely stem from a range of systemic factors, including intensive caseloads, limited staffing and resources, and an ever-increasing set of policies and the demands they create. Not least, they likely result from a lack of institutionalized evaluation and monitoring of policies and practices throughout the criminal justice system, a theme to which I return in the final chapter.

Discussion Questions

What are the benefits of evaluating the implementation of a criminal justice policy? What are the problems of not evaluating the implementation of a criminal justice policy?

How do you conduct an implementation evaluation?

How do implementation evaluations and performance monitoring differ? How are they similar?

Because criminal justice policies frequently involve many activities, and because it may not be possible to evaluate all such activities, what criteria should we use for selecting the policies whose implementation we will evaluate?

What are the main reasons why criminal justice policies frequently are poorly implemented?

What steps can be taken to increase the number and quality of implementation evaluations of criminal justice policies?

7

Outcome Evaluations and Impact Evaluations

I N OUR DAY-TO-DAY LIVES, MOST OF US CARE DEEPLY ABOUT A DECEPTIVELY simple bottom-line question: Does something (e.g., a strategy, tool, or product) work? We use a certain toothpaste – does it reduce cavities more so than some other toothpaste? We use a certain means of transportation – does it get us to our destination faster than some other? We confront a colleague – did it change his or her behavior or make us feel better? In these and a thousand other instances, we tend to go with whatever we think works best.

What does it mean, though, to say that some approach "works" or that it works better than another does? Here, matters get a little complicated. Consider the toothpaste example. We may think it is a good idea to buy a special type of toothpaste, call it A. Should we buy it? Will we obtain a better result using it rather than our current toothpaste? Perhaps a researcher undertakes a study and shows that a group of people who used toothpaste A had fewer new cavities than they acquired on, say, an annual basis, prior to using it. That improvement seems self-evident to be a good thing, but can we trust that it resulted from using the toothpaste? No. Perhaps the improvement would have occurred regardless of the change in toothpaste. So, all that we can say is that an important outcome (fewer cavities) improved after using the new toothpaste.

The researcher then proceeds to conduct a new study. He or she randomly assigns people to the toothpaste A group and others to the toothpaste B group. Lo and behold, toothpaste A "works": people who brush their teeth with it experience fewer cavities compared to people who use the other toothpaste. Because we have an appropriate comparison – the hallmark of an impact evaluation – we have more trust that toothpaste A actually caused a reduction in cavities. By contrast, the earlier outcome evaluation documented only that use of toothpaste A was associated with fewer cavities.

What if we want to know about whether toothpaste A is better than, say, toothpaste C, D, or E? Answering these questions requires that we repeat the experiment, only this time we must randomly assign people to the toothpaste A group and others to the toothpaste C, D, and E groups. Perhaps toothpaste A wins the contest again. If so, we may feel even more confident about selecting it.

However, we face a dilemma. What if we care not only about reducing cavities but also about preventing tartar buildup? Or reducing tooth sensitivity? If the experiments did not directly test for effects along these dimensions, we would have no clue about how to proceed. Or, rather, we would be left with the competing claims made by the manufacturers, claims that, needless to say, may be incorrect or misleading.

This example involves a rather mundane task we all face. Even so, it illustrates the simple goal of outcome and impact evaluations, respectively: (1) to establish whether a policy is associated with some intended outcome or set of outcomes (this is an *outcome evaluation*) and (2) to determine whether the association is causal (this is an *impact evaluation*). It also illustrates some of the complexities, such as determining the appropriate basis of comparison and selecting relevant outcomes, that outcome and impact evaluations entail. It shows, too, how the specific comparisons used in such evaluations may influence the findings and how we should interpret them.

Outcome evaluations and impact evaluations are critical for criminal justice policy. If a policy "works," we might want to continue supporting it. If a policy does not "work," then scarce resources should be allocated to another that does or to efforts to improve the policy's design or implementation. Put simply, we want to promote effective policies and weed out ineffective ones.

This chapter describes how outcome and impact evaluations differ and then focuses particular attention on impact evaluations because these ultimately provide the foundation for demonstrating policy effectiveness more convincingly. Specifically, it discusses the basic logic of impact evaluations, the methodologies for conducting them, the importance of identifying unintended effects, and the limitations and importance of impact evaluations. Following this discussion, two case studies of prominent criminal justice policies are provided. One examines drug courts and the other examines gun laws. As with the other chapters, the case studies serve to illustrate key ideas and themes. Finally, the chapter concludes with a discussion of whether criminal justice policies in the United States rest on strong, empirical evidence of their effectiveness.

What Are Outcome and Impact Evaluations?

Outcome and Impact Evaluations: Step 4 in the Hierarchy

Once we have established the need for a policy, the theory or design of it, and established that the policy has been well implemented, we are set to proceed to the fourth step – assessing association and causation – in the evaluation hierarchy. *Outcome evaluations* describe the types and levels of outcomes associated with a particular policy. *Impact evaluations* go one step further by establishing whether a policy not only is associated with the outcomes but also whether it actually produces or causes them.

The two types of evaluation involve related efforts. For that reason, they sometimes get discussed as if they constituted one and the same endeavor. They do not. Outcome evaluations identify types, levels, or changes in an outcome or set of outcomes and their association with some policy. An outcome evaluation might, for example, document that 20 percent of arrested domestic violence offenders subsequently recidivated. From this information, we have established an association between the policy and an outcome (recidivism). However, we do not know whether the policy (e.g., a mandatory arrest law) created this level of recidivism. Perhaps it is indeed lower than what would have happened without the policy; however, perhaps it is not.

Put simply, outcome evaluations do not allow us to make causal claims. Why should we care? The answer is simple: we want to know that a policy produced some outcome so as to inform decisions about whether to continue or expand the policy. If the outcome would have happened anyway, then why bother with the policy, especially if it entails considerable costs? Why, for example, bother buying toothpaste if brushing alone, with no toothpaste, is equally effective?[1] Or, using an example of more direct relevance for criminal justice: if mass incarceration has not caused decreases in crime, and, ideally, large decreases in crime, why bother with it?[2]

Causal claims can be made easily; establishing them empirically is another matter. Advocates frequently make compelling arguments about a particular policy and then assert that it must be, nay, is effective. The claims sound more compelling when coupled with information about outcomes. "Because of this new antigang initiative, gang-related crime is down 50 percent." "Only 10 percent of our prison program graduates recidivate, well below the 60 percent recidivism rate among all inmates." The figures sound impressive. However, they ignore the possibility that these outcomes would have occurred anyway, regardless of the interventions.

Making that assessment – showing what would have happened without a policy – presents a significant challenge. Nevertheless, it is an important one to address if we value the notion of evidence-based policy. It also is important because common sense frequently misleads us by creating a seemingly irrefutable logic that some policy must be effective.

In class, I sometimes use an example that Ludwig Wittgenstein employed to show how common sense can lead us astray.[3] Imagine that we stretch a cord around the earth's equator. What happens if we add thirty-six inches of cord and allow it to rise proportionally above the earth? Intuition leads most of us to say that the change would be so small as to be unobservable when, in reality, the cord would rise almost six inches. Indeed, it would rise by the exact same amount if the example involved a soccer ball, the sun, or any other sphere. Inspection of the formula shows why: $R2 - R1 = ((C + k)/2\pi) - (C/2\pi) = k/2\pi = k/6.28$, where $R2$ is the new radius and $R1$ is the old radius, C is the initial circumference, k is the addition to C (i.e., the extra thirty-six inches added to C in this example), and π is a constant (3.14). As can be seen, the change in radius (i.e., $R2 - R1$) caused by adding thirty-six inches is equal to $k/6.28$, or $36/6.28$, which amounts to 5.73 or, with rounding, 6 inches. Observe that no matter how large the circumference of any given sphere, the change in radius will be the same, as it is purely a function of k and not C.

This type of problem – wherein common sense leads to incorrect assumptions – holds particular salience for criminal justice policy. Approaches billed as commonsensical pervade the criminal justice system, and many of them, such as boot camps, faith-based programs, and Scared Straight types of prison visitation programs, to name but a few, may not be effective.[4] At the same time, the increased emphasis on accountability and evidence-based practice dictates that criminal justice policies should be found to be effective through research rather than incorrect assumptions about what "works."

Causal claims thus matter a great deal. Associations frequently occur even when no real effect exists. The associations appear compelling if coupled with a logical argument about why the association reflects a causal relationship. However, many causal claims, even those coupled with seemingly airtight logical arguments, fail to be supported by research. For that reason, we want an evaluation research approach that can help establish that a policy creates (and is not simply associated with) an intended outcome. We want, for example, to be able to trust that mass incarceration actually reduces crime, that supermax housing indeed makes prison systems safer, and that mandatory arrest laws in fact reduce domestic violence revictimization.

An outcome evaluation provides the initial groundwork for making causal claims but provides little to no comparative framework for establishing causality. By contrast, an impact evaluation directly establishes whether a policy produces specific outcomes and does so by using control groups or conditions. Put differently, an impact evaluation employs a comparative framework and, in so doing, transforms an outcome evaluation into a study that can make a more credible claim about causality.

So, if outcome evaluations do not allow for causal claims, why undertake them? The benefits are several and parallel those for implementation studies. Outcome evaluations prompt policy makers and criminal justice administrators to clarify the relevant criteria for identifying policy effectiveness. In addition, they can be used to hold agencies and organizations accountable. With an implementation evaluation, we establish accountability, in part, by showing that expected activities, services, or practices were undertaken as intended. With an outcome evaluation, we establish it by showing that the outcomes have or have not occurred.[5] We cannot demonstrate that the policy produced them, only that expected types and levels of or changes in outcomes occurred.

More specifically, if a clear foundation exists for anticipating certain levels of outcomes, then the tracking of outcomes can allow us to ascertain whether they accord with what should occur. For example, case processing standards have been established for how long it should take a case to proceed through juvenile court.[6] If we view the number of days from referral to sanctioning as an outcome, we can monitor it and determine if all youths are processed within the time span recommended by the standards. Should there be a clear delay in processing or should there be a clear increase from one year to the next in processing times, we know that the particular jurisdiction is underperforming or that some exigency has influenced the court's performance. Similarly, if a program, such as multisystemic therapy (MST), has been consistently identified as producing a certain level of success (e.g., a 45 percent reduction in recidivism relative to the recidivism of control groups), that benchmark can be used to determine whether the program, as implemented in a specific locale, is performing as well as it should.[7]

A Closer Look at Outcomes

A brief discussion of outcomes is warranted given their centrality to impact evaluations. As discussed in Chapter 5, an *outcome* "is the state of the target population or the social conditions that a [policy] is expected to have changed."[8] It differs from an *output*, which typically refers to the services or activities undertaken by a policy.[9] To illustrate, a prisoner reentry program may provide inmates with training on how to interview for jobs with the goal of helping inmates to obtain employment and to reduce recidivism. The training constitutes an output whereas the outcomes would include how well inmates learn to interview and whether they obtain jobs or commit crime.

One type of outcome, service quality, bears special mention because it leads us to consider a much broader spectrum of criminal justice outcomes than we otherwise would consider. Service quality can, as Harry Hatry has emphasized, be viewed as an important type of outcome for a simple reason: "Although [quality of service] characteristics do not measure a final result, they are important to program customers and thus can be considered intermediate outcomes an agency should track."[10]

This distinction holds special relevance for the criminal justice system because many aspects of its operations and policies can be viewed as falling under the rubric of "service quality," and so should be viewed as outcomes rather than as outputs. For example, court processing time constitutes a central dimension of what it means to provide fair and just treatment to those accused of an offense and to victims and communities, who typically expect and want a rapid response to crime. It thus can be viewed as representing an outcome rather than an output.

For any given part of the criminal justice system, a number of service quality dimensions should be considered as outcomes, either because they are important to the public or because they relate to such overarching goals as public safety and justice. Examples of such outcomes include the timeliness of service provision (e.g., how rapidly police respond to calls); the accessibility and convenience of a service (e.g., how easily program participants can access court-mandated drug treatment); accuracy of assistance or information (e.g., how accurate the information is that a prison publicizes about visiting hours); courteousness of service delivery (e.g., how courteous probation officers are with parents of juvenile offenders or victims); condition and safety of facilities (e.g., how safe a prison is for inmates, staff, or visitors); and customer satisfaction (e.g., how satisfied members of particular neighborhoods are with community policing services).[11]

It is important for both outcome and impact evaluations to examine all relevant policy outcomes and, where that may not be possible, to highlight which ones could not be included. In criminal justice, conversations about the bottom line typically lead to a focus on crime and recidivism as critical outcomes. That makes sense, given that safety constitutes a paramount concern for the public. However, retribution and justice represent important concerns as well. More generally, many outcomes are relevant for assessing the impacts of the criminal justice system and the policies, programs, and practices that constitute it. Consider restitution programs aimed at compensating victims or neighborhoods in some manner, whether financially or through community service. Relevant outcomes not only would include recidivism but also might include monetary payments to victims or reductions in graffiti and garbage in the community.

For any given set of outcomes, evaluators ideally should identify those that should be given more weight.[12] For example, a screening and assessment instrument might help probation departments to identify more quickly who should be detained and to classify more accurately those individuals at greatest risk of recidivating. A reduction in the amount of time it takes to process cases constitutes an important outcome in its own right. However, arguably the more important one is whether fewer individuals released under their own recognizance commit additional crimes. Even more important might be whether the crimes were violent or serious. If so, we would want to disaggregate any recidivism measure into types of crimes or some classification system for capturing the severity of an offense.[13] It is not always possible to arrive at a consensus about which outcomes matter most. The fact that policies frequently have multiple goals nonetheless dictates that some attempt is made to identify those that matter most.

Evaluators also should build on theory evaluations to distinguish between short- and intermediate-term (proximal) outcomes and longer-term or end (distal) outcomes, as discussed in Chapter 5.[14] In the previous example, faster processing of cases would constitute a short-term or proximal impact whereas reduced offending would constitute a longer-term, end, or distal impact. This distinction matters because evaluators frequently face situations where they cannot measure or assess longer-term, end outcomes. In these situations, they ideally can assess impacts on short- or intermediate-term outcomes. If the policy's causal logic is credible, improvements in these outcomes might reasonably be viewed as producing improvements in the longer-term outcomes.

Evaluators also should distinguish between *in-program outcomes* and *after-program outcomes* (also discussed in Chapter 5). Some programs, such as prisoner reentry initiatives, occur for an extended period of time. For example, a released prisoner might reside at a halfway house for one year. The ultimate goals of the program likely would be to help the ex-prisoners to secure stable employment and housing, avoid drug use or addiction, obtain treatment if needed, and, not least, commit less crime. Observe, however, that such outcomes might occur while individuals participate in the program, not just after they complete it. We know, for example, that the likelihood of ex-prisoners recidivating is greatest in the months immediately following release from prison.[15] In these cases, we would want to identify impacts that resulted from the program, distinguishing those that occurred while in the program (and that perhaps resulted from partial program exposure) from those that occurred after release from or completion of it.

Finally, any analysis, whether of outcomes or of any other policy dimension, is only as good as the data on which it rests, and so considerable care should be expended trying to create the best outcome measures possible. Frequently, researchers must make do with available data (e.g., police records) because insufficient resources exist to create data better suited to answering an evaluation research question. That challenge confronts almost all researchers; even so, it must be addressed to produce credible policy impact estimates. Ultimately, we want outcome measures that are reliable and valid. A reliable variable is one that consistently produces the same measurements when used repeatedly to measure some phenomenon. To illustrate, a reliable scale is one that consistently returns the same weight measurement when we stand on it. A reliable measure of self-reported offending is one for which a respondent consistently reports the same type or level of offending. Valid measures are those that measure whatever they are supposed to measure. For example, a valid weigh scale would report our correct weight when we stand on it. A valid measure of recidivism would be one that captured true offending. In criminal justice research, recidivism measures frequently may not be valid. For example, rearrest may capture not only offending but also policing practices; as such, the measure may not accurately reflect the criminal behavior of all subjects in a study.[16]

How to Conduct an Impact Evaluation

Here we will focus on the steps involved in conducting an impact evaluation. What about outcome evaluations? The approach for them overlaps that for conducting implementation evaluations. Conceptually, there is little difference that bears mention, save for the fact that one collects information not only on various dimensions of implementation but also on relevant outcomes. The overlap between implementation and outcome evaluations is reflected in part by the fact that performance-monitoring efforts typically involve tracking measures of both.[17] Because Chapter 6 discusses these steps and because identification of actual impacts holds special importance for judging policies, the focus here will be on impact evaluations, and, in particular, their logic; the methodologies for undertaking them; and the importance of examining unintended effects.

The Basic Logic: Identifying a Causal Effect

The basic idea or logic of an impact evaluation is to examine what would have happened if a policy had not been implemented. Evaluators sometimes refer to this state – what would have happened – as the counterfactual condition. The *counterfactual* "is an estimate (either quantitatively or qualitatively) of the circumstances that would have prevailed had a policy or program not been introduced."[18] If we can accurately estimate the counterfactual, and if the relevant outcomes prove to be better in the policy-targeted group or area, we have greater trust that the policy caused the improvement.[19]

Here, the devil is in the details. It seems simple enough – we want to know if a policy produces some outcome. That is, what would have happened if we had not intervened? The problem stems from the fact that we must infer what would have occurred. The individuals in a drug treatment program participated in it, for example. We cannot undo that fact and then see what would have happened to them if they had not participated. Instead, we must use methodologies that allow us to develop a credible estimate of the level of or change in an outcome (e.g., recidivism) were we able to undo the intervention and then go back in time and see how reality would have unfolded.

Clearly, we cannot go back in time (yet). Thus, we have to approximate what would have happened. To do so, we can use experimental and quasi-experimental methodologies. The credibility of estimates derived from these methodologies ultimately rests on clear conceptualization of the policy and relevant counterfactual conditions. And that, as will be discussed later, is where matters become more complicated.

Perhaps the foremost challenge involved in undertaking a credible impact evaluation lies in identifying the appropriate counterfactual condition so that we can make appropriate apples-to-apples comparisons that in turn enable us to estimate a policy's impact on one or more outcomes. Consider a typical scenario. The media profiles some program and touts its effectiveness by comparing the recidivism of participants with that of an inappropriate comparison group. A typical statement runs something like, "Look at the much lower recidivism of the program participants. Even if it's not a perfect comparison being made, it's clear that this program is effective." Not true.

To illustrate, programs may appear to have strong effects purely because they "cream" – whether intentionally or not – the "best" participants. Put differently, they select participants who are least likely to recidivate, or participants self-select themselves into the program. For example, inmates who

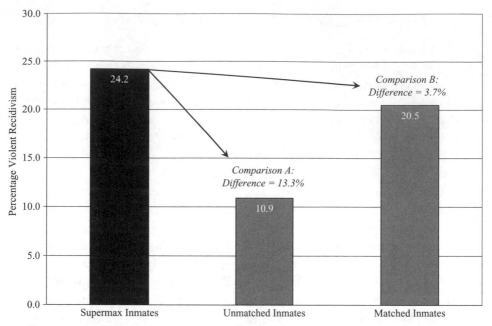

Figure 7.1. Supermax housing impact on violent recidivism.

volunteer for faith-based prison programs likely differ in important ways from those who do not.[20] In particular, they may be less likely to recidivate. As a result, comparing recidivism outcomes between this group and "average" inmates constitutes an apples-to-oranges comparison that tells us little about the program's effectiveness. This problem, termed a *selection effect*, is but one of many that can lead to inappropriate comparisons and thus to incorrect or less-than-credible estimates of policy impact.

To illustrate the point further, consider the impact of supermax housing on violent recidivism. A colleague and I examined this issue by examining violent felony reconvictions, within three years of release, among Florida supermax inmates and their counterparts.[21] As can be seen in Figure 7.1, almost one-fourth (24.2 percent) of supermax inmates recidivated. One might be tempted to compare this rate of recidivism to that of general population inmates, as depicted by comparison A in the figure. It is apparent that supermax inmates recidivate at a considerably higher rate. Whereas 24.2 percent of released supermax inmates committed new violent crimes, only 10.9 percent of unmatched general population inmates did so. A seemingly straightforward interpretation would be that supermax prisons caused inmates to escalate their violent offending, creating a rate of violent recidivism more than double that of other inmates.

The problem with such a comparison lies in the fact that supermax inmates do not represent a random sample of the general inmate population. Rather, they have been selected for placement based on their behavior or concern that they pose a threat to officers and other inmates. Indeed, if one examined the characteristics of the two groups, these differences would be apparent. Supermax inmates in the study typically had a history of committing more violent crimes and, while in prison, engaged in more defiant and violent behavior than other inmates. Thus, on the basis of these factors alone, we could anticipate that these inmates would be more likely than other inmates to commit violent crime upon release.

By juxtaposing the recidivism of supermax inmates to that of general population inmates, we make the mistake of undertaking an apples-to-oranges comparison. The result? We risk making the attendant mistake of assuming that any difference in recidivism results from the effects of supermax incarceration. This problem plagues many criminal justice policy evaluations. Apples-to-oranges comparisons are made and then any differences get interpreted as evidence that a particular policy effectively reduces recidivism or crime.

What we want instead is an apples-to-apples comparison of inmates in supermax housing with general population inmates similar to them in all relevant respects except the supermax incarceration experience. For legal and ethical reasons, correctional system officials cannot randomly assign inmates to supermax confinement or to general population prisons. This approach, which entails an experimental design, provides a stronger basis for estimating the counterfactual. However, if, as appeared to be the case in our Florida study, many inmates eligible for supermax confinement never get placed in it because of limited supermax housing, then the opportunity arises for identifying an "apples" comparison group. Using a statistical methodology, aptly termed *propensity score matching*, for identifying such a group, we were able to create an apples-to-apples assessment of supermax and nonsupermax inmates. The result, depicted as comparison B in the figure, shows that supermax inmates still were more likely than other inmates to commit violent crimes upon release back into society. However, the difference between their rate of violent recidivism (24.2 percent) and that of the matched group of inmates (20.5 percent) was substantially smaller. Instead of the 13.3 percent difference that emerged from the apples-to-oranges comparison of supermax inmates and their unmatched counterparts, a 3.7 percent difference emerged.

The focus on supermaxes illustrates the logic of an impact evaluation as it applies to criminal justice policies, programs, and practices aimed at

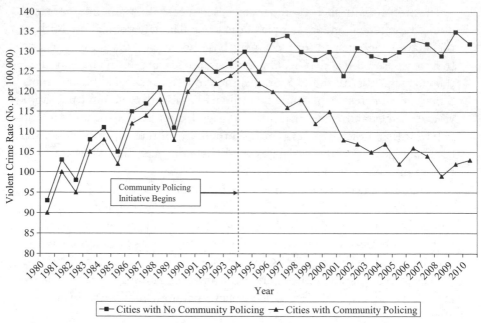

Figure 7.2. Impact of community policing on violent crime.

reducing individual-level offending. However, a similar logic applies to *area-level*, sometimes referred to as *community-* or *ecological-level*, efforts aimed at reducing crime rates. These efforts typically aim to influence the behavior of large numbers of individuals who reside in particular areas. As such, they have the potential to exert a greater effect on the overall volume of crime in a particular jurisdiction or state. Consider, for example, that a program that reduces the recidivism of released inmates may only be available for a relatively small group of inmates. Thus, the aggregate impact may be small. By contrast, even a modest reduction in a county's or state's crime rate can generate a sizable aggregate impact.

Figure 7.2 depicts an impact evaluation counterfactual logic for community policing, a widely prevalent type of areal (or ecological-level) intervention. Community policing initiatives, which spread rapidly throughout the United States in the 1990s, aim to reduce crime rates through a number of strategies, including the development of better police and resident communication and collaboration. A critical question is, however, whether community policing effectively reduces violent crime. That is, does it reduce such crime relative to what otherwise would happen? To answer that question, an impact evaluation would develop a counterfactual. For example, we could identify areas that adopt community policing and examine whether reductions in violent crime rates before and after the intervention exceed those in similar areas that do not implement the intervention.

To simplify the discussion, let us assume that in 1994 a set of cities all agreed to implement community policing at the same time. (In reality, cities have adopted community policing in different years and for different periods of time.) To assess the impact of community policing, we could undertake an interrupted time-series analysis. Such an analysis strives to determine whether a change in some trend results from an intervention.[22] The approach we take here is identical to that of the earlier supermax example in that a critical first step involves identifying an appropriate comparison group. In this case, we would want to identify cities that did not adopt community policing but that were nearly identical to those that did. We would want to establish, among other things, that the violent crime rate trend in these communities – prior to the intervention – was similar to the preintervention trend in those that adopted community policing. Otherwise, we would risk making an apples-to-oranges comparison.

Assume that we in fact can identify such cities. Our goal now is to compare the violent crime trends in the community policing cities to determine not only if violent crime rates went down but also to determine if the reductions exceeded those in the cities without community policing. Inspection of Figure 7.2 reveals what community policing advocates expect would happen. Specifically, soon after cities began implementing community policing, violent crime rates began to decline steadily. Crime rates fell from roughly 127 violent offenses per 100,000 residents in 1994 to a low of 99 violent offenses per 100,000 residents in 2008. By contrast, in the comparison group cities, violent crime continued its steady rise. In short, in this hypothetical example, community policing shifted the upward trend in violent crime to a downward trend. The fact that violent crime continued to increase in the comparison cities suggests that the effect was a real one. That is, assuming that we can trust the study results, it appears that community policing caused the crime reduction and that, if it had not been adopted, violent offending would have continued to increase just as it did in the comparison cities.

The information about the comparison sites is critical for making the causal claim that community policing caused a reduction in violent crime. Consider, for example, that without the comparison, we might be tempted to believe that the reduction in violent crime was even greater. Observe that for the comparison group, violent crime rates continued to rise after 1994, but that they rose at a slower pace than in the years prior. The slower rate of increase can be seen in the flatter slope. Violent crime was increasing, just not at the dramatic rate that it increased from 1980 to 1994. Without this point of comparison, we might be tempted to conclude, incorrectly, that the slope from these years would continue indefinitely. In turn, the downward slope – that is, the steadily declining rate of violent crime in the community policing cities – would seem even more impressive. As it is, the decline remains impressive, just not as much as it would be if crime rates in the comparison cities increased at the same rate from 1980 to 2010. (The verdict is still out on whether community policing reduces crime rates. Some studies suggest that it does, and others suggest it does not; in both cases, many of the evaluations have been criticized as methodologically flawed.[23])

Here, as with the supermax example, identifying an appropriate basis of comparison constitutes a critical challenge. Cities do not all adopt community policing in the same way or to the same extent. Indeed, what community policing is may vary from one city to another.[24] Similarly, cities that do not adopt community policing may differ from cities that do in ways that may not be readily addressed. For example, City A may adopt community policing and City B may not. The cities may have experienced different types and levels of crime, and the trends in such crime may differ. In addition, they may differ in a host of ways that relate to crime rates. Thus, it may not be appropriate to use City B in an impact evaluation of City A's community policing effort. The same issue applies at lower units of analysis. For example, within a city, some neighborhoods may be more willing to embrace community policing.[25] Yet that willingness may also indicate that these neighborhoods systematically differ from those that do not. Thus, we may have little ability to create a true apples-to-apples comparison.

Different Methodologies: Experiments and Quasi Experiments

The two basic methodologies for assessing whether a policy produces an impact are experiments and quasi experiments, the latter of which try to approximate true experiments. Numerous sources discuss the technical details of these methodologies and interested readers should consult them.[26] Here, the emphasis will be on the conceptual underpinnings of these methodologies. That focus stems from a prominent theme running throughout this book – namely, clear conceptualization can be far more critical than complicated research designs to conducting credible and useful evaluation research, as well as to knowing how to put specific study findings into appropriate context.

We start first with experiments because they are considered to be the "gold standard" in research and because they establish the bar by which other research methodologies are judged.[27] The essence of an experiment consists of the following: we randomly assign subjects (e.g., individuals, areas) to either an intervention or a no-intervention group. Typically, these would be referred to as the treatment and control groups, respectively.

Randomization is critical to experiments because we want to know that the only thing that created any difference in outcomes is the intervention, not some characteristic unique to the treatment group. Successful randomization results in equivalence, with treatment and control groups sharing, among other things, similar characteristics and histories, similar predispositions or propensities for the outcome, and similar experiences (save for the intervention) during the study period. Larger samples tend to be more equivalent, which is why, to the extent that resources permit, researchers tend to favor including as many subjects as possible.[28] Ultimately, should we be able to randomize subjects successfully, we have more trust than we would with nonexperimental studies that any identified treatment effects are real. By contrast, nonexperimental studies allow for a variety of influences that alter the composition, propensities, or experiences of comparison group subjects and so engender less trust that the results are credible.[29]

The logic of an experiment applies equally to any unit of analysis. For example, regardless of whether an intervention targets individuals, families, specific groups (e.g., women, minorities, immigrants), schools, communities, cities, or states, an experimental design requires randomization. Clearly, however, randomization with larger units of analysis is typically more difficult and expensive.[30] Even so, if a policy targets a particular unit of analysis, then an experiment (as well as a quasi-experiment) would want to focus on it. If, for example, an intervention, like community policing, aims to affect crime in a set of areas, then such areas should be the unit of analysis for the study.

Ultimately, the aim of an experiment is to show that an intervention produced, or did not produce, a specific level or change in an outcome. Randomization, for example, allows one to create simple comparisons, such as the percentage of treatment group subjects who recidivated compared to the percentage of control subjects who recidivated. However, because randomization does not produce exact equivalence, we must take recourse to tests of statistical significance to determine if the differences, if any, that we observe could occur by chance.[31] On the basis of these tests, we may conclude, if an effect is identified, that it is real (i.e., that it did not occur by chance). That assessment may be altered if, among other things, we observe small effects and the sample sizes are small.

Quasi-experimental research designs emulate the spirit of an experiment but typically lack the critical feature of them – randomization. The logic

remains the same, but the procedures differ. Consider the supermax illustration discussed earlier. We cannot ethically assign inmates to supermax
incarceration on a random basis. So, an experiment is ruled out. However,
it appeared that many inmates were eligible for supermax incarceration but
were not placed in it as a result of limited supermax cells. In this context,
we could try to approximate an experiment by identifying inmates eligible
for supermax incarceration but who did not actually experience it purely
because of capacity constraints, and then compare their recidivism with
those of actual supermax inmates.

With experiments, one of the most critical tasks is to achieve true randomization; with quasi-experimental research, the analogous goal is to create as
much equivalence as possible between the treatment and control groups.
(Some researchers reserve the term *control group* for the subjects identified
in experiments and *comparison group* for the nonrandomly identified subjects
identified in quasi experiments.) The problem lies in the fact that achieving
such equivalence can be extremely difficult, especially if the data necessary
for creating equivalence do not exist. Consider sentencing research. A large
body of studies has examined the death penalty and attempted to answer
a basic question: Does the death penalty reduce crime and, in particular,
murder? There remains much debate among scholars about the answer, in no
small part because of the intrinsic difficulties of achieving equivalence when
comparing states that have the death penalty with those that do not.[32] The
death penalty has not been randomly implemented among different states,
and states that have death penalty laws and that aggressively use them may
differ in ways related to the murder rate. Unless one can fully account for
these differences, estimates of the deterrent effect of the death penalty will
be biased.

Another sentencing example involving efforts to estimate the impact of
transfer of juvenile offenders to the criminal justice system. Clearly, transferred youths may well differ from those who are not transferred. They may
have committed more serious or violent crimes and have histories of chronic
offending. They may be more combative, hostile, or defiant in the courtroom. Their parents may be less able to afford quality legal counsel. They
may be less competent to stand trial. Assume, for the sake of argument, that
all of these factors feature prominently in courtroom decisions to transfer
youth. Now, imagine that we want to examine the impact of transfer on
recidivism. To this end, we try to identify a comparable group of youth who
were not transferred. Eventually, using court records data, we find a group
that looks similar with respect to age, sex, race, ethnicity, prior record, and
current offense type. That is well and fine, but the question we face is

whether we have sufficient equivalence to trust the results of a comparison of the transferred youth with this control group. Arguably not. Recall that we have not matched on such characteristics as the quality of legal counsel or competency to stand trial. Such factors not only may influence decisions to transfer but also may influence recidivism. To the extent that the influence exists and we have failed to address it, our estimate will be biased. That situation in fact describes many of the extant studies of transfer as well as evaluations of other sentencing policies.[33]

A diverse range of methodologies exist to create equivalent groups.[34] There are, for example, matching procedures, as discussed earlier. Also, many multivariate statistical approaches allow one to statistically control for multiple (hence, multivariate) differences that might bias treatment-versus-control effects. These approaches attempt to control for factors that may affect selection into treatment (i.e., a policy, program, practice) and that may affect the outcome. A little-used but powerful approach to creating control groups involves regression-discontinuity designs. These designs work well in situations where we know exactly how participants are selected into groups and we have a measure (e.g., a score on some variable) used to facilitate such selection.[35] Here, we know in advance what the selection process is and thus can more directly incorporate it into the statistical analyses.

A much more commonly used approach involves *pre-post analyses* wherein one compares outcomes for a group or area at one point in time and then at a second or later point in time. When no control groups or areas exist, such estimates typically risk generating biased estimates of impact because they allow time for many influences other than the policy to affect the estimates. Even with control groups or areas, the estimates can be biased if they do not adjust for differences in the experiences, events, or contexts (other than that of the policy) between the treatment and control groups or areas. For ecological-level studies of areas, time-series analyses typically are used to identify whether trends in or changes in outcomes varied pre- and postintervention.

Which approach to use? There really is no easy answer. Each policy and the context in which it exists dictate which approaches can or should be used. Resources and data availability constrain what can be done. The creativity of the researchers comes into play as well. In the end, Rossi and his colleagues have advocated a "good enough" rule, one that seems eminently reasonable: "Choose the strongest possible design from a methodological standpoint after having taken into account the potential importance of the results, the practicality and feasibility of each design, and the probability that the design chose will produce useful and credible results."[36]

Critical Conceptual and Analytical Issues

Regardless of the methodology used in an impact evaluation, the basic conceptual steps involved in identifying policy effects remain the same. We need clear information about the goals of the policy so that we can identify relevant outcomes, we need to identify the intended targets (e.g., specific individuals, groups, or areas), and we need to create control groups that are sufficiently similar as to allow for appropriate comparisons of levels or changes in outcomes. Should we fall short on these or other dimensions, or should studies we read or review fall short on them, then serious questions arise about the credibility of the resulting impact estimates. With that said, several critical conceptual and analytical issues bear emphasis because they affect how impact evaluations are undertaken and the credibility of any estimated impacts they generate.

First, impact assessments are, by their very nature, comparative – the main challenge, or trick, lies in identifying the appropriate comparison.[37] To illustrate, consider faith-based prison programs, such as the widely publicized InnerChange Freedom Initiative.[38] They have garnered considerable media and political attention, and frequently they are touted as highly effective. Compared to what, though? Should the comparison be to other programs? That would seem odd in a context where many of the inmates, in the absence of the faith-based program, receive little to no programming, especially in times when correctional system resources face budget cuts or considerable expansion without a commensurate increase in funding for programs and services. So, perhaps the comparison should be to "business as usual" – that is, a comparison to what the inmates otherwise would have received. Observe here, however, that what inmates typically receive will vary greatly from one prison to the next. That possibility would dictate that we would want to create a control group from inmates residing at facilities where the faith-based program participants originated. Even then, we face a dilemma: the inmates in the faith-based program would have volunteered, because states cannot force prisoners to participate in religious programs. Thus, we need to identify inmates who somehow look similar in relevant respects, including their willingness to volunteer for an intensive faith-based program, to arrive at an apples-to-apples comparison.[39]

Second, evaluators should strive to identify, a priori, the type and magnitude of effect expected, the time period within which it should occur, and, not least, whether the effect matters.[40] The expected effect and the time frame within which it should occur provide important information for designing an evaluation. For example, we might anticipate that a statewide sentencing law would not create a substantial effect on sentencing practices or crime rates for at least one or two years after being enacted. If so, the appropriate assessment would involve examining changes in sentencing practices or crime rates one year or two years after the law went into effect.

A related endeavor involves describing whether a particular effect is or would be consequential. Tests of statistical significance provide little to no foothold for addressing this issue. With sufficiently large samples, one can typically achieve statistical significance even when the substantive effects are trivial. A policy may reduce the number of crimes in a city from 10,000 to 9,990, but such a difference would not likely register with the public as being noteworthy. But on what basis, then, do we determine if an effect merits our attention? No single strategy works best. Ideally, one can find a comparative foundation on which to make a judgment. To illustrate, if most programs in a state prison have, on average, a recidivism rate of 40 percent, it might be appropriate to use that number as a point of comparison for assessing whether the recidivism rate of a program that targets similar inmates is noteworthy.

Third, with both experiments and nonexperiments, evaluators should compare all subjects in the treatment group with all those in the control group. For example, we would not want to compare the recidivism rates of only those treatment group subjects who completed treatment with all subjects in the control group. Doing so creates an apples-to-oranges comparison. The issue is especially relevant for many criminal justice programs that require subjects to undertake many tasks. For example, participants in the Inner-Change Freedom Initiative have to complete sixteen to eighteen months of programming, including Bible study, mentoring, life skills training, educational classes, and the like. Were one to focus only on program completers, it would eliminate any equivalence with the control group and create misleading results about the putative effectiveness of the program. In essence, if we focus only on completers, we are cheating by "creaming" the "best" treatment subjects who naturally, even with no programming, would likely fare better on a range of outcomes.[41]

Fourth, many factors can threaten the internal validity of an impact evaluation – that is, the extent to which we can have trust that a policy actually caused an effect on some outcome.[42] As alluded to earlier, selection bias constitutes a common threat to validity. However, many other threats to internal validity exist – including history, maturation, testing, instrumentation, statistical regression, mortality, ambiguous temporal sequence, and selection-based interactions – and should be examined before we trust that an estimated policy impact is likely to be real.[43] For example, it may be that any identified effect really stems not from the policy but from historical events that occurred during the period under which the study was undertaken. Consider that many policies, especially those that target areas (e.g., counties, cities, states, countries), operate in a context in which many other crime-causing factors exist and in which many other crime-fighting efforts are being undertaken. In such a context, it becomes extremely difficult to isolate any unique crime-reducing effect of a single policy.

Not least, many factors can threaten the external validity of an impact evaluation – the extent to which we can have trust that a causal claim produced by a study of a particular policy can be generalized to different populations or in different areas.[44] Here, again, caution is warranted. In some cases, we may be confident that a result can be generalized, but frequently it cannot. For example, faith-based programming might exert a greater, or perhaps lesser, effect in reducing recidivism if it occurs in settings where educational or vocational training opportunities exist or it may help men more so than women. Only multiple studies expressly designed to examine such possibilities can delimit the generalizability of findings from any one study. Consider, too, that treatment effects may vary by dosage and that any such effect would raise questions about the external validity of a study that did not explore this possibility. Observe, for example, that one supermax facility might greatly reduce violence throughout an entire prison system but that the law of diminishing returns may apply to each additional supermax. That is, each new facility may create smaller reductions in violence as compared with the reductions created by the first one. An impact evaluation not expressly designed to test for dosage effects would risk creating the appearance that a single constant effect exists, when in reality the effectiveness of supermax housing may vary according to the number of such institutions a state possesses.

The Importance of Identifying Unintended Effects

The goal of impact evaluations is to determine if a policy produces the desired effect. However, many policies may have unintended effects, which, to the extent possible, should be identified. Otherwise, we risk creating an unbalanced assessment of a policy, one that could be overly positive or negative.[45] Consider several illustrative examples. Community-based crime-prevention efforts might reduce crime in some areas but increase it in others. Conversely, their positive influence may be greater than typically assumed – for example, they might decrease crime in targeted areas and also in nearby or similar communities.[46] Or consider prison classification systems, which might actually increase rather than decrease recidivism. Gerald Gaes and Scott Camp recently identified just such a possibility. They conducted an experiment in which they randomly assigned inmates to higher-security custodial facilities and found that these inmates had substantially higher recidivism rates than their counterparts.[47] A third example – interventions that involve group influence, a hallmark of incarceration and many treatment programs – may cause more offending rather than less among participants.[48]

One of the most prominent unintended effects that many crime policies may create is *net widening*. Diversion programs, for example, aim to channel offenders, where possible, from more serious sanctions to less expensive and potentially more effective alternatives. Studies show, however, that sometimes these efforts do not actually divert cases but instead pull in a previously unsanctioned population, thereby expanding the correctional system.[49]

By definition, when something is unintended, we do not anticipate or expect that it will happen, which can make identifying it difficult. Nonetheless, careful reviews of the research literature as well as discussions with criminal justice administrators, practitioners, offenders, victims, and other criminal justice actors and stakeholders can be used to identify potential unintended effects.

Experiments Are Not the Only or Best Option

Experiments typically are held up as the gold standard for policy impact evaluation. In reality, however, they can and frequently do suffer from many problems. For that reason, they are not magically better than quasi-experimental designs. Indeed, quasi-experimental designs frequently can be conducted in contexts where experiments cannot. They can be cheaper, too.

Thus, although experimental impact evaluations can advance efforts to identify effective criminal justice policies, we should be aware of their limitations and, concomitantly, the fact that in many cases they are not the only or best option for assessing policy impacts.[50] To underscore this point, let us turn to several specific considerations that can influence whether we want to pursue experiments or whether we can trust or generalize from their results. In the next section, we will focus on a more general set of considerations that affect the credibility and usefulness of both experimental and nonexperimental impact evaluations.

One problem with experiments is that they may lead us to focus on policies with more certain, but also smaller, returns. The trade-off stems from the fact that a greater emphasis on methodological rigor biases studies toward interventions with a more narrow scope, such as programs that serve a specific at-risk population or that consist of a single-factor intervention. The reason is simple – these interventions lend themselves more easily to randomization and in turn the production of less equivocal results. In contrast, interventions such as community policing, which typically target large populations and areas and consist of multiple strategies to reduce crime, cannot easily be studied through randomization. That situation arises because of the difficulty in identifying appropriate comparison sites, the multidimensional nature of the intervention, and the prohibitive costs of large-scale, multisite experimental evaluations.

Another problem already mentioned is that experiments are costly and can run for many years.[51] Many criminal justice systems may not be able to afford experiments for most of their policies. They also may not have the luxury of waiting the four or five or more years it may take to conduct an experimental impact evaluation. By contrast, quasi-experimental designs that rely on existing data sometimes can be conducted at little cost and in a relatively short amount of time.

Ethical considerations limit whether experiments can be used to assess a policy's impacts. We cannot, for example, randomly assign people to arrest, detention, prison, supermax facilities, the death penalty, faith-based programs, states with specific sex offender laws, or other such policies. We also typically cannot randomly assign poverty reduction, community policing, and neighborhood empowerment programs, or other such areal-level efforts, to some areas in a city or to some cities and not others.

Experiments may be poorly implemented or suffer from large or nonrandom subject attrition, whereby experiments miss their intended targets.[52] In turn, the integrity of the experiment suffers and so, too, does any finding resulting from it.[53] Consider the Minneapolis Domestic Violence Experiment. Although well conducted in many respects, the experiment also suffered from a number of problems. For example, "officers had advance knowledge of the response they were supposed to make and therefore could reclassify a domestic violence case if they not wish to make the assigned response" and, in 17 percent of the cases, the "officers gave a 'treatment' that they were not supposed to."[54] Such problems do not necessarily compromise the experiment's results, but they raise flags about whether the results might have differed if these problems had not occurred. The same holds true of experiments conducted on many other criminal justice policies.[55]

Finally, impact evaluations conducted under laboratory-like conditions, what are termed efficacy studies, may point to unrealistically promising results as compared to what would be found with evaluations conducted under real-world conditions, what are termed effectiveness studies.[56] Consider the fact that new programs sometimes receive greater funding and scrutiny than long-standing ones. The funds may allow for fuller program implementation and the scrutiny may lead staff to comply more fully and enthusiastically with program protocols. We might well find a program effect under these conditions but find none when the program is implemented as it likely would be in the real world – that is, with less funding and potentially less attention to protocols. Put differently, efficacy studies produce results that may not accurately reflect what would happen in the real world. Some research suggests, for example, that the benefits of the popular multisystemic therapy (MST) program may be considerably lower in real-world settings as opposed to ideal settings.[57]

Factors That Can Impede the Credibility and Usefulness of Impact Evaluations

Many factors can affect the credibility and usefulness of results of both experiments and nonexperiments. These factors, including a range of specific problems and limitations, should not lead us to give up on impact evaluations. Far from it. However, awareness of some of them can sensitize us to the need to conduct such evaluations carefully and to interpret the results of them with equal care. It also can highlight the central importance, again, that clear conceptualization holds for undertaking evaluation research that generates credible and useful results and also for correctly interpreting impact evaluation findings.

Failure to Follow the Evaluation Hierarchy

An impact evaluation's results are only meaningful if we can assume that the policy addresses a real need, rests on a credible theory, and was implemented well. For example, if a theory evaluation identified a policy as having a weak theoretical foundation or an implementation evaluation showed that a policy was poorly implemented, we should be skeptical about any impact evaluation demonstrating a positive policy impact.

Consider something as mundane as the possibility that scheduling could influence whether probationers violate court orders. Edward Humes, for example, learned in his investigation of the Los Angeles juvenile court system, that probationers who relied on public transit frequently could not make their appointments on time or had to miss school and thus be truant to make it on time.[58] Here, we have a probation office practice, what amounts to a type of policy, whose design (e.g., the times when appointments are scheduled) impedes implementation. In such a context, we should be skeptical about any impact evaluation that finds that these check-ins fail to reduce recidivism.

Internal Validity

Unless considerable care is undertaken with an impact evaluation, the real risk arises that it will lack internal validity. Put differently, and as discussed earlier, we will not be able to trust that a policy caused some identified level or change in an outcome. For example, a quasi-experimental evaluation may show that a faith-based program reduced recidivism. If, however, selection effects were inadequately addressed (e.g., the possibility that inmates with a low propensity to recidivate volunteered for the program), we cannot be confident that the program produced the change.

External Validity

There may also be threats to external validity, also discussed earlier, that undermine how much we should trust or act on findings from an impact evaluation. For example, a drug court may be found to be effective with one population or in one area but not with other populations or in other areas. Until and unless such possibilities have been addressed, we typically should proceed cautiously in assuming that an identified effect will occur in other contexts.

Substitution Bias and Appropriate Comparisons

A related issue concerns the nature of the control group experience and how that may influence estimated policy effects. Impact evaluations typically proceed on the assumption that the control group does not receive the intervention. However, that assumption does not hold when substitution bias occurs. This bias "arises when members of an experimental control group gain access to close substitutes for the experimental treatment"; when that occurs, "control group outcomes no longer correspond to the untreated state."[59] The more general issue, which involves experimental and nonexperimental evaluations, is one of making appropriate comparisons.

Lawrence Sherman has noted that "the problem of differing control groups is basic to experimental design. To say that a program increases literacy by 50 percent is to imply a comparison: a 50-percent increase relative to what?"[60] Consider two studies involving drug courts. In one community, numerous treatment services exist for offenders in the control group, and in the other community few such services exist. We could conduct the studies using identical individuals involving identical courts, and yet, because they occur in separate communities, the results might differ substantially. The issue is one of external validity, but it also is one of making appropriate comparisons. Drug courts may be effective, but perhaps only if the comparison is to individuals who receive almost no services. If so, mention of that comparison becomes critical to guiding the design of studies and also to delimiting their relevance or generalizability.

Poor Policy Implementation

Early stages of policy implementation may undermine integrity of policy, thus creating a biased assessment of impact.[61] Frequently, federal agencies and foundations express interest in supporting evaluations of new policies. The idea makes sense – take a good idea; test it; and if it is found to be credible, then market it. However, many new policies require much tinkering to iron out a wealth of details. The space shuttle *Challenger* exploded in 1986 because of a faulty O-ring design.[62] Such seemingly small details clearly may have dramatic impacts, and, so, too, with criminal justice policies. For example, a failure to implement the full amount of drug treatment, in the right dosage and manner, might well be sufficient to reduce any impact a drug court might have.

Lack of Sufficient Statistical Power

We should be cautious in accepting the results of impact evaluations that lack sufficient power.[63] Statistical power refers to "the probability that an estimate of [a policy's] effect will be statistically significant when, in fact, it represents a real effect of a given magnitude."[64] Studies ideally should have sufficiently high statistical power to minimize what is termed *type II error*. That is, we want to minimize the probability that we will say that a policy has no effect when in fact it does.[65]

The problem lies in the fact that real effects may exist, but the studies, as designed or implemented, cannot detect them. In a concluding section of articles, the assessment in these cases tends to be "we found no treatment effects" or the treatment "doesn't work."[66] Such phrasing misleads readers because the studies frequently could only have detected effects of a large magnitude. Thus, to be technically correct and not misleading, the descriptions should be that "the study identified no statistically significant treatment effects and *could not have so identified any effect size of less than X percent.*" Even this phrasing, however, will not likely offset initial impressions of a policy's ineffectiveness.

The ubiquity of the problem cannot be overstated. Summarizing the results of a meta-analysis of 556 delinquency intervention studies, Rossi and his colleagues found that "many effects of a magnitude that might well represent important program benefits were not found to be statistically significant . . . mainly because of small sample sizes and underutilization of control variables."[67] Notably, in more than half the cases where a 24 percent reduction in recidivism was reported – a reduction that even a casual observer might view as compelling evidence of treatment effectiveness – no statistically significant effect surfaced.[68] Such a pattern accords better with an assessment that the studies suffered from small sample sizes than that no true effect existed.

The problems attendant to underpowered studies include not just the failure to identify a meaningful effect. They also include the involvement of subjects in a study that is unlikely to create accurate impact assessments[69] and the possibilities that a program may close, a law may be repealed, or a less effective alternative will be adopted in place of the policy subject to the evaluation.

No Criteria for Determining Significant Policy Effects

Unless criteria exist for determining "how large is enough," it is difficult to arrive at a reasonable assessment of whether a policy's impact warrants much attention.[70] Relative to some comparison group, how much of a reduction in recidivism should we see before we determine that a program is "effective"? How much should crime rates be reduced? In most areas of criminal justice policy, no clear criteria exist. Some foothold for making an assessment comes from cost-efficiency analyses, however. As will be discussed in Chapter 8, such analyses, cost-benefit analyses in particular, enable researchers to document the monetary benefit resulting from a policy.

Failure to Illuminate the "Black Box"

Impact evaluations typically will have limited credibility if we lack documentation about whether an identified impact is associated with elements of policy implementation and of intervening causal linkages – the policy "black box" – held to produce the impact.[71] Unfortunately, many impact evaluations proceed without an implementation focus and thus produce findings of questionable validity. For example, if an experiment shows that restorative justice programs reduce offending, the finding would be more compelling if the study also showed that the reduction could be linked clearly to changes in the factors identified by these programs, such as increased understanding of how their behavior harmed others, what contributed to their behavior, and what could be done about it.[72] Ultimately, the problem of "black box" impact evaluations lies in the fact that the "the evidence . . . does not cumulate. The end result . . . is just a list of programs that 'work' and 'don't work,' but no understanding of why they succeed or fail."[73]

Insufficient Attention to All Relevant Outcomes

Finally, an impact evaluation that focuses only on one or two relevant outcomes of many will have limited relevance and, indeed, may produce misleading or distorted impressions about a policy. For example, a study of the effects of supermax prisons that examines only prison homicides and not assaults or inmate compliance with rules would provide important but limited insight into the effectiveness of these facilities.[74] The same would be true of a study that only examined their effects on recidivism.[75] With drug courts, recidivism constitutes a central goal. However, clearly such courts also aim to reduce drug dependence. Should a drug court help reduce dependence but not reduce recidivism, we might be less than thrilled, but we would be more cautious in dismissing such courts than would be the case if no effects were documented for either outcome.

Solutions

Many of the previously mentioned problems and issues can be addressed through carefully conceptualized research designs (and sufficient funding to undertake them). Indeed, the importance of conceptualization is why they warrant discussion here. Criminal justice policy makers, administrators, and practitioners frequently have considerably more insight than researchers into the range of issues that may affect an evaluation. A drug court administrator, for example, would be well positioned to highlight which outcomes should be included in an impact evaluation and also the possibility that a particular court's focus on, say, first-time felons might limit the generalizability of any results to other groups. The administrator also would likely be able to identify implementation problems that could affect impact evaluation results. Attention to the types of problems and issues listed here can go a long a way toward placing impact evaluations on solid footing and toward helping researchers and others put estimated policy impacts in a proper, comparative context.

Clearly, and as will be discussed in Chapter 9, a greater investment in more and better experimental and quasi-experiment research is needed. Such an investment would pay dividends to efforts aimed at identifying and implementing evidence-based policies. It also would serve as a corrective against the potentially misleading results that stem from studies that use weak research designs. Studies show, for example, that weak research designs typically are more likely to identify significant effects, but these effects are less trustworthy than those produced by strong research designs.[76]

In addition, increased use of meta-analyses, which use quantitative methods to summarize the results of many evaluations, can provide an important aid in efforts to identify effective policies.[77] Such analyses constitute a major advance in summarizing what is known about a large body of research. Yet they also average across many studies, thus obscuring significant, important results from particular studies.[78]

One solution that should not be pursued is to require more impact evaluations of all the policies, programs, and practices that comprise the criminal justice system. It is unreasonable to expect that virtually every implemented policy be shown to be effective. Undertaking rigorous impact evaluations of policies is costly and time consuming, and virtually no state or local jurisdiction can afford to undertake impact evaluations of more than a handful of their crime policies. Does this fact provide license for policies to be enacted without fear of criticism, because no study will show that they work or not? No – there are many policies that research shows can be effective, and studies can be done at relatively minimal cost to monitor and improve implementation to ensure that policies have the best chance possible to be effective.

Consider an analogy to medicine. Society expects that doctors will be trained in and use treatments that science has shown to be effective with particular diseases.[79] The expectation in fact differs from practice. Sherman has observed that "in medicine as in government, much of what is done proceeds from theory, conjecture, and untested new ideas" and, citing Michael Millenson's discussion of a U.S. Office of Technology Assessment study, "that 85 percent of everyday medical treatments had never been scientifically tested."[80] Nonetheless, we do not typically expect that doctors will reinvent the wheel by showing that their particular use of a treatment is effective. Rather, we expect doctors to implement effective treatments appropriately, and the hope is that the treatments work in particular cases.

If they do not, it is understood that treatment is effective "on average," not necessarily in each and every case. If doctors refused to or did not want to be monitored, one of course might be concerned. By the same token, one should expect crime policies to have a solid theoretical and research-based foundation and that assessments be undertaken to ensure that these policies are well implemented, but impact evaluations of every criminal justice policy simply are unnecessary.

Why Are Outcome and Impact Evaluations Important?

Outcome and impact evaluations serve multiple purposes. As alluded to in Chapter 3, they can be useful for helping to draw attention to and clarify the ultimate goals of a policy and, by extension, the relevant criteria for judging policy performance. That alone constitutes a critical step in evaluating policies – without clarity about all relevant goals, we cannot provide a balanced assessment of impact.

Outcome evaluations by themselves, without an accompanying impact evaluation, should typically not be used to make causal claims about policies, but they can provide a relatively inexpensive platform on which to improve policy performance. For example, a clear trend downward on some outcome (e.g., recidivism) might indicate that a particular program has a problem that merits attention. Even so, because many factors other than a policy can influence outcomes, it can be difficult to place information about outcome levels or changes in proper context. The result can be inappropriate or misleading statements about policy impacts, especially if no information is provided about the quality of implementation or about factors, such as a downturn in the economy, which might account for observed outcomes.[81]

Impact evaluations provide information about policy effectiveness and, in turn, can contribute to debates about which policies merit greater support and which do not. Effectiveness ultimately constitutes the central goal of social policy. As such, assessing policy impact is absolutely essential. Without such assessments, we cannot know if policies can be deemed to be successful or therefore whether they should be continued, expanded, modified, or eliminated.[82]

Ultimately, outcome and impact evaluations further the larger criminal justice policy goal of ensuring that scarce resources get allocated to policies with the best chances of producing solid returns. Such a benefit serves not only to increase the accountability, effectiveness, and efficiency of the criminal justice system. It also highlights a moral issue – when scarce resources wind up supporting ineffective policies, it means that we have missed an opportunity to allocate funds toward effective ones. That in turn means that more crime, more victimization, and less justice occur.

Case Studies: *Drug Courts* and *Gun Laws*

To help illustrate the central idea underlying impact evaluations, two case studies of widely popular policies are next presented. The first focuses on drug courts and the second on gun laws. I review each policy and the assessments of impact to date, and then discuss several observations and implications related to the policies and impact evaluations of them. After the case studies, we turn to the question of what impact evaluations say, if anything, about a broader range of criminal justice policies.

Drug Courts

THE POLICY. The first drug court emerged in 1989. Since then, the expansion of drug courts has been nothing short of remarkable – as of 2008, more than 2,100 such courts were in operation.[83] Some scholars have described this growth as reflecting a drug court "movement," one buoyed by concern about increased drug arrests in the 1980s and 1990s and by disenchantment with traditional handling of drug-using offenders.[84] Processing tended to go slowly and it seemed that drug-involved offenders typically received light sentences and little to no supervision or treatment. Against that backdrop, the federal government invested millions of dollars and established the Drug Courts Program Office to facilitate the development of more drug courts.[85] A perfect storm of sorts thus arose – a perceived need existed, a new policy emerged that had elements that appealed to conservatives and to liberals (e.g., tougher supervision and thus greater accountability while also offering treatment), and funds were made available to implement the policy.

The basic idea of a drug court is simple. Justice system actors and treatment professionals combine their efforts to provide more rapid sentencing, close supervision, drug testing, drug treatment, and ancillary services. In turn, and as depicted in Figure 5.2, participants should experience decreased drug abuse and addiction (through treatment and drug testing) and increased mental health and employment (through provision of therapy, training, and other services). As a result, they should commit less crime through decreased drug use and addiction, increased mental health and employment, and the deterrent effect of increased supervision and monitoring.

The idea appears simple but in reality it is not. The specific procedures, programming, and theory of any given drug court can vary greatly. Jeffrey Butts and John Roman, for example, have identified a number of conceptual frameworks that have been used to structure and describe drug courts.[86] The amount of variability across the frameworks highlights the fact that any given drug court may differ from another enough so that any contrast could constitute an apples-to-oranges comparison.[87] Consider, for example, some of the following ingredients jurisdictions may, but need not necessarily, use to structure their drug courts and examples of the questions that arise in each instance: integrated justice system processing and treatment (integrated how?), nonadversarial processing (what precise balance of adversarial and nonadversarial should exist?), identification of "eligible" participants (based on what method of assessment or on what criteria?), provision of treatment (what types, in what doses, for how long?), drug testing (for what drugs, how frequently, and for how long?), judicial involvement (type and frequency of court check-ins?), intensive supervision (type and number of court or personnel contacts?), rapid sanctioning (how much time between a violation or crime and a court sanction?), and court collaborations with other agencies and community programs and groups (what types of collaborations exactly?).

The populations targeted by drug courts vary as well. For example, some drug courts focus on first-time or less serious offenders, while others focus on more serious, high-risk offenders; and some focus on adults while others focus on juveniles.[88] The populations actually served may also vary. In some areas, drug courts may see more methamphetamine abusers, while others may see more heroin abusers. Some drug courts may even target offenders with no serious drug problems.[89] Not least, the contexts in which drug courts operate may vary. One court may operate in an area where traditional criminal justice processing, sanctioning, and treatment are substantially better than in an area where another drug court operates. Or it may operate in a context where more community or agency support and resources exist to provide the greater collaboration, supervision, treatment, and ancillary services (e.g., job skills training, family therapy) that constitute the hallmarks of the drug court ideal.[90]

IMPACTS OF DRUG COURTS. The rapid growth in drug courts stands out in part because it emerged in the absence of strong or compelling evidence that these courts effectively reduce drug abuse or addiction or recidivism. Two decades after the first drug courts emerged, what do impact evaluations say about the effectiveness of this specialized system of justice?

Before turning to research that answers that question, we should consider several possibilities that emerge if we think about drug courts from a theory or implementation evaluation perspective. Given the variability in the theory and design of drug courts, we might expect less-than-consistent evidence about their effectiveness. In addition, the fact that these courts involve a multitude of strategies and services, require substantial collaboration and cooperation among diverse parties, and, not least, entail considerable investments that may not be adequately sustained over time, we might anticipate that studies reveal minimal impacts, on average. The reason is simple – sustaining full and high-quality implementation along these different dimensions is challenging.[91] Finally, we also might anticipate that in contexts where the theory is clearly articulated and the implementation is strong, some drug courts demonstrate strong positive effects.

So, what do existing studies reveal? Several comprehensive reviews exist, including a 2006 meta-analysis of fifty-five published drug court impact evaluations,[92] and most point to a few themes. First, relatively few methodologically sound studies have been conducted; second, studies to date provide suggestive evidence that drug courts may reduce recidivism more so than such interventions as traditional probation; and, third, few impact evaluations have been coupled with strong implementation evaluations to test the theoretical logic of drug courts.[93]

The results from some impact evaluations are encouraging. At the same time, the question arises: why the equivocal results? The first theme provides a critical part of the answer. To date, few studies have used randomization, and several of those that did suffered implementation problems. Among the quasi-experimental studies that have been undertaken, roughly half have failed to use statistical controls to take into account differences between treatment and control groups that might bias the estimated effects.[94]

The factors discussed here likely contribute to the equivocal results. For example, variable implementation of drug court components (e.g., drug testing, court check-ins) may reduce the likelihood of successful outcomes. As a result, some drug courts may be more effective than others and some models or approaches may be more effective than others. Wilson and his colleagues have noted, for example, that "drug courts that used a single drug abuse treatment provider had slightly larger effects, on average, than those drug courts that used multiple drug treatment providers."[95]

OBSERVATIONS AND IMPLICATIONS. Although drug courts appear likely to reduce drug abuse and recidivism, "the evidence is not convincing from a social scientific standpoint."[96] Several strategies exist for improving the state of evidence. Drug courts can develop more consistent theoretical rationales and protocols and emphasize strong implementation. Without such emphases, virtually any social policy faces a reduced likelihood of producing significant effects.

From a research perspective, more and better impact evaluations are needed, including more experiments and quasi-experiments that use adequate statistical controls.[97] In addition, such studies should be coupled with theory and implementation evaluations that test the drug court causal logic. Assume, for example, that drug courts produce consistently strong reductions in recidivism. What exactly produces this effect? Monitoring and supervision? Drug testing? Drug treatment? The combination of these activities or their use in conjunction with other services (e.g., family therapy, job and life skills training)?

Not least, a stronger body of evidence is needed that identifies the populations and areas for which drug courts are most effective and that investigates potential unintended effects, such as the diversion of resources from traditional courts. Answers to such questions are critical because they would allow policy makers and administrators to emphasize the activities that create the largest effects and deemphasize those that have small or no effects, to target the populations and areas where the greatest effects could be achieved, and to minimize potentially harmful unintended effects.

Gun Laws

THE POLICY. The Second Amendment to the U.S. Constitution states: "A well regulated militia, being necessary to the security of a free state, the right of the people to keep and bear arms, shall not be infringed." The phrasing has caused no small amount of debate. Gun proponents typically interpret it to mean that citizens can own guns and that laws cannot impose restrictions on ownership, while opponents argue that it refers only to agents of the State, such as law enforcement officers.

The legal issues aside, the United States has embraced gun ownership – an estimated 200 million to 250 million firearms are in circulation today – and, relative to other countries, has been far less willing to limit such ownership.[98] It is estimated that "4.5 million new firearms are sold each year," contributing to an ever-increasing pool of available guns.[99] Even so, considerable concern has emerged about the possibility that gun availability increases violence and that, in particular, it contributed to dramatic increases in violent crime in the 1980s and early 1990s.

It in fact remains unclear the extent to which guns cause or prevent violence. They clearly are, however, implicated in violence.[100] For example, in 2004, guns were involved in the death of 29,569 Americans, whether through homicide, suicide, or accidents.[101] The relationship, however, may not be causal. For example, guns may be used to facilitate other types of crime and contribute to deaths or serious injuries that otherwise would have constituted simple assaults, but they also may be used in self-defense and thus deter potential victimization.[102]

Against this backdrop, a large array of gun laws have been created by federal, state, and local governments in recent decades in an attempt to control access to firearms and to deter the use of firearms to commit violence or other crime. The laws cumulatively provide fewer restrictions than exist in most developed countries, but they nonetheless constitute an impressive effort. Consider, for example, the eight types of laws examined by a 2003 special task force convened by the Centers for Disease Control and Prevention (CDC): "bans on specified firearms or ammunition, restrictions on firearm acquisition, waiting periods for firearm acquisition, firearm registration and licensing of firearm owners, 'shall issue' concealed weapon carry laws, child access prevention laws, zero tolerance laws for firearms in schools, and combinations of firearm laws."[103]

IMPACTS OF GUN LAWS. So, do such laws work? Many studies have examined specific gun laws. Here, I focus on gun laws broadly and, in particular, on the evidence from the CDC's task force, which involved a panel of national experts. The review stands out because of the large number of prominent scholars involved in the assessment of the extant literature and because of the rigorous criteria used to assess the quality of gun law impact evaluations and estimated effects on violence reduction.

The CDC study identified fifty-one studies that met its criteria for inclusion and that examined one or more of the eight types of laws. The assessment was simple and depressing: "Evidence was insufficient to determine the effectiveness of any of these laws."[104] Put differently, the laws could be effective, but the social science for establishing that claim was, in the panel's view, inadequate. The CDC presented a somewhat more complicated assessment for many of the laws: some studies suggest that a given law reduces firearm violence, others that it has no effect, and still others that it might increase such violence. The mixed set of findings, when coupled with the fact that many of the studies suffered from important methodological limitations, not surprisingly led to the assessment that we simply do not know as yet whether these laws effectively reduce firearm violence. A similar verdict of the effects of other gun policies, including sentencing laws that provide for enhanced penalties in cases involving illegal use of firearms, has emerged from other prominent reviews, including a 2005 assessment by the National Research Council.[105]

OBSERVATIONS AND IMPLICATIONS. Much remains unknown about the effectiveness of gun laws because too few methodologically rigorous impact evaluations have been conducted. The problems with prior studies have been varied. For example, many have not quantified the extent of policy implementation.[106] Requiring waiting periods between the application for and acquisition of firearms does not mean that such periods are actually observed by sellers or purchasers. What effect would emerge under full versus partial compliance? Studies to date have not investigated that issue in relation to most gun laws.

Another problem lies with the lack of reliable or valid outcome measures. Law enforcement data frequently have been used in gun law evaluations, primarily because of their relative availability. Unfortunately, many crimes go unreported and the underreporting may vary across areas.

These problems are compounded by a third: the use of inappropriate comparisons. Some studies provide postintervention assessments of firearm violence in a given area and infer a causal effect from a decline in such violence. Yet such declines may have been consistent with a general downward trend in violence rather than a crime-reducing effect of gun policies.[107] Other studies compare different areas but fail to take into account differences between the areas that might contribute to estimated impacts. For example, in many cross-sectional studies, researchers compare one state (e.g., Massachusetts) with another state (e.g., Mississippi). These states may differ, however, in ways that could account for differences in gun-related violence; these differences, rather than specific gun policies, may contribute to an appearance of a crime reduction. Philip Cook and Jens Ludwig have emphasized that we may try to address this apples-to-oranges problem by introducing statistical controls; the problem is that the controls typically used may not be adequate and do not account for much of the variation in crime rates.[108]

The abundance of firearm and crime prevention laws itself creates a problem. With so many laws, tremendous challenges arise in trying to isolate the effect of one law from the effect of all others, to say nothing of changes in society at large. Consider the 1993 Handgun Control and Violence Prevention Act, known as the Brady bill, which was designed to regulate firearm purchases.[109] It went into effect at almost the same time as several other national crime-control efforts emerged. For example, the Community-Oriented Policing Program was created in 1994 and provided several billion dollars in funding; similarly, the Local Law Enforcement Block Grants Program was enacted in 1996 and provided almost $3 billion in funding.[110]

To be sure, some firearm policies may be effective. For example, Cook and Ludwig have argued that gun registries and "intensive police patrols directed against illicit gun carrying in high-violence neighborhoods" may help deter crime.[111] Other gun experts, such as Gary Kleck and Don Kates, suggest that "narrowly targeted gun control measures like bans on felon gun possession and background checks" may be effective.[112] Any effect on aggregate crime, however, would be contingent on not impeding "gun access for self-defense by generally law-abiding people."[113]

The larger point here is the need for better data and research to provide an evidence-based foundation for reducing gun-related crime. One scholar has observed that "the gun issue . . . has been fought not on the battleground of objective criteria, but instead on the turf of raw emotion."[114] That problem is compounded when the available research evaluating the impact of gun laws is limited and flawed.

Are Current Criminal Justice Policies Effective?

The earlier chapters argued that many criminal justice policies lack a clearly established need or theoretical foundation and that they frequently are poorly implemented. We can anticipate, therefore, that many criminal justice policies are ineffective or are unlikely to be effective. The fact remains, however, that we know little about the effectiveness of most parts of the criminal justice system and policies aimed at reducing crime and increasing justice.

Why? Many policies, including the multitude of programs, practices, rules, laws, and the like that comprise the criminal justice system, either have not been evaluated or the extant impact evaluations, whether experimental or nonexperimental, lack sufficient rigor to produce credible results that we can trust.[115] Consider the results from the widely cited report by Sherman and his colleagues.[116] The authors developed a five-point system for ranking studies, where 0 = no confidence in results, 3 = minimum degree of methodological rigor, and 5 = high confidence in results. Only 30 percent of the 440 studies that they reviewed scored a three or better.[117] Similarly, David Farrington and Brandon Welsh conducted a review in which they found not only that randomized experiments in criminology were relatively rare (they found eighty-three that were conducted from 1982 to 2004) but also that, among those that they examined, only one in five produced what they termed "significantly desirable results."[118] Put differently, 80 percent of the studies produced null findings.

An optimistic stance would be to assume that, the aforementioned issues notwithstanding, criminal justice policies typically produce intended outcomes. That stance runs counter to much of the available evidence to date, including numerous studies documenting implementation problems with crime policies. There are, I believe, some grounds for optimism, which I discuss in the conclusion. For example, Farrington and Welsh's review provided suggestive evidence, based on a small handful of experiments per policy type, that correctional therapy, drug courts, and batterer intervention programs may reduce offending. Nonetheless, I believe the weight of the evidence suggests grounds for pessimism about the effectiveness of many of the most prominent criminal justice policies that have been pursued in recent decades. That said, I should emphasize again that few impact evaluations systematically examine the effectiveness of a given criminal justice policy on the full range of relevant outcomes but instead focus on one (e.g., recidivism). As such, they provide a highly incomplete picture of policy effectiveness.

Consider first the two case study illustrations. Despite the rapid increase in drug courts and plethora of gun laws that exist, few methodologically rigorous impact evaluations of them exist. Those that do exist have either produced equivocal results or suggest that these efforts do little to reduce recidivism or crime. To be certain, exceptions exist and strong theoretical arguments can be made to lend credence to the view that drug courts and various gun laws are effective. And they may well be. To date, however, strong and consistent evidence is lacking. At the same time, compelling arguments can be made that these popular crime-prevention strategies are unlikely to produce positive outcomes without considerable improvements in implementation.

A similar assessment can be made about the policies examined in the previous case study illustrations. Mass incarceration may have reduced crime in recent years. However, scholars disagree about that assessment and almost all extant impact evaluations rest on strong assumptions that may be incorrect. Few impact evaluations exist of sex crime laws and fewer still exist that examine supermax prisons. Some of these assessments suggest potential harms rather than benefits. For example, supermax prisons may actually increase recidivism. Faith-based programs and transfer laws have been widely studied, but, again, few impact evaluations exist that credibly address selection effects and other methodological issues that compromise the credibility of identified effects. As with supermax prisons, studies suggest that transfer laws may actually worsen rather than improve recidivism outcomes. Not least, it remains unclear whether mandatory domestic violence or prosecution laws effectively reduce domestic violence. In almost every instance, variable implementation of the policies within and across states makes it difficult to establish when "the" policy exists. It also makes it difficult to determine the precise conditions under which any identified effects from specific studies could be expected to emerge were the policy to be adopted elsewhere.

When we canvass the literature on other parts of the criminal justice system, much the same summary assessment can be made. Consider, for example, the starting point for criminal justice – arrest. Ideally, arrests would produce deterrent effects. They would, for example, deter individuals from committing crime. However, they also may inform arrested or would-be offenders about the relatively low risks of apprehension and thus motivate them to engage in more crime. It is no simple matter to isolate the effect of arrest, separate from the effects of, say, the sanctions that may result from arrest. Even so, as David Huizinga and Kimberly Henry found in their recent review of the literature, the studies that address the issue in a credible manner suggest that arrests, on average, either have no effect on crime rates or recidivism or they actually increase both.[119]

How about the deterrent effects of the large number of "get tough" sentencing laws? Here, again, concrete and consistent evidence of the crime-reducing effects of specific laws is largely lacking.[120] Among other things, little is known about the relative effectiveness of diverse types of sentencing laws, how any estimated effectiveness may vary over time, and how dependent any effects are on the amount and quality of implementation.[121] At the same time, evidence exists that points to potentially harmful effects of these laws via increased incarceration. Devah Pager has found, for example, that "ex-offenders are one-half to one-third as likely to receive initial consideration from employers as equivalent applicants without criminal records. Mere contact with the criminal justice system . . . severely limits subsequent job prospects."[122] In turn, such individuals face increased risks of recidivating, risks that can create damaging ripple effects on the communities to which they return.[123]

Prisoner reentry programs have flourished in response to the dramatic increase in released inmates and the attention it has received from policy makers and researchers. Some studies point to effective practices. For example, a National Research Council commission examined the literature on community supervision and found evidence that drug treatment and cognitive-behavioral therapy can reduce recidivism.[124] At the same time, it underscored the need for a much larger body of methodologically rigorous studies to identify the precise policies and practices that could improve reentry outcomes.

Additional policies could be listed, but the same theme would emerge – although many criminal justice policies exist and although many of them may be effective, there simply are too many questions to trust that the policies indeed are effective. That said, exceptions certainly exist, which I discuss in Chapter 9.

Conclusion

Outcome and impact evaluations enable us to assess policy effectiveness. For that reason, they constitute a critical place in the evaluation hierarchy. Ultimately, if a policy does not produce an intended outcome, then what good is it? An outcome evaluation by itself cannot establish policy effectiveness – that is, it cannot establish that a policy actually caused an intended outcome. It can, however, be used to help identify critical goals and inform judgments about policy performance, especially when criteria exist for the levels or changes in outcomes that can be reasonably expected given appropriate policy implementation. A performance-monitoring system that tracks outcomes can be used in a similar manner and also can help identify when problems exist that should be addressed, such as a dramatic decline in outcomes.

Impact evaluations provide a direct test of policy effectiveness. They can consist of randomized experimental designs or, when such are not possible or feasible, any of a range of quasi-experimental designs. Experiments are the gold standard in evaluation research because, if implemented well, they allow us to feel confident that a real policy impact – a causal effect – exists or does not. Even so, they can suffer from many problems that can undermine the credibility of the results. They also can be quite costly and lead to an overly narrow focus on the types of policies that can be more easily subject to an experiment but that also may affect fewer individuals or areas.

For these reasons, quasi-experimental research designs can be helpful. They typically cost less; can be conducted when ethical or other issues preclude experiments; and, if implemented well, can produce credible assessments of impact. However, ensuring that a close approximation to an experiment has been achieved can be difficult. The risk thus arises that a quasi-experimental impact evaluation may generate spurious results, creating the appearance of an effect when none exists.

Regardless of the type of impact evaluation undertaken, careful attention to methodological rigor allows us to have greater trust in the results. To that end, we want to be clear about a policy's goals, the full set of outcomes relevant to assessing the policy, and the appropriate comparisons that should be used to draw inferences about policy effectiveness. We also want evidence that a policy does not produce harmful unintended effects. Not least, we want evidence from theory and implementation evaluations that help us to trust that any identified policy effects result from the policy.

As with the other types of evaluation, the quality and relevance of impact evaluations stems as much from clear conceptualization of key issues (e.g., identification of a policy's goals and appropriate bases of comparison) as it does from a familiarity with complicated research methodologies. Here, again, no single template or approach exists for conceptualizing the research questions relevant for evaluating the impact of a given policy. Instead, a thoughtful and deliberate approach, informed by an understanding of evaluation research, completion of prior steps in the evaluation hierarchy, and knowledge of the particular features and context of a policy, is likely to produce the best results.

Unfortunately, as the case study illustrations and different examples highlighted, methodologically rigorous impact evaluations of criminal justice policies occur far too rarely. In addition, evidence that these policies produce their intended impacts typically is lacking or equivocal, although exceptions certainly can be identified. As discussed in the final chapter, this state of affairs underscores the importance of substantially increasing the amount and quality of impact evaluations in criminal justice.

Discussion Questions

What are the benefits of evaluating the impacts of a criminal justice policy? What are the problems of not evaluating the impacts of a criminal justice policy?

How is an outcome evaluation different from an impact evaluation?

What is the basic logic of an impact evaluation?

How do you conduct an impact evaluation?

Why do experiments not always tell us much about whether a criminal justice policy will be effective in the real world?

Because it is not possible to conduct impact evaluations of every criminal justice policy, what criteria should we use for selecting the policies we will evaluate?

What are the main reasons why so few high-quality impact evaluations of criminal justice policies are conducted?

What steps can be taken to increase the number and quality of impact evaluations of criminal justice policies?

8

Cost-Efficiency Evaluations

W HEN ALL IS SAID AND DONE, WE NOT ONLY WANT CRIMINAL JUSTICE
policies to produce intended outcomes, like less crime; we also
want the most "bang for the buck." That is, we want policies that provide
the most benefit for the least cost.

Most of us implicitly apply this logic in our day-to-day decision making.
For example, we typically want a mode of transportation, such as a car,
that reliably gets us to our destination, but we also want to pay as little as
possible for it. Although the decision-making calculus may be complicated,
the formula that we apply is not: among the available cars from which
we can choose, we want the one that maximizes the benefit (e.g., reliable
transportation) and minimizes costs (e.g., purchase price, repairs, fuel) over
some set period of time.[1]

The formula applies as well when we have competing goals, but the calculations can be a bit more challenging. Perhaps we have a car that will no
longer run. Then we learn that we have a dental problem that, if untreated,
will lead to substantial pain. We need the car to get to work, but we also need
surgery to live without pain. If we have the funds and no other competing
demands, we could pay for both. Problem solved. However, many people
face a real dilemma: buy a car or pay for surgery?[2] Without a common metric for making a comparison between the qualitatively different outcomes
(employment versus pain), we face a somewhat greater challenge in determining which decision will yield the most benefit for the least cost. Even so,
the focus on comparing benefits with costs remains the same.

Cost-efficiency evaluation involves this same type of logic and it comes
in two varieties, one for each of the two situations just mentioned. *Cost-
effectiveness analysis* is used to determine which of several approaches is best
for achieving a given outcome, and *cost-benefit analysis* is used to determine
which of several approaches that target qualitatively different outcomes

creates the most benefit relative to costs. To illustrate, law enforcement agencies must make decisions about which strategies most efficiently prevent crime. Cost-effectiveness analyses can be helpful in comparing such strategies. However, these agencies also must make decisions about other strategies that target other outcomes, such as efforts to reduce fear of crime and to provide emergency services that may save lives.[3] Here, the outcomes (crime, fear of crime, lives saved) differ, and so we need a common metric for comparing the strategies that target them so that, in the end, we can compare which one produces the most benefit for the least cost.

Efficiency is of paramount importance to society and most organizations, especially when the risks are great (e.g., increased crime, fear, and injustice) and resources are scarce. That situation aptly characterizes criminal justice. For these reasons, cost-efficiency evaluation stands at the top of the evaluation hierarchy and is central to creating a more accountable and effective criminal justice system.

This chapter describes efficiency evaluation and the differences between cost-effectiveness and cost-benefit analyses. It focuses particular attention on the logic of such analyses and the basic steps involved in conducting them. It also highlights the central limitations and benefits of efficiency evaluation for criminal justice policy. The chapter then provides two case studies, one on community policing and the other on private prisons, to illustrate the idea of such evaluations. Paralleling the approach taken in previous chapters, it concludes by exploring the research foundation for assessing the efficiency of prominent U.S. criminal justice policies.

What Is a Cost-Efficiency Evaluation?

Cost-Efficiency Evaluation: Step 5 in the Hierarchy

THE EFFICIENCY MANDATE. The fifth and final step in the evaluation hierarchy involves cost-efficiency evaluation. Efficiency stands as perhaps the central guiding mandate of government – the aim is to provide services and achieve goals at the least cost and, more generally, to provide the maximum benefits to society. Achieving that mandate can be difficult when so many competing goals exist (e.g., education, public safety, roads) and when, in each instance, different approaches exist for trying to achieve them.

Regardless, the mandate exists and is embodied in virtually any taxpayer-funded effort. For example, when states allocate a certain amount of funds to corrections and not to education, they implicitly assume that the benefits of doing so exceed those associated with allocating the funds to education.

They may not conduct a study to test that assumption, but they nonetheless follow the logic. Similarly, when a department of corrections decides to build and operate a supermax prison, they assume that doing so produces benefits, relative to the costs, that exceed what could be obtained through other investments.

Despite policy makers' calls for greater accountability, evaluations of the efficiency of public policies occur infrequently. Certainly, and as will be discussed later in this chapter, they occur rarely in criminal justice. The end result? Policy makers and criminal justice administrators perforce must make assumptions – ones that could be incorrect – about the relative benefits and costs of various policies, programs, and practices.[4] This situation in turn creates substantial doubts about whether the government operates as efficiently as it could.

In the meantime, crime clearly creates substantial costs for society. As noted earlier, criminal justice expenditures in 2006 were $215 billion, a figure that does not factor in the costs of victimization or other adverse effects of crime.[5] In 1993, the last year for which a comprehensive assessment was conducted, the costs were estimated to be $450 billion.[6] Many scholars dispute the validity of this estimate, noting, among other things, that they build on cost estimates associated with extreme rather than run-of-the-mill crimes.[7] Even so, the expenditures alone and the dramatic increase in them over the past two decades highlight the fact that society has invested heavily in criminal justice and presumably expects some return on that investment.

COST-EFFECTIVENESS ANALYSIS VERSUS COST-BENEFIT ANALYSIS. Efficiency evaluations can consist of either cost-effectiveness analysis or cost-benefit analysis. *Cost-effectiveness analyses* identify the cost per outcome (e.g., for every dollar spent, one crime was averted). They are useful when comparing policies that target the same outcome. In the beginning of this chapter, the comparison of vehicles illustrated the logic of a cost-effectiveness analysis – the consumer aims to identify which vehicle will, over some period of time, provide the most reliable transportation for the least cost.

Cost-benefit analyses – sometimes referred to as benefit-cost analyses – identify, in monetary terms, policy costs and benefits (e.g., for every dollar spent, two dollars were saved). They are useful when comparing policies that target different outcomes (e.g., one aiming to prevent teen pregnancies and another aiming to reduce crime). The vehicle-versus-dental-care example at the beginning of the chapter illustrated the logic. In the example, the person attempts to identify whether achieving one goal (buying a car) will produce more benefits than achieving another (obtaining dental care), relative to the costs of producing these benefits.

To illustrate further the distinction between the two types of analyses, consider the following two scenarios. First, you are the mayor a small town of 30,000 people, one that includes many of your best friends and family members. You have only $1 million to spend on efforts other than the bare bones minimum of paying for such services as roads, schools, and a medical clinic. In the course of the past year, the number of aggravated assaults increased by 10 percent, from 100 to 110. You want to address the problem and task a committee with presenting several options. They convene and recommend that you consider one of the following policies: longer prison terms for individuals who commit assaults (assume here that incarceration costs are paid for by the town), an employment training and placement program for at-risk populations, or a gang-reduction initiative. In each instance, the policy goal is the same – reduce assaults. Which policy do you select? Cost-effectiveness analyses would develop cost estimates for each policy and use information from impact evaluations of the policies. They then would create policy-specific estimated costs for, say, avoiding some number of assaults. The policy that costs the least to produce this result would be the most cost-effective.

Now, imagine a second scenario. Here, again, you are the mayor of a small town of 30,000 people and you have $1 million to spend on social problems. When you look over the past year, you see that assaults have increased 10 percent. However, you also see that teen pregnancies and the number of homeless people have both increased by 10 percent as well. To simplify matters, assume that in each case, a 10 percent increase amounts to ten additional cases (e.g., ten additional assaults, ten additional teen pregnancies, ten additional homeless persons). For the sake of argument, assume that impact evaluations have been conducted and show that, for $1 million, (a) a policy exists that will result in five fewer assaults in the coming year, (b) another policy will result in five fewer teen pregnancies, and, (c) a third policy will result in five fewer homeless persons. The investment cost in each instance is the same, but the outcomes differ. And therein lies the rub: an assault differs from a teen pregnancy and both differ from homelessness. What we need is a way to establish a basis of comparison. *Monetizing* – putting a dollar value on – a given unit of outcome enables us to establish comparability among the three outcomes. In turn, we then can create policy-specific estimates of costs versus benefits. The policy with the greatest return, as expressed in dollars, would be the most cost beneficial, all else being equal.

In some cases, cost-effectiveness analyses may suffice and have the virtue of sparing evaluators the difficult challenge of arriving at defensible monetized estimates of impact. The valuation of a life, for example, is a contentious issue.[8] The problem lies in the fact that many criminal justice policies and programs have multiple goals. Unless we factor all of them into an efficiency analysis, we end up with an unbalanced comparison. Enter cost-benefit analyses. They enable us to use a common metric – money – to compare a diverse set of outcomes. It might seem that cost-effectiveness studies would be suitable for a large swath of criminal justice initiatives aimed exclusively at reducing recidivism. However, different crimes have different costs. A rape, for example, typically would be presumed to produce more harm than theft of a bicycle.[9] For this reason, cost-benefit analysis is useful, and indeed, necessary, for recidivism studies if we are to develop valid comparisons among policies.

How to Conduct a Cost-Benefit Analysis

Here, we will examine cost-benefit analysis and a number of conceptual elements central to undertaking one. The focus on cost-benefit analysis stems from the fact that the logic and steps involved parallel those for a cost-effectiveness analysis; the main difference is that cost-benefit analysis requires that we monetize all outcomes.

The focus on conceptual considerations stems from several considerations. First, it accords with a theme running throughout this book – namely, clear conceptualization is critical to undertaking and understanding policy evaluation, and, in many respects, it matters far more than the use of sophisticated research designs. That idea holds true with cost-benefit analysis as much as it does for needs, theory, implementation, and outcome and impact evaluations. Indeed, cost-benefit analysis, as Mark Cohen has emphasized, "is often more of an art than a science."[10] Second, an emphasis on conceptual considerations provides a more direct link to the discussions in the earlier chapters. For example, the veracity of a cost-benefit analysis rests heavily on a credible estimate of policy impact. Indeed, it can reasonably be said that a cost-benefit analysis is only as credible as that of the estimated impacts on which it rests.[11] However, such estimates frequently may not exist, as Chapter 7 highlighted. By implication, any cost-benefit analysis premised on an assumed impact should be viewed with considerable caution. Third, many excellent detailed accounts of the concrete nuts and bolts of cost-benefit analysis already exist and so do not need to be covered here.[12]

Many distinct tasks go into a cost-benefit analysis. Broadly, however, six steps need to be taken: (1) state the policy question, (2) identify the perspective of analysis, (3) identify all relevant costs and benefits, (4) assign values to costs and benefits, (5) compare the costs and benefits of one or more policies, and (6) assess the sensitivity of the results to critical assumptions and detail all relevant assumptions and limitations. Each step is described next.

1. STATE THE POLICY QUESTION. The relevant policy question and perspective of analysis may seem obvious, but frequently they are not. Identifying them can require a great deal of conceptual footwork. For example, we might be interested, as a general matter, in whether the benefits of a particular policy, say, a supermax, exceed the costs. But such a question lacks specificity. In reality, we likely want to know if building a new supermax facility would be cost beneficial relative to some other alternative. Or we likely want to know if an existing supermax constitutes a cost-beneficial investment as compared to the costs and benefits of tearing it down and investing in a different type of facility or perhaps some other strategy or set of strategies for improving order and safety in a prison system. In short, the central challenge, at bottom, is similar to what we face when conducting or critiquing impact evaluations – identifying the relevant basis of comparison.

To make a useful determination about appropriate comparisons, we typically need information about relative efficiency, that is, the efficiency of one approach as compared to another. To this end, it can be helpful to have a thorough needs evaluation from which to work. Such an evaluation can provide important context for describing the specific problems and the possible solutions to them. Perhaps, for example, a jurisdiction has experienced a jail-overcrowding problem. A needs evaluation might show that a large number of low-risk first-time offenders are being jailed prior to trial. If so, an efficiency analysis for a proposed jail might want to include not only the returns expected from constructing a new jail but also those that might accrue from a distinctly different policy option, namely, using jail space primarily for medium- and high-risk offenders.

2. IDENTIFY THE PERSPECTIVE OF ANALYSIS. Different perspectives exist – programs, government agencies, particular communities, cities and counties, states, and society, to name but a few – and each possesses a unique view that might well shape the specific questions posed in an efficiency evaluation. The societal perspective appears to be the one most frequently used. Government programs, for example, exist to help the public. Thus, their costs and benefits should be assessed with respect to society at large,

TABLE 8.1. The influence of the perspective of analysis on the classification of costs and benefits: An illustration using supermax prisons

	Perspective of analysis		
	Department of Corrections	Society	Local community
a. Improved prison management	Benefit	–	–
b. Fewer in-prison assaults	Benefit	–	–
c. Improved postrelease success for general population prisoners	Benefit	Benefit	–
d. Weakened supermax inmate family relationships	–	Cost	–
e. Increased recidivism of supermax prisoners	Cost	Cost	–
f. Increased mental health problems among supermax prisoners	Cost	Cost	–
g. Increased domestic dispute incidents among prison staff and families of supermax prisoners	Cost	Cost	Cost
h. Additional property taxes	Cost	Cost	Benefit

Source: Adapted from Lawrence and Mears (2004:10).

not some particular agency or group. However, cost-efficiency scholars disagree about the best or most appropriate perspective.[13] Consider, for example, that a government agency charged with public health might reasonably ignore the crime-reduction benefits of drug treatment, while a criminal justice agency might ignore the public-health benefits of reduced drug abuse.[14] Why? When a department of corrections hires more staff, that investment comes from its budget not that of other state agencies. Accordingly, the department would likely include the additional staff as part of a cost-benefit analysis aimed at determining whether this investment or some other (e.g., purchase of equipment or technology) produced the most returns for some outcome of interest of direct relevance for the department (e.g., systemwide order and safety). In turn, any resulting cost-efficiency estimates of this investment might look appreciably different from those produced from different perspectives of analysis (e.g., those of a department of public health).

To illustrate this point, consider, again, supermax prisons and the undertaking of cost-benefit analyses from three distinct perspectives – a department of corrections, society, and a local community.[15] Table 8.1 presents those perspectives and shows how some outcomes might be treated by each. Consider the first two outcomes, improved prison management (row a) and reduced in-prison assaults (row b). From a corrections perspective, both changes, potentially resulting from supermax incarceration, would constitute a benefit and so should be included in a cost-benefit analysis. However, from the perspective of society or a local community, neither outcome constitutes a benefit or cost. Neither outcome, for example, necessarily contributes to greater public safety.

When we turn to improved post-release success for general population inmates (row c), the picture changes slightly. Success might consist of lower recidivism rates, which a department of corrections would want to include in a cost-benefit analysis. From a societal perspective, lower recidivism clearly would stand as a benefit as well, and so from this perspective should be included in such an analysis. A benefit to the local community would be unlikely given that state prison inmates typically come from places other than the area where a given prison is located. However, should many of the released inmates return to that area, then a cost-benefit analysis from a local community perspective would want to include information about lower rates of recidivism.

Supermax housing might weaken inmates' ties to their families and weaken or disrupt family relationships (row d). An effect on inmates' families would not constitute a cost to the department of corrections. However, it might well constitute a cost to society, as depicted in the table.

If supermax incarceration were to increase rather than decrease recidivism (row e), then it would be a cost rather than a benefit, one that would be relevant from the perspectives of both the department of corrections and society. It also is possible that supermaxes increase mental health problems (row f), or so critics contend. Any increase would also count as a cost from these same perspectives.

The possibility exists that working in supermax facilities increases stress and domestic disputes among staff who work in them and the inmates placed there (row g). If such effects indeed exist, they likely would count as costs from each of the three perspectives of analysis.

Finally, we turn to an instance in which an outcome may be a cost or benefit. Increased property taxes (row h) may result when a department of corrections, and, by extension, society, invests in a supermax prison. These thus would be counted as costs from department of corrections and societal perspectives. However, for a local community, such taxes might well be treated as a benefit because of the increased revenues.

This example illustrates that no single or correct perspective of analysis exists. It also illustrates how the perspective of analysis can determine the classification of outcomes as costs or benefits. In turn, it demonstrates the critical importance, when presenting or interpreting cost-efficiency results, of clarifying the perspective of analysis used and how the results might differ if other perspectives were used.

3. IDENTIFY COSTS AND BENEFITS. The third step in conducting a cost-benefit analysis entails identifying all relevant costs and benefits. As the discussion of step 2 indicates, the perspective of analysis will determine what is counted as a cost or a benefit and, more generally, what costs and benefits should be considered. A systematic and detailed theory evaluation can aid in this effort by highlighting a policy's critical features, processes, and outcomes. Once we have selected the perspective and consulted a theory evaluation, the next step involves cataloging any cost or benefit related to the policy of interest.

In a cost-benefit analysis, a cost consists of anything that entails a loss and a benefit costs of anything that entails a gain, as expressed monetarily. To illustrate, expenditures – such as capital and operating costs associated with building and running a supermax prison – would be counted as costs, while improvements in outcomes (e.g., recidivism) would be counted as benefits. Whether a given item is classified as a cost or benefit ultimately depends, however, on whether it produces a (monetized) loss or a gain. For example, if a supermax prison increases recidivism, it creates a loss; accordingly, the increased recidivism would be classified as a cost. If, however, it decreases recidivism, it creates a gain or improvement; accordingly, the decreased recidivism would be classified as a benefit.

From an accounting perspective, several distinct types of costs and benefits should be cataloged. Numerous sources discuss these in detail, and Cohen and others have done so within a criminal justice framework.[16] Consequently, here we will review only some of them to illustrate the conceptual and analytic work involved in undertaking and interpreting a cost-benefit analysis.

Costs and benefits can be classified in many ways, but one of the most important distinctions is between costs and benefits that are direct versus indirect. *Direct* costs and benefits "are those that are closely related to the primary objective of the [policy]."[17] Direct costs of supermaxes, for example, include construction, personnel, technology, and other inputs, whereas direct benefits might include reduced violence and disorder throughout the prison system. *Indirect* costs and benefits "are by-products, multipliers, spillovers, or investment effects of the [policy]," what sometimes are referred to as *externalities*.[18] Indirect costs can be intended or unintended. An intended indirect cost might include overhead associated with operating a supermax and an unintended indirect cost might include increased systemwide violence or disorder that results from the use of supermax housing. An indirect benefit of a supermax might be reduced recidivism; it would be classified as indirect in states that expected no recidivism-reducing effect of supermax prisons.

Costs and benefits can also be classified as tangible and intangible. *Tangible* costs and benefits are those that we can easily identify and monetize, whereas *intangible* costs and benefits may be difficult to identify or monetize.[19] Tangible costs might include, for example, victimization costs, such as medical expenses and lost wages. Tangible benefits might include reduced crime. Among released offenders, it might include improved physical or mental health, and, in turn, a reduced need for and use of social services or health care.[20] Intangible costs might include increased pain and suffering or fear of crime and reduced quality of life, while intangible benefits might include decreased pain and suffering and increased quality of life.

Not least, costs and benefits can be classified as fixed and marginal. *Fixed* costs and benefits are constant, regardless of the size of or change in a policy. For example, if we purchase a video surveillance system, that cost remains the same whether we use it or not. By contrast, *marginal* costs vary depending on the size of or change in a policy or some feature of it. Should more drug-addicted offenders enter prison, more expenses may be incurred to provide treatment and thus would constitute a variable cost. Many criminal justice cost-benefit analyses use marginal capital and operating costs.[21] Ultimately, the decision about what to include depends heavily on the specific focus of the cost-benefit analysis. For example, if a jurisdiction were deciding whether to expand drug treatment offered by an existing program, we would focus on marginal costs; most fixed costs would be irrelevant because the program already exists.[22]

Several observations about costs and benefits bear mention. First, different types can be combined to help guide our efforts to identify all relevant costs and benefits. For example, there may be direct intangible benefits (e.g., a community policing program makes residents feel safer) and indirect intangible benefits (e.g., a community policing program helps preserve neighborhoods or facilitates efforts at revitalizing them).[23] It may not always be easy to identify or classify them, but all such possibilities should be explored to ensure as comprehensive a listing of costs and benefits as possible.

Second, opportunity costs are an important consideration in cost-benefit analyses. "The *opportunity cost* of using a resource is the value of its next most valuable alternative use."[24] For example, an office might be needed to support a particular crime-prevention initiative. If used in this manner, it no longer can be used in other ways. We cost the office, therefore, by measuring the value of whatever its next best use would be (e.g., its rental value).[25] Unfortunately, it may not always be clear what the next-best use is or what value to include, which can create uncertainty in cost-benefit estimates.[26] Also, what an opportunity cost is may depend on the perspective of analysis. How a prison system would have used funds for a supermax may vary, for example, from how state legislators would have used them.

Third, in developing a list of costs and benefits, we invariably will run into situations where we are not sure what to include.[27] Here, an important rule of thumb can guide us: in general, we want to include only those costs and benefits related to the policy under consideration and that we would not otherwise occur.[28] For example, if a supermax wing is added to an existing prison facility, we would include only the personnel costs associated with operating that wing, not the entire prison facility. The reason parallels the logic of impact evaluations – we want a clear assessment of a policy's costs and benefits relative to what would have happened without that policy.

Fourth, the credibility of a cost-benefit analysis depends heavily on accurate cost and benefit estimates. For this reason, we typically want to proceed with an efficiency analysis only (a) if we have a credible estimate of policy impact or (b) if we want to explore how large an impact would have to be – and whether the magnitude of impact is reasonable to expect – to break even with our investment. If no impact evaluations have been conducted or those that exist rest upon a weak research design, then, by extension, we should have less trust in any efficiency estimates.

4. ASSIGN VALUES. Once all costs and benefits have been identified, we then want to assign monetary values to them. This step can be aided by recourse to data from agency records.[29] However, it can be highly controversial because there may be little agreement about how to monetize some costs and benefits, especially intangible ones. Tangible costs and benefits "typically pass through a market system and have a price, such as articles of clothing or computer equipment."[30] In these cases, we can readily compile monetary values for each cost and benefit.

Intangible costs and benefits, however, typically have no market and thus no price. For example, no market exists for fear, pain, or suffering. Our option in this case is to proceed with a cost-benefit analysis that excludes such items. In so doing, however, we understate or overstate the true relationship between total costs and benefits. Our other option is to rely on imperfect estimates of intangible costs and benefits. The risk, again, however, is that we understate or overstate the total costs relative to the benefits. No simple solution to this quandary exists, especially given that "the largest component of crime costs is quality-of-life or intangible costs."[31] However, one safe approach involves conducting the analyses in different ways and reporting how the results vary.

In recent years, a number of methods have emerged for developing monetary estimates of the cost of crime.[32] For example, one can combine information about a range of dimensions – including victims' lost productivity, medical care, mental health care, police and fire services, social and victim services, and property loss and damage – to develop crime-specific cost estimates.[33] It also is possible to survey the public and ask them how much they would be willing to pay to avoid victimization of family members or themselves. In this way, we can obtain an indirect estimate of crime costs and arguably closer estimate of true market-derived crime costs, were such available.[34]

For criminal justice policies aimed expressly at reducing crime, accurate information about impacts on trajectories of offending is especially important. Many recidivism studies track offenders for only one to three years. However, if positive effects wash out shortly after this time span, or, alternatively, if they continue for many years after, we would want to revise our estimates of the crime-reducing effects of the policy and thus our cost-benefit analyses.[35] Criminal justice policies necessarily involve a focus on retribution, and so ideally cost-benefit analyses would also take this fact into account. However, few studies assess the economic returns that retribution produces and how those returns vary across policies.[36]

Finally, relatively little attention has been given to developing monetary estimates associated with noncrime outcomes (e.g., increased employment and education, decreased drug abuse).[37] If no such outcomes existed, this situation would not be problematic. However, many criminal justice policies create benefits that go well beyond crime and so ideally should be included in efficiency analyses.[38]

5. COMPARE COSTS VERSUS BENEFITS OF ONE OR MORE POLICIES. Once all costs and benefits have been identified and monetized, it is a simple matter to sum them and then create a bottom-line assessment. Before doing so, however, a process called *discounting* must be undertaken. Any multiyear endeavor, which characterizes most criminal justice policies, accrues costs and benefits over time, with some costs occurring at different times than some benefits. This fact introduces a complication: the value of money today, the present value, is more valuable than money in the future, regardless of inflation. Consider, for example, that a bank might pay 4 percent interest on a $100 investment in a savings account. After one year, we would have $104. From an economist's perspective, the $104 a year from now has a present value of $100 in current dollars and so the discount rate would be 4 percent.

Cost-benefit analysis addresses this fact – the relatively greater value of money in the present than in the future – through discounting. Specifically, "the estimated costs and benefits are arranged over time (usually a number of years) and then those two annual flows of dollars are discounted to present value."[39] (Discounting is not an adjustment for inflation; the latter typically is addressed using constant dollars in all analyses.[40]) The U.S. Office of Management and Budget publishes guidelines that recommend a 7 percent discount rate on public investments.[41] However, the Washington State Institute for Public Policy used a 3 percent discount rate in what many view as one of the more rigorous cost-benefit analyses of a wide range of criminal justice policies.[42] Because selection of the discount rate can greatly influence cost-benefit estimates, it is important to assess the effects of using different rates and to identify a rate appropriate to a particular policy context.[43]

Selection of the policy time span used can also exert a strong effect on cost-benefit estimates. We want to select an appropriate time span that accurately reflects the duration or lifetime over which a policy will generate costs and benefits. In so doing, we need to calibrate our estimates of specific costs and benefits to adjust for changes in their timing and magnitude. To illustrate, crime rate reductions might not begin for a year or two until after a community-focused prevention program has begun and the effect may be more pronounced initially before then tapering off. Conversely, some costs, such as those associated with constructing a prison, are incurred in the first year and, in cost-benefit analyses, are amortized (spread out) over a number of years.

Once the process of discounting has been completed, the summed costs and benefits can be used to generate the *net benefit* (i.e., benefits – costs) – technically the net present value – or a *benefit-cost ratio* (i.e., benefits/costs) over the life course of a policy. For example, if a policy produces $1,000,000 in discounted benefits and has discounted costs of $700,000, the net benefit would be $300,000 and benefit-cost ratio would be 1.43. The benefit-cost ratio does not reflect issues of scale. For example, two policies could have identical benefit-cost ratios, but one could be much larger in scale and thus produce, in aggregate, a greater benefit. For that reason, it typically is preferable to present, at a minimum, the net benefit.[44]

Table 8.2 provides an illustration from a report a colleague, Sarah Lawrence, and I produced on cost-benefit analysis of supermax prisons.[45] To convey the basic logic better, the illustration focuses on the question of whether upgrading a building to a supermax facility is cost beneficial and it makes a number of simplifying assumptions. For example, it assumes a one-year time frame and does not incorporate all relevant costs and benefits. In a real cost-benefit analysis, these and other assumptions would need to be revised. As can be seen in the table, the total benefits add up to $640,000 and the total costs add up to $886,000. The net benefit thus is negative (−$246,600) and the benefit-cost ratio is less than 1.0 (.72). In this example, then, supermax housing is not cost beneficial.

A nice feature of cost-benefit analysis consists of the use of a standardized metric, money, which enables us to readily compare the net benefits of different policies. All else being equal, for example, we would want to select the policy that provided the largest net benefit. For example, if a dispersion strategy for managing violent or disruptive inmates produced a net benefit of $100,000, then, as compared with a supermax, it would clearly be the preferred choice. "All else being equal" constitutes a critical qualification, however. For example, cost-benefit analyses at best serve as one part of a general decision-making process. And some decisions, such as the perspective of analysis, may entail political decisions that ultimately can only be resolved within the political arena.[46]

6. ASSESS SENSITIVITY AND ARTICULATE LIMITATIONS. Of course, it might be that estimated cost-benefit estimates are incorrect or are sensitive to minor changes in assumptions about critical costs and benefits. It also is quite possible that a number of important limitations exist. Perhaps, for example, an important intangible cost or benefit was not included or an estimated cost or benefit derived from the use of data of questionable reliability or validity. Perhaps, too, evaluators were unable to determine if the costs and benefits differentially accrued for one group or area as against another (e.g., perhaps crime reductions occurred primarily in one neighborhood but the costs were borne by all county residents). For these reasons, an absolutely essential part of any cost-benefit analysis involves (1) explicit mention of all relevant limitations and (2) assessment of the sensitivity of the results to changes in such dimensions as the magnitude of certain impacts, the monetized values in cases where debate exists about the appropriate

TABLE 8.2. Cost-benefit analysis of a supermax prison

	Measure	Number of units	Per unit value ($)	Total ($)
Benefits				
Reduced violence among inmates	No. of inmate-on-inmate assaults	150	1,200 per assault	180,000
Reduced violence against staff	No. of inmate-on-staff assaults	50	1,200 per assault	60,000
Fewer violent incidents requiring hospitalization	No. of hospitalizations	40	2,500 per incident	100,000
Less stressful living conditions	No. of inmate grievances filed	200	500 per grievance	100,000
Less stressful working conditions	No. of sick or personal days taken	250	800 per day	200,000
				640,000
Costs				
Construction costs	Sum of charges related to construction		–	500,000
New equipment and technology	Cost of new equipment and technology		–	25,000
Staff hiring and training	Personnel costs for hiring and training	80	20 per hour	1,600
Personnel costs	Personnel costs for five new officers	10,400	30 per hour	312,000
Utilities	Additional amount of monthly utility bills	12	4,000 per month	48,000
				886,600
			Net Benefits (Benefits – Costs) =	**–246,600**
			Benefit-Cost Ratio (Benefits/Costs) =	**.72**

Source: Adapted from Lawrence and Mears (2004:32).

TABLE 8.3. Sensitivity analysis: An illustration using supermax prisons and assumptions about reductions in inmate-on-inmate assaults

Number of reduced inmate-on-inmate assaults per year	Net benefit	Benefit-cost ratio
75 (low impact)	−$336,000	.62
150 (expected impact)	−$246,600	.72
300 (high impact)	−$66,000	.92
355 (break-even impact)	No gain or loss	1.00
400 (best-case impact)	$173,400	1.20

Source: Adapted from Lawrence and Mears (2004:33).

values to use, the discount rate or time horizon, and the specific treatment of certain cost and benefit items.

To demonstrate how cost-benefit analyses might easily change if we use different assumptions, let us return to the supermax illustration. Table 8.3 models several different scenarios. This exercise is termed *sensitivity analysis* and allows us to determine how much efficiency estimates will change based on different assumptions, such as the expected or estimated values of costs and benefits.

The first scenario assumes a low impact of supermax housing on inmate-on-inmate assaults; here, such housing only produces 75 fewer assaults. The second assumes the expected impact of 150 fewer such assaults. The third assumes a considerably larger impact of 300 fewer assaults. The fourth shows the number of reduced assaults (355) required to break even (i.e., for benefits and costs to equal one another). And the fifth assumes a best-case scenario impact of 400 fewer assaults.

As we can see, the low, expected, and high impact scenarios consistently result in a net loss. To break even, we would need a reduction in assaults that is halfway between the optimistic high-impact- and best-case-scenario impacts. Only in the best-case scenario would we achieve a net benefit ($173,400).

To reiterate, these estimates do not reflect the true impacts or costs and benefits of supermax prisons. The information for an accurate assessment remains lacking to date. Instead, the estimates, and how they vary with key assumptions, serve to underscore several themes of this chapter. First, credible estimates of impact are absolutely essential for deriving efficiency estimates that we can trust. If impact evaluations produced flawed assessments, efficiency evaluations will also be flawed.

Second, efficiency analyses can be useful for providing information about the potential returns on certain policy investments and also the uncertainty associated with those returns. In the present example, a cost-benefit analysis shows that supermax housing produces a net loss rather than a net benefit. That assessment is reinforced by the sensitivity analyses, which show that a net loss is relatively certain – indeed, only a best-case scenario would return a positive net benefit. However, we just as easily could have modeled a situation in which changes in the assumed impacts of supermax prisons consistently produced net benefits. The point in either case is that sensitivity analyses, if conducted with reasonable estimates about likely costs and benefits, can provide important information about whether investing in a policy makes sense.

The importance of sensitivity analysis is difficult to overstate – even slight changes in assumptions can result in dramatically different results. For example, assumptions about such issues as tax credits or the assumed medical costs of inmates at different custody levels can profoundly alter an efficiency estimate of prison privatization, as has been detailed by Gerald Gaes and his colleagues.[47] Similarly, altering the time span can easily reverse an efficiency assessment. Eugene Bardach, for example, has shown how changing the underlying time-span assumptions in an analysis of mandatory minimum sentencing laws for drug offenses can dramatically change an assessment of efficiency. In his analyses, the use of short time horizons make it appear that longer prison sentences are more cost-effective, whereas longer time horizons highlight that conventional enforcement and sentencing strategies, as well as treatment, may be more cost-effective.[48]

Limitations of Cost-Efficiency Evaluation

Many cost-efficiency evaluations are subject to what might be called the house-of-cards criticism. That is, they build on a wide range of implausible or untested assumptions, unreasonable time frames or discount rates, or incorrect cost and benefit estimates (e.g., the magnitude of expected policy impact may be substantially off the mark). In such cases, any resulting net benefit or cost-benefit ratio may include so much error as to be meaningless.

"Garbage in, garbage out" captures the problem in a more colorful way. Consider, for example, an efficiency evaluation in a context where an impact evaluation suffered from a number of critical flaws. Perhaps, for example, it failed to control adequately for selection biases. The result? An efficiency evaluation then proceeds to produce inflated cost-effectiveness or

cost-benefit estimates. Or perhaps the impact evaluation failed to identify or quantify important negative unintended effects. Once, again, the
efficiency estimates would be inflated. To illustrate, a cost-efficiency evaluation of supermax prisons that failed to include information about potentially
adverse effects on inmate mental health would overstate the benefits of these
prisons relative to their costs.

Another important limitation stems from the perspective of analysis.
Quite simply, the perspective taken may influence the results because it
"may require selectively taking different costs and outcomes into account,
depending on the perspectives and values of sponsors, stakeholders, targets, and evaluators themselves."[49] Consider the possibility that a crime-
prevention program may reduce crime in one area but do so primarily by
displacing it to a neighboring county or state. (Alternatively, it may reduce
crime in both places.[50]) From the perspective of the county with the crime-
prevention program, the program created a benefit (i.e., reduced crime).
From a societal perspective, however, the program produced no benefit. It
merely displaced crime and consumed resources in the process. The problem
in such situations lies in the fact that only careful consumers of cost-benefit
research may appreciate how different the results might be were a different
perspective to be used, especially if descriptions of the results neglect to
highlight the potential variability of the results.

One of the more prominent limitations of efficiency evaluations concerns
intangible costs and benefits. What, for example, is the proper or accurate
monetary value of fear, trust in and satisfaction with criminal courts, and
any of a number of crimes? Estimates exist, but scholars disagree about
their validity.[51] Similarly, what value should be put on procedural injustice?
Such injustice first has to be documented. Perhaps a prison system unfairly
places some inmates in supermax housing or a local law enforcement agency
disproportionately pulls over minority speeders. The next logical step might
be to factor a reduction in such injustice as a benefit or an increase as a
cost. However, few credible estimates exist for placing a monetary value on
a "unit" of perceived or actual injustice.

These observations underscore the fact that cost-benefit analysis "is not a
value-free concept but instead involves definitions and explicit boundaries to
determine whose costs and benefits matter."[52] For example, a conventional
cost-benefit analysis would not consider the pain and suffering that inmates
experience while incarcerated, but most inmates presumably would hold a
different view about that decision.

Although some of these limitations can be avoided, some cannot.
That does not necessarily undermine the value of cost-efficiency evaluations. Instead, it simply highlights the importance of presenting important

assumptions and caveats alongside of efficiency estimates. For example, one can explicitly state that a particular efficiency evaluation did not include information about a policy's effects on procedural injustice. Such steps can help to avoid what James Kee has referred to as the "black box syndrome," which occurs when researchers are "tempted to hide the messiness of the analysis from the decision maker" and instead report concise synopses that omit or gloss over important limitations, even when the "messiness" might reveal contradictory results depending on the assumptions used in the analyses.[53] Recall, again, that society and various agencies implicitly undertake cost-efficiency evaluations every time they invest in a particular policy and not another. In such cases, the same limitations apply but arguably are greater because a variety of assumptions go unarticulated and untested.

Why Are Cost-Efficiency Evaluations Important?

Cost-efficiency evaluations serve several important purposes. First, they provide a general sensitizing function similar to that of needs and theory evaluations by clarifying a policy's goals, the outcomes relevant to assessing those goals, and a policy's costs. For example, an ex ante efficiency evaluation (i.e., one that occurs prior to funding a new initiative) can build on needs and theory evaluations by drawing attention to the importance of identifying the exact measures that will be used to assess policy impact.[54]

Second, they can provide guidance about how likely it is that a given policy or set of policies will produce substantial returns. Impact evaluations do not provide such information, and precisely for that reason typically lead to different policy implications than do cost-efficiency evaluations.[55] Here, again, ex ante efficiency evaluations can be helpful. Such evaluations necessarily must proceed with estimates of expected rather than actual benefits. When, however, reasonable grounds exist for anticipating a level of impact and for monetizing it, they can provide a reasonable foundation for producing efficiency estimates that in turn can be credibly used to inform policy deliberations.

Third, ex post efficiency evaluations (i.e., those that occur after a policy has been implemented and its impacts have been assessed) provide critical information for deciding whether to continue, expand, or terminate a policy. Cost-effectiveness analyses can inform such decisions, but cost-benefit analyses provide a far more useful platform for them. A cost-effectiveness analysis tells us which of several options may produce a given outcome (e.g., reduced gang-related crime) for the least amount of money. That information can be quite useful in deciding among these options. However, it provides little foothold for comparing policies with different goals, including policies that target different crimes. By contrast, cost-benefit analyses enable us to develop comparisons, using a standardized metric (i.e., dollars), of the policies' relative costs and benefits.

Fourth, cost-efficiency evaluations – because of all the elements that go into them – force us to be explicit about the range of goals that inform our judgments about a policy's worth, to identify potential unintended effects, to acknowledge empirically unverified assumptions that substantially influence our assessments, and also to acknowledge the value judgments that contribute to support or opposition to a policy. A cost-efficiency evaluation might show, for example, that supermax prisons produce more benefits than costs, but only if we assume moderate to strong reductions in disorder and violence. And it might highlight that it cannot address concerns about whether supermax confinement constitutes a humane form of incarceration, but that such concerns should be considered as part of a balanced deliberation about the merits of supermax prisons.

Fifth, in some cases, efficiency evaluations can be used to monitor performance. If, for example, the estimated efficiency of a community policing program declines over time, it might indicate a need to examine the program more closely. Perhaps smaller reductions in violence are occurring than in the early phases of the program and could be increased with more consistent or higher quality implementation. Clearly, we could monitor crime rates over time and arrive at a similar concern. Efficiency estimates, however, would enable us to put a dollar value on what the changes mean in bottom-line terms – that is, the returns on a continued investment in the policy.[56]

Case Studies: *Community Policing* and *Private Prisons*

Community policing and private prisons have both emerged as prominent policies in recent decades. Although community policing is more widespread, prison privatization has steadily increased, tapping in part into a broader societal shift toward privatizing government functions. Here, the two policies are presented as case studies to illustrate the importance of cost-efficiency evaluations and some of the ideas central to conducting and interpreting them. After discussing these case studies, the discussion turns to an exploration of the state of criminal justice policy as viewed through an efficiency lens.

Community Policing

THE POLICY. Policing models have changed over time.[57] Until recent decades, the traditional policing approach centered on a reactive model in which patrol officers would wait for calls for service.[58] Under this model, the locus of control for identifying and addressing problems rested primarily with the police, not the community. Moreover, police supervisors dictated the focus and nature of police activity. The result? Officers tended to feel isolated from the community, and residents tended to resist or feel ambivalent toward the police.

Community policing emerged in part as a response to the perceived ineffectiveness of this model in responding to crime. During the 1980s, when violent crime rates were on the rise, law enforcement agencies across the country revised their approach. They zeroed in on the idea that their officers and the communities in which they worked held unique insight into ways in which crime might be better prevented and addressed. The result? Community policing. This new model aimed to develop community-police relationships that would be collaborative in identifying crime and how best to solve it.[59]

The end goal of community policing is to reduce crime. However, other goals exist as well. Successful community policing ventures should also lead to greater community order and to residents feeling safer. Residents also should have greater trust in the police and feel more satisfied with them. Even if these other goals did not reduce crime, they would be considered important ends in and of themselves. That fact means that efforts to evaluate the impacts of community policing should take the different goals, not just crime, into account.[60]

COST-EFFICIENCY OF COMMUNITY POLICING. Almost no research exists on the cost efficiency of community policing despite the popularity of this approach to law enforcement and the substantial federal and state funding of it.[61] Regardless, any efficiency evaluation would be problematic because of the limited evidence of community policing impacts on fear of crime; trust in and satisfaction with the police; disorder; and, not least, crime.[62] To be certain, studies exist that suggest that community policing can yield improvements along all of these dimensions.[63] However, few such studies rely on rigorous methodologies, and many of them provide no such evidence.

At the same time, considerable and consistent evidence exists that documents the fact that the implementation of community policing initiatives is highly variable. This fact alone suggests that any potential impacts – and thus efficiency – may be highly variable. They may depend greatly, for example, on the characteristics of communities. They also may depend on the precise activities that constitute community policing (e.g., shorter response times, information sharing with the public, meetings with residents, problem-solving cooperative efforts with residents). Not least, they depend on the intensity and quality with which communities and the police undertake such activities.

This situation characterizes another popular and widely prevalent law enforcement strategy that emerged during the 1980s and 1990s: problem-oriented policing. The main difference between the two approaches is that "community policing has a softer image and more preventive orientation . . . , relying more on engaging the public as partners in reducing crime and disorder than on aggressive law enforcement."[64] By contrast, the problem-oriented approach retains a fundamentally police-centered emphasis, one in which the police identify problems – in particular, the root causes of crime – and then develop and assess responses to them.[65] As with the literature on community policing, few rigorous evaluations of this widely used strategy exist, but some studies suggest that it may modestly reduce crime.[66] With problem-oriented policing, the primary outcome is crime, not fear of crime or public trust in or satisfaction with the police.

OBSERVATIONS AND IMPLICATIONS. Community policing has cost billions in taxpayer dollars. Between 1995 and 2000 alone, for example, $8.8 billion in federal funding went to support the hiring of more police officers and to improving community policing efforts nationwide.[67] Yet basic questions remain about whether such investments have produced appreciable impacts on crime or other community policing goals. It thus is too soon to know whether any impacts, should they exist or be of any sizable magnitude, are cost efficient.

What, though, would cost efficiency look like? One approach would be to identify the extent to which the cost of preventing crime is lower than traditional policing or other new approaches to policing. Cost-effectiveness analyses would facilitate such comparisons. However, they would require treating all crime as more or less equal. One solution would be to weight some crimes more than others, which is precisely what a cost-benefit analysis would allow. A cost-benefit analysis would be especially relevant for assessing the efficiency of community policing, given that it aims to improve several qualitatively distinct types of outcomes (e.g., crime, disorder, fear). Among other things, it would provide a basis for comparing community policing benefits with those of police strategies that aim exclusively to reduce crime.

Although reliable impact estimates of community policing do not yet exist, cost-efficiency evaluations nonetheless could prove useful in identifying whether expected impacts would, at a minimum, offset the costs. Perhaps, for example, small to modest reductions in crime alone would suffice to break even. However, perhaps large reductions, especially in serious or violent crime, would be required.

The fact that community policing targets multiple outcomes means that comprehensive cost-benefit analyses would need not only valid impact estimates for each outcome but also valid estimates of the monetary value of them. For example, we would need defensible estimates of the value of specific types of crime and the fear of each type. Such estimates could be derived from a number of sources, including surveys that ask people how much they would be willing to pay to obtain reductions in crime.[68]

The perspective of an efficiency analysis would be especially critical to consider when interpreting any results. For example, if we focused exclusively on neighborhoods where community policing was implemented, we might find that this strategy was cost-efficient. However, consider the possibility that crime could have increased in other nearby neighborhoods where community policing was not implemented. If we focused on the perspective of the neighborhoods, we might find that the strategy was inefficient because of crime displacement effects. If we focused on the entire county, city, or town, we presumably would average out these estimates. Doing so, however, would obscure area-specific costs and benefits that might be important to recognize. Such possibilities illustrate the importance of exploring multiple perspectives of analysis and whether efficiency estimates vary or overlap when doing so.

Private Prisons

THE POLICY. Calls for privatizing government functions emerged as a prominent theme in the 1980s and 1990s, one that resonated strongly in the corrections arena. The embrace of privatization can be seen in national statistics. By 2000, there were 87,369 inmates held in private facilities, and by 2008, that number had increased by 47 percent to 128,524 inmates and accounted for 8 percent of the total state and federal prison population.[69] The privatization efforts have been more successful at the federal level: as of 2008, 16.5 percent of federal inmates were housed in private facilities, more than double the 6.8 percent of state prisoners in such facilities.[70]

Why privatize prisons?[71] The main argument is that private prisons can provide the same care and control and achieve the same or better outcomes for less cost. Some people feel that the government operates inefficiently, and so they assume that privately run prisons must be more efficient. Others feel that government agencies operate quite efficiently and that, from an ethical standpoint, certain functions – such as housing, managing, and treating prisoners – should only be undertaken by government. From this perspective, the idea of private companies making a profit by performing a state function (i.e., punishment) seems inappropriate. A related argument suggests that a profit motive creates an incentive to cut services and treatment, regardless of the well-meaning intentions of private company administrators or staff.

COST EFFICIENCY OF PRIVATE PRISONS. An evidence-based approach to corrections cannot address the ethical critiques of prison privatization. It can, however, inform debates about the basic assumptions needed to support a cost-efficiency argument. What specific information would help?

Consider first the initial premise – that government-run prisons operate inefficiently. Do they? In fact, no standardized metric for prison efficiency exists. If it did, certain elements would be essential to include. For example, prisons typically must provide education and job training of some type and also physical and mental health services. They must maintain order and safety and do so in a humane and legally allowable manner. Not least, they typically must strive to minimize inmate recidivism.

If we reflect on these dimensions, it becomes evident that a cost-effectiveness study would be insufficient. Certainly, one could develop cost estimates and then juxtapose them against the number of inmates served who recidivate. Doing so would, however, ignore a number of other outcomes that would be relevant in any comparison. Perhaps, for example, the rate of inmate-on-inmate assaults in a privately run facility is twice that of a government-run prison. Such assaults would be critical to any comparison, as would such outcomes as the prevalence of postrelease mental illness, homelessness, and unemployment resulting from the incarceration experience. Of course, we could line up all relevant outcomes and provide a cost-effectiveness assessment for each outcome (e.g., the cost per assault, the cost per recidivism event, the cost per mental illness). However, because the outcomes qualitatively differ from one another, we need a common metric, such as money, to create a uniform basis of comparison. In short, what we want is a cost-benefit analysis of public prisons to establish a baseline value of efficiency. This type of analysis, by and large, has not been conducted.

Next, consider a second premise implicit in the first; private prisons can provide the same services and the same or better outcomes as public prisons but at lower cost. The operational costs typically are relatively straightforward to compare. If we could accept the ceteris paribus (all else equal) assumption, we could stop there. That assumption is, however, highly questionable. What if implementation evaluations were to show that private prisons offer fewer services, that inmate abuse and drug use occurs more frequently in them, and that inmate visitation and treatment for physical or mental health problems occur less frequently? And what if impact evaluations were to show that postrelease outcomes, such as recidivism, employment, and homelessness, were worse as compared to public prisons? Alternatively, what if private prisons fare better on all these dimensions? Any substantial deviations would greatly alter any efficiency analysis.[72]

So, what does the research say? Some studies suggest that private prisons are no more cost-efficient than public prisons, and a small handful suggest that they may be slightly more cost-efficient.[73] The more relevant findings, however, are that (a) few cost-efficiency studies of private prisons exist, (b) those that do exist use widely varying and frequently inappropriate methodologies, and (c) none systematically compare public and private prisons – much less ones that are comparable in all respects (e.g., types of inmates, custody levels) – with respect to the implementation of required services and activities or to a range of in-prison and postrelease outcomes.[74] The result, then, is a situation in which only apples-to-oranges comparisons can be made.

OBSERVATIONS AND IMPLICATIONS. Public prisons may be inefficient and private prisons may be the solution to this problem. As with community policing, such claims remain largely undocumented. It thus remains unknown whether the privatization trend has been beneficial. What is known is that existing efficiency estimates produce widely varying estimates depending on the methodologies and assumptions used to produce them.[75]

This situation reflects a broader problem in the field of corrections – namely, few states or jurisdictions have performance-monitoring systems in place sufficient for creating valid comparisons of the performance among public prisons, much less the performance of public versus private facilities, along a range of dimensions (see, for example, Table 6.1).[76] Such monitoring would facilitate implementation, impact, and efficiency evaluations. In addition, it would enable evaluators to identify facility-specific cost-benefit estimates. This specificity is important because facilities vary greatly in the types of inmates they house and in the type and quality of administration and staffing. Average estimates among public prisons or among private prisons obscures this variation and creates the incorrect impression that, say, all private prisons are cost-beneficial when perhaps only some of them are.[77]

The good news is that increased attention has been given to efficiency evaluations of private prisons and that concrete guidance for conducting them now exists. Gaes and his colleagues, for example, have provided a clear set of guidelines to undertaking such evaluations.[78] These guidelines may promote greater consistency and rigor in prison efficiency analyses, which in turn should allow a body of work to emerge that more definitively identifies when, and under what conditions and with what populations, prison privatization results in taxpayer cost savings.

Are Current Criminal Justice Policies Cost Efficient?

By and large, the answer to this question is we don't know. The vast bulk of criminal justice policies have not been subject to cost-efficiency evaluations, and extant efficiency evaluations typically suffer from critical methodological shortcomings or rely on sufficiently different methodologies as to make comparisons from one efficiency analysis to another meaningless.[79] Comparison of existing cost-benefit analyses of various policies, for example, is problematic because they frequently use different costs and benefits and different approaches to computing and monetizing them.[80]

The problem is actually worse – credible efficiency estimates depend on credible assessments of impact, but such assessments are also in short supply. Thus, even were we to undertake efficiency evaluations of the major criminal justice policies in place today, any resulting estimates would be vulnerable to the legitimate criticism that they do not accurately reflect true costs and benefits. Consider, for example, the policies examined in the case studies, including, from this chapter, community policing and private prisons, and, from previous chapters, mass incarceration, sex crime laws, supermax prisons, faith-based prison programs, transfer laws, mandatory domestic violence arrest laws, drug courts, and gun laws. The precise impacts, intended or otherwise, of these efforts remain unclear.

Much the same can be said of many other criminal justice policies. Consider unemployment checks, which recently have been lauded as a way to protect employers and their staff and customers while others have criticized them as constituting a significant barrier to gainful employment among released prisoners. We know little, however, about how these checks affect ex-prisoner postrelease employment.[81] Even if we had robust estimates of the impacts, a great deal more information would be needed for cost-benefit analyses. As Richard Freeman has noted, we would want reliable and valid estimates of such dimensions as "the impact of the reduced lower hiring on ex-offender criminal behavior; the costs of this additional criminal behavior; . . . the potential differential productivity between someone without a criminal record and someone with a record; and the possible deterrent effect of information on criminal behavior nonoffenders."[82]

Consider, too, the many practices and decision-making points in criminal justice, which constitute, in their own right, policies. Most go unexamined and yet hold the potential to create considerable costs and benefits for society.[83] For example, when law enforcement agencies mistakenly target low-crime rather than high-crime hot spots for more intensive attention or when offenders receive treatments, sanctions, or classifications that do not match their particular risk and needs profiles, more recidivism and crime is likely.[84] Without reasonably precise estimates of the impacts of these decisions, as well as the range of policies and programs that populate the criminal justice landscape, credible efficiency estimates will remain ephemeral.

One bright spot is the fact that economic analyses have begun to filter into more criminal justice research and policy evaluation.[85] Another is that policy evaluation appears likely to become more frequent and rigorous given the sustained calls for increased government accountability and evidence-based practice. Any such trend likely bodes well for the frequency and quality of efficiency evaluations.

Still another bright spot exists – a few rigorous efficiency evaluations suggest that some criminal justice policies are in fact cost efficient. Steve Aos and his colleagues, for example, have conducted some of the most comprehensive criminal justice efficiency analyses to date. For each of a range of policies, they created per-participant "net present values of the long-run benefits of crime reduction minus the net up-front costs."[86] They found that, from crime victim and taxpayer perspectives, the net present values of many policies were positive.[87] To illustrate, consider the per-participant net present values – in parentheses and 2006 dollars – of the following evidence-based, adult-focused policies that they identified: vocational education in prison ($13,738); intensive supervision, treatment-oriented programs ($11,563); general education programs in prison ($10,669); cognitive-behavioral therapy in the prison or community ($10,299); drug treatment in the community ($10,054); correctional industries in prison ($9,439); drug treatment in prison ($7,835); adult drug courts ($4,767); employment and job training in the community ($4,359); and electronic monitoring to offset jail time ($870).[88]

The net benefits for youth-focused interventions were, in many cases, greater. Policies with positive net values included: multidimensional treatment foster care ($77,798), diversion for low-risk offenders ($40,623), family integrated transitions ($40,545), functional family therapy for youths on probation ($31,821), multisystemic therapy ($18,213), aggression-management training ($14,660), teen courts ($9,208), juvenile boot camps ($8,077), juvenile sex offender treatment ($7,829), restorative justice for low-risk offenders ($7,067), interagency coordination programs ($5,186), and juvenile drug courts ($4,622).[89]

These estimates hinge heavily on assumptions Aos and his colleagues made about the estimated impacts of the different policies. Although they employed a rigorous set of criteria for identifying well-evaluated policies and for estimating impacts, other scholars might disagree about some of the analyses and assumptions. Estimates of incarceration costs and benefits are, for example, heavily contested.[90] In addition, estimated impacts stemmed in some cases from only a few studies, and the efficiencies of many policies could not be evaluated because too few or no credible impact studies existed. Regardless, the approach taken by Aos, and the fact that they conducted the efficiency analyses at the behest of the Washington State Legislature, illustrates both that cost-efficiency analyses can feasibly be undertaken in criminal justice and that they can be used to inform policy debates and discussions.

Finally, an important bright spot involves estimates of the costs of crime. Cohen and his colleagues, as well as other scholars, have devised increasingly sophisticated approaches to identifying the costs of crime to society. By one account, the "present value of saving a fourteen-year-old, high-risk juvenile from a life of crime [ranges] from $2.6 to $5.3 million."[91] Such information can be used to anchor efforts to provide realistic and defensible estimates of savings stemming from different criminal justice policies. At the same time, meta-analyses increasingly have provided more credible estimates of impacts that may be safely assumed for a variety of well-implemented policies.[92]

Such efforts hold the potential for increasing the use of efficiency evaluations to inform policy debates and decisions. Among other things, they can be used to explore the assumptions underlying current policies. For example, for more than one hundred years, U.S. taxpayers have funded the operation of an entirely separate system of justice for juveniles, an administrative encumbrance justified by the logic that the benefits necessarily offset the costs. A cost-efficiency analysis could be used to identify the implicit assumptions about the greater improvements that youth face when processed under this system of justice.[93] Such assumptions could be juxtaposed against the best available evidence concerning adult and juvenile justice system policies and interventions. Clearly, an efficiency evaluation alone would not determine the fate of the juvenile justice system. Just as clearly, however, it could be used to clarify precisely what we expect in the form of returns from this system.

Conclusion

Cost-efficiency evaluations constitute the final step in the evaluation hierarchy and enable us to assess the returns on criminal justice policy investments. Two types of such evaluations exist. Cost-effectiveness analyses identify policy costs and the outcomes that they produce. They are useful primarily when comparing two or more policies that share the same goals. Cost-benefit analyses identify policy costs and the benefits, expressed in monetary terms. They are useful for comparing two or more policies that have different or nonoverlapping goals. Efficiency evaluations can highlight whether a policy's impact justifies the expense required to produce it. More generally, they can inform and complement deliberations about whether policies should be implemented, continued, expanded, or terminated.

Few efficiency evaluations occur in criminal justice, in part because economic analysis has not featured prominently in the training of criminologists and criminal justice scholars.[94] Regardless, the end result consists of a situation in which the vast bulk of criminal justice policies proceed based on hunches and assumptions about both the costs and the benefits of these policies. Such a situation clearly runs counter to the recent calls for increased government accountability and effectiveness. Fortunately, it may well change in coming years because of this trend and because of the increased infusion of economic analyses into criminological research.

The basic steps in efficiency evaluations are straightforward, although each step can entail considerable complexity. The steps include (1) clearly stating the policy question; (2) determining the perspective of analysis, (3) identifying all relevant costs and benefits; (4) assigning monetary values to the costs and benefits; (5) contrasting the total costs and benefits; and (6) conducting sensitivity analyses to determine the consistency of the results under different sets of assumptions and, in this same vein, articulating any and all relevant limitations that may affect the credibility or interpretation of the results.

A number of limitations may undermine the credibility of efficiency evaluations. For example, they may proceed based on estimated impacts that themselves lack credibility. The case studies of community policing and private prisons, as well as the other examples discussed in the chapter, illustrate the pervasiveness of this particular problem. The limited information about the impacts of various criminal justice policies – including the magnitude of the impacts and how much they can be expected to emerge in a

diverse set of contexts – severely hamstrings the validity of efficiency estimates. Other limitations, such as the challenge of monetizing certain outcomes (e.g., rapes, murders, fear of crime, satisfaction with law enforcement
performance), exist as well.

Even so, it bears emphasizing that society implicitly conducts an efficiency
evaluation every time it invests in a policy. The sole difference is that no
empirical analyses inform the implicit evaluation and the limitations remain
obscure. Society arguably is better off with explicit rather than implicit
analyses. Why? When we fail to identify the assumptions on which our
decisions rest, we risk selecting policies that rest on highly questionable
or incorrect assumptions. When we identify these assumptions, we have
a better chance of flagging those that lack merit and in turn create the
opportunity for selecting a policy that we can better trust will provide the returns we hope for and expect. Such improvements are critical given the
stakes involved (e.g., crime, victimization, injustice) and the scarce resources
with which the criminal justice system works.

Criminal justice policies and the debates about them are influenced by
many factors. Efficiency evaluations constitute but one of them. Nonetheless, they can provide critical information to improve the quality of deliberations about a diverse range of criminal justice policies. However, for
them to be useful and to be used appropriately, it is critical that we be
aware of their conceptual underpinnings and their limitations. Even the
best efficiency evaluations, for example, require judgment calls about such
issues as the appropriate perspective of analysis, which outcomes should be
weighed more heavily, and the extent to which estimated policy impacts can
be trusted.

Discussion Questions

What are the benefits of evaluating the cost efficiency of a criminal justice
policy? What are the problems of not evaluating policy cost efficiency?

What is the difference between a cost-effectiveness analysis and a cost-
benefit analysis? When do you use one versus the other?

How do you conduct a cost-benefit analysis?

What are the main challenges in conducting cost-efficiency evaluations of
criminal justice policies?

Because it is not possible to conduct cost-efficiency evaluations of every
criminal justice policy, what criteria should we use for selecting policies
that we will evaluate?

Given that policy makers and the public frequently seem to place a high premium on the idea of getting the most "bang for the buck," why are cost-efficiency evaluations of criminal justice policies so rare?

What steps can be taken to increase the number and quality of cost-efficiency evaluations of criminal justice policies?

9

Conclusion

I CONCLUDE THIS BOOK ON WHAT I BELIEVE IS AN OPTIMISTIC NOTE. AS THE preceding chapters suggest, there is much cause for concern about the lack of accountability in criminal justice, as reflected in the absence of any systematic empirical monitoring of even the most prominent policies. We also should be concerned about the lack of effective or efficient policies in criminal justice or, more precisely, the lack of evidence that existing policies are effective or efficient. That said, many opportunities exist for dramatically improving the situation at relatively little cost. In this chapter, I briefly restate the argument that more and better evaluation research is needed. I then describe a number of opportunities and strategies both for increasing the quantity and quality of criminal justice evaluation research and for integrating such research into policy making and everyday practice.

The Need for More and Better Criminal Justice Evaluation Research

As noted at the outset in Chapter 1, this book was written with several goals in mind. The first was to describe what an evaluation research approach is and how it can be used to inform criminal justice policy, including various laws, programs, rules, protocols, and practices that make up the criminal justice system. This goal was motivated by the observation that policy makers, criminal justice administrators and practitioners, and even researchers frequently do not know what evaluation research is or, by extension, that different types of evaluation can be conducted. It also was motivated by the fact that the essentials of an evaluation research approach can be learned or at least appreciated without having a background in research or statistics. It was motivated, too, by the observation that in an era of heightened attention to government accountability and evidence-based practice, few students or

TABLE 9.1. Prominent American criminal justice policies as viewed through an evaluation research framework

Question	State of evidence
Are the policies needed?	Minimal
Do they rest on sound theory and design?	Minimal
Are they typically implemented in a consistent and appropriate manner?	Minimal
Are they associated with and do they produce their intended impacts on intended outcomes?	Minimal
Are they cost efficient?	Minimal

scholars are formally introduced to evaluation research. Not least, it was motivated by the belief that an understanding of evaluation research can assist criminal justice policy makers, administrators, and practitioners to be better requesters and consumers of policy research and to appreciate the benefits of such research. In so doing, they can help facilitate efforts to overcome or mitigate some of the barriers, described in Chapter 2, to accountability and research-based policies.

The second goal was to argue that many of the most prominent policies on the criminal justice landscape rest on an unstable or weak research foundation, even though we now live in an era in which increasingly greater emphasis has been given to the importance of government accountability, evidence-based practice, effectiveness, and efficiency. This argument was presented through a series of chapters, each of which focused on a different type of evaluation – needs, theory, implementation/process, outcome and impact, and cost efficiency – and provided case studies that illustrated the application of these types of evaluation to prominent criminal justice policies.

To convey how bleak the situation seems to be, Table 9.1 presents what I believe a fair summary is of the state of evidence for many of these policies, as viewed through an evaluation research framework. Briefly, there appears to be minimal evidence that the policies are needed, that they rest on sound theory or design, that they are implemented in a consistent or appropriate manner, that they achieve their intended goals (i.e., impacts), or that they are cost efficient.

Chris Eskridge has observed that, "by and large, the crime prevention programs that we utilize in the United States have not been systematically evaluated."[1] Much the same can be said about almost every aspect of the criminal justice system and the efforts not only to reduce crime but also to achieve justice for the accused, victims, communities, and society at large.[2] Exceptions certainly exist. However, by and large, as the case studies and various illustrations indicate, there remains a dismaying paucity of evidence of accountability or effective policy or practice.[3] Indeed, at a more general level, we have little information about the quality of the day-to-day decisions made by the various actors throughout the criminal justice system. Their decisions, as well as any errors in judgment that they make, occur largely within a "black box."[4]

The third goal was to argue that evaluation research should be increased, improved, and integrated into criminal justice policy making and practice. Clearly, as discussed earlier, evaluation research constitutes but one platform of any strategy to improve criminal justice policy.[5] In addition, as Peter Rossi has observed, "Even at its best, applied social research does not substitute for the political process."[6] Without such research, however, we can say little that is meaningful about whether local, state, or federal governments have targeted the most pressing problems, whether they have done so using the best theory and empirical studies, whether they have implemented policies appropriately, whether the policies are effective, and whether particular policies achieve their goals in the most efficient, least costly manner. In short, without more and better evaluation research, we cannot easily hold government accountable or successfully create, identify, or implement effective and efficient criminal justice policies. Fortunately, many steps can be taken to greatly improve the research foundation of the criminal justice system.

Using Evaluation Research to Improve Criminal Justice Policy

If we accept the premises that (1) more and better evaluation research should exist and (2) it should inform policy-making efforts and the programs and everyday practices that collectively comprise the criminal justice system, the question arises, How do we improve the current situation? Table 9.2 outlines a number of strategies that can be taken. In each instance, these strategies, culled from recommendations found in many scholarly accounts, can be viewed as largely untapped opportunities, ones where even modest advances may produce large improvements.

Educate and Train Students and Researchers in Evaluation Research

Education and training in evaluation research are critical elements of any effort to increase the amount and quality of such research in criminal justice.

TABLE 9.2. Strategies for increasing and improving the evaluation research foundation of criminal justice policy

- Educate and Train Students and Researchers in Evaluation Research
- Promote Applied Research in University Settings
- Integrate Applied and Basic Research Efforts
- Create Ties among Researcher, Policy Maker, and Practitioner Communities
- Require Use of the Evaluation Hierarchy in Developing and Assessing Policy
  - Require Needs, Theory, and Implementation Evaluations of Policies
  - Conduct Impact Evaluations Strategically
  - Conduct Break-Even Cost-Efficiency Evaluations to Assess Sensitivity
- Institutionalize Evaluation Research into Criminal Justice System Operations
- Create Independent Criminal Justice Research Agencies
- Develop a "Bank" of Knowledge about Effective and Ineffective Policies

Indeed, it is difficult to imagine how substantial improvements can occur without creating a cadre of people who know about and can undertake different types of evaluation while taking into account the unique research contexts and challenges in criminal justice.

Two groups constitute obvious targets for education and training in evaluation research: (1) undergraduate and graduate students and (2) researchers. Many students, including those in prominent universities, as well as students in what many consider to be the higher-tier criminology and criminal justice programs, receive little by way of an introduction to evaluation research.[7] For example, few programs offer a course on policy research. The bar thus is quite low for increasing the number of students who understand such research.

To be certain, many programs require that students take introductory research methods or statistics courses. However, such courses typically provide, at best, a little insight into how one might evaluate policies. It is analogous to taking a course on how to bake a cake. You might learn about a select set of ingredients, the importance of sequencing the mixing of ingredients, and how long to bake the cake and at what temperature. However, you would learn little about how to make healthy meals, much less how to make healthy meals that address the needs and preferences of different individuals, to make meals for different-sized groups, or to create meals within varying budget and time constraints. Stated more directly, effective evaluation research requires more than knowing about specific methods; it requires knowledge of different types of evaluation and of how to adjust research methodologies to fit the specific needs of diverse stakeholders within what frequently are highly restrictive time and budget constraints.

One recommendation, therefore, is that universities and colleges emphasize evaluation research. Such a focus would directly respond to national, state, and local calls for more accountability across diverse social policy sectors. A related recommendation is that criminology and criminal justice programs offer courses specifically focused on introducing students to a wide array of policies and to different ways of evaluating such policies. No single best way exists for structuring such courses. However, the main ingredients would likely consist of reading about different policies and evaluation approaches and taking part in exercises aimed at helping local criminal justice agencies with particular policy questions. This training ideally would include a focus on how to effectively communicate research results to policy makers and practitioner communities.[8] Examples of such courses exist, especially in public policy programs, but at present are not offered on a regular basis by many criminology and criminal justice programs across the country.[9]

Another recommendation is that criminal justice researchers be provided formal training in evaluation research. It may seem odd to suggest that researchers should be trained in evaluation research. Yet, as was emphasized earlier, many researchers – regardless of whether they work in universities or colleges, research organizations, or criminal justice system agencies – lack a familiarity with the specific types of evaluation that exist and the unique considerations and constraints associated with such evaluations. Clearly, many criminal justice researchers have considerable experience, much of it learned on the job, and so may not need such training. Even so, they might well benefit from policy evaluation courses. Researchers in these settings typically will not have the time to take an entire course at, say, a local university or college. In this case, they might instead take intensive one- or two-week courses. Few places offer such courses, but they might do so if the demand were sufficient and if, as discussed later, universities promoted applied research.

Promote Applied Research in University Settings

Historically, university faculty members, especially those in the social sciences, who have engaged in applied research – that is, in the evaluation of social policies – have been less likely to be tenured or promoted or to receive the prestige of their counterparts who have focused on more theoretically focused pursuits, such as investigating the causes of crime.[10] A practical response to such a situation is of course to shy away from applied research. However, the deprioritization of applied research creates multiple problems. It drives some of the people best situated to create and undertake complicated and sophisticated research designs away from tackling the difficult challenge of assessing important social policy issues. It results in students receiving little formal education or training in evaluation research. It contributes to a situation in which many policies go unevaluated. And it results in missed opportunities to examine important theoretical questions. To illustrate, studies of prisoner reentry programs hold the potential not only to shed light on whether such programs effectively reduce recidivism but also to create insights into the causes of desistance from crime, a topic of central prominence in criminology.[11] Similarly, studies of supermax prisons can contribute to efforts to understand how social order is maintained.[12]

Today, many universities, and certainly many criminology and criminal justice programs, place a greater value on policy research than they have in the past.[13] Nonetheless, it remains the case that such research stands at the periphery of many programs, as reflected in part by the lack of course offerings on policy evaluation, administration, or planning. In addition, the journals considered to be the most prestigious in criminology – and thus that typically are most relevant to tenure and promotion decisions – do not prioritize policy evaluation. As but one illustration, in his 1997 presidential address to the American Society of Criminology, Charles Wellford observed that from 1986–1996, fewer than 5 percent of all studies published in *Criminology*, the highest-ranked journal in the field of criminology, focused on the topic of justice.[14] Of course, the percentage would assuredly have been higher if Wellford had included studies that focused on recidivism or, say, assessments of community policing programs. The point, however, is that a critical policy issue, justice, has gone largely unexamined in at least one of the highest-ranked criminology journals and, more broadly, that theory-related questions rather than policy-related ones tend to be prioritized by such journals. To be sure, the prominence of such journals as *Criminology and Public Policy*, published by the American Society of Criminology, and *Crime and Delinquency*, which focus almost exclusively on policy-related questions, helps to offset that situation. Even so, they enjoy less prestige than higher-tier journals. That in turn affects whether scholars pursue publication in them.[15]

A central implication of such observations is that applied research should be made a priority in university settings. Many strategies can be pursued for doing so. For example, centers or institutes can be established that are charged with training students and faculty in policy research, in securing external funding for policy evaluations, and in developing ties with criminal justice policy makers, administrators, and practitioners.[16] Also, the infrastructure for competing with nonacademic research organizations could be improved. Doing so would enable university researchers to respond more easily in a timely and effective manner to calls for evaluations and also to be able to undertake complicated research tasks, ones that frequently involve the collection of data across multiple sites over many years.[17] Tenure and promotion criteria could involve explicit weighting schemes that reward policy evaluation research. Universities, and the colleges, schools, and departments within them, could advertise the fact that many of their graduates find work in nonacademic research settings.[18] More generally, the mission of universities could be revised to make service to the community – at local, state, and national levels – a priority, not only through educating students but also through facilitating efforts to provide empirical assessments of critical policies, programs, and practices and to make presentations to policy makers and practitioners.[19] Such a shift could be paralleled by changes in professional organizations as well. Joan Petersilia, for example, has advocated that the American Society of Criminology work to help tailor "the academic model to accommodate the mission of criminal justice research" and to define its "research mission to include assistance in the field."[20]

Universities face some risks by focusing on applied research. For example, such research typically requires that one focus on the questions that most matter to policy makers and practitioners or on the hot button issues of the day. The attendant risk, then, is that research becomes politicized, with scholars essentially serving to promote, directly or indirectly, political agendas.[21] In addition, scholars may fail to focus on important questions relevant to understanding crime causation and to reducing crime. For example, in the 1970s, much research attention focused on the impacts of punishment, driven in no small part by federal funding priorities. Arguably, this emphasis resulted in too-little investment in research on alternative strategies for reducing crime.[22] To illustrate, consider that well into the 1990s, relatively little research systematically examined the range of factors that can impede or facilitate the successful reentry of people released from prison.[23] Such concerns notwithstanding, it bears emphasizing that researchers in university settings enjoy considerable leeway to pursue a variety of research topics and to do so in ways that reflect consciously or unconsciously held ideological beliefs.[24] The solution for the universities, then, would not seem to lie with divorcing applied research and basic research from one another, but rather achieving an effective balance between the two.

Integrate Applied and Basic Research Efforts

These observations lead to another recommendation – applied and basic research efforts should be integrated where possible. Multiple benefits can result from such integration. First, a large body of evaluation research points to the notion that the most effective policies tend to be those with strong theoretical foundations.[25] The involvement of theoreticians in evaluation research thus could help increase the chances of research increasing the effectiveness of policies. For example, they might identify certain activities or causal linkages critical to reducing crime and in turn highlight policy dimensions that should be enhanced or increased. Such steps would be especially useful during the formative stages of policy development and implementation. That said, their involvement in impact evaluations could be useful as well by helping to identify factors that could undermine policy effectiveness.

Second, many insights now considered to have stemmed from basic research in fact emerged from applied research endeavors. Thus, the inter-action of applied and basic researchers holds the potential for substan-tially advancing knowledge about basic research questions.[26] As Rossi once observed about past presidents of the American Sociological Association: "Many [Association] Presidents are not generally remembered as applied social researchers because, over time some of their most important applied research has been redefined as basic research."[27] Extending this observation, he noted that the boundary between basic and applied research is frequently not very clear. Why? Basic and applied research efforts may morph from one emphasis (i.e., basic or applied) into another or indirectly influence one another.[28] To illustrate, "some contributions of applied work (such as the concept of personal influence and opinion leadership) are directly and eas-ily traceable to the applied work from which they originated. Others, like the concept of relative deprivation, are indirect contributions arising out of commentaries upon or secondary analyses of applied work."[29] Such exam-ples apply as well to criminology as they do to sociology. As one case in point – relative deprivation is a concept central to social disorganization and strain theories.[30]

In short, a focus on applied research can increase the amount and quality of basic research and can do so in direct and indirect ways. As but one additional example, consider that much basic research increasingly involves a reliance on secondary data sets. That is, scholars increasingly use data that have been collected for other purposes to test their ideas. The problem lies in the fact that the data frequently may not provide the best measures for testing particular theories.[31] The obvious solution is to collect better data, but doing so can be costly and time consuming. As a result, many university researchers may shy away from such efforts and thus investigate topics that may be less important or more tangential to tests of prominent theories. Involvement in evaluation research, however, could provide unique opportunities to create data more directly relevant to testing these theories. Studies of prisoner reentry programs constitute a case in point. Many such studies aim to assess the impact of the programs on recidivism and, to this end, collect new data based on interviews with program participants and comparison group subjects. Here, one might cost-effectively include survey questions that could inform the evaluation and concomitantly serve to test competing theoretical arguments about the causes of desistance from crime.

A related example involves risk prediction instruments, created for the purpose of identifying which convicted offenders pose the great risk to society in terms of the likelihood of committing new crimes. Many such instruments exist, yet frequently they lack any reference to factors central to many mainstream criminological theories.[32] Even so, they serve a critical role in the criminal justice system and garner considerable attention. For that reason, development and refinement of them will likely continue for many years to come. Any such efforts likely would benefit from the involvement of criminological theorists and, at the same time, would offer many opportunities for developing new data and, in turn, testing and refining crime theories.

Create Ties among Researcher, Policy Maker, and Practitioner Communities

A critical step toward enhancing the previously mentioned efforts and, in so doing, increasing criminal justice evaluation research, is to create stronger ties between the research community and policy maker and practitioner communities.[33] As it now stands, such ties frequently are weak to nonexistent. Where they exist, they typically result from the efforts of senior researchers – whether in academic or in nonacademic settings. Even then, the ties too often result from chance meetings or circumstances.

Stronger ties would create many benefits. Academic researchers would have greater access to unique sources of data and thus opportunities for testing and refining theories. Students in turn would likely obtain more hands-on experiences in conducting such research. Practitioners would receive much-needed assistance in evaluating their efforts and might well receive such assistance free or at low cost. In addition, policy makers and criminal justice administrators would be provided more empirical evidence about various policies. That would position them better to debate the merits of the policies, how to improve them, and whether to discard them in favor of some alternative approach.

Established ties would also serve as a check against shoddy research or "gotcha!" studies that aim primarily to show that an agency or program has failed miserably. Such studies contribute to unwillingness among criminal justice agencies and programs to participate in research. To be clear, researchers should not shy from presenting negative findings. However, a productive evaluation research endeavor is one where such groups know at the outset that negative findings may arise and will be presented. And it also is one where researchers strive to provide a balanced presentation of the findings, regardless of whether they think a particular policy is good or bad. By forging strong collaborative ties, the researcher and policy maker and practitioner communities can help to avoid such circumstances, while the involvement of multiple research groups or independent consultants has the potential to help prevent unconscious ideological biases from unduly biasing research designs or the presentation of findings.[34]

Another benefit of stronger ties between the researcher and policy-making and practitioner communities would be increased mutual appreciation by these groups of, on the one hand, the nuances of research and, on the other hand, the challenges and contexts of policy development and implementation. For example, researchers might become more attuned to the need to present findings in simpler, more accessible ways, and to produce findings quickly.[35] They also might be less likely to dismiss practitioner views as biased or irrelevant and be more likely to gain insights into policy that otherwise would be difficult if not impossible to generate. As Carol Weiss and her colleagues have noted, "The professional judgment of the people on the scene is influenced not only by self-interest and constrained values; it also is grounded in practical wisdom and tacit knowledge. They know the local history, the people involved, the interpretations that participants provide, and all the other experiences that frame a given program."[36] For their part, policy makers and criminal justice administrators might become more sophisticated and realistic in their requests for research and also develop a greater awareness of study limitations and how to interpret research findings.

Many strategies exist for promoting stronger ties between researchers and policy maker and practitioner communities. Professional organizations, such as the American Society of Criminology and the Academy of Criminal Justice Sciences, could take the lead in promoting such ties. They could, for example, encourage members to support these types of efforts, create committees tasked with developing guidelines or how-to manuals for the research community to use in the field, make presentations to state and federal legislatures on a regular basis, include evaluation research trainings as part of their annual meetings, and prod universities to recognize applied research as a critical component of tenure and promotion decisions.[37] Some movement in that direction has already occurred. For example, Todd Clear, who served as a president of both of the aforementioned professional associations, has advocated that these organizations take the lead in educating and training policy makers about the importance of seeking diverse scientific opinions about crime and justice policies.[38] Similarly, Petersilia has advocated that the American Society of Criminology take steps to make "policy makers (including funders) and practitioners confident that [criminological] research is relevant and responsive to their needs – without compromising the higher objectives of research."[39]

Other strategies exist as well. Policy makers could require that researchers weigh in on any legislation that would have a large financial impact or that was being considered for widespread implementation.[40] At a national level, the federal government can play a prominent role in promoting evaluation research and in fostering ties between the research and policy maker and practitioner communities.[41] Criminal justice agencies also could forge ties with local universities and research organizations to raise awareness about the data possibilities, the research opportunities, agency resources and needs, and the constraints under which the agencies operate. In short, the development of these ties can be pursued by multiple groups using different strategies.

Require Use of the Evaluation Hierarchy in Developing and Assessing Policy

A potentially more contentious recommendation for increasing the amount and quality of criminal justice evaluation research is to require that the evaluation hierarchy be used in the development and assessment of policy as well as in deciding whether a given policy should be retained, modified, expanded, or eliminated. Some examples of this approach have been implemented in several states, including Indiana, Oklahoma, Oregon, and Washington, but the implementation is partial and does not include the full evaluation hierarchy.[42] I argue that (1) needs, theory, and process evaluations should be conducted for policies that consume, or may obligate, a large amount of resources or funds; (2) impact evaluations should be conducted strategically, with a focus primarily on efforts where the gain in knowledge will be substantial; and (3) cost-efficiency sensitivity analyses should be conducted on policies that may entail considerable costs.

REQUIRE NEEDS, THEORY, AND IMPLEMENTATION EVALUATIONS OF POLICIES. The argument for requiring needs, theory, and implementation evaluations of criminal justice policies – especially those that entail large costs – is straightforward: anything less will almost invariably result in a substantial waste of resources.[43] Policies that are not needed may be implemented; policies that lack any coherent theoretical foundation, much less one supported by empirical research, may be adopted; and needed and theoretically grounded policies may be poorly implemented.

Requiring needs, theory, and process evaluations would, of course, entail costs, but the costs need not necessarily be exorbitant. For example, state, county, or city criminal justice agencies might conduct annual crime surveys at relatively low expense to obtain independent and generally more valid assessments of crime and thus the need for a response of some type. They also could survey employees to identify areas of operations that merit attention. To illustrate, a survey of prison employees might reveal that certain types of inmate disturbances or management practices have adversely affected staff or inmate morale.[44] Similarly, a survey of criminal court administrators might identify case-flow disruptions and strategies for increasing case processing.

One way to ensure that such evaluations occur is for state legislatures or local governmental authorities to require that criminal justice system agencies allocate, say, 5 percent of agency or policy funds for research. In addition, they could require that needs and theory evaluations precede the funding of any new crime initiatives and that implementation evaluations be part of any initiatives that receive funding. Doing so would substantially increase the ability of agencies and policy makers to target the most important needs, to do so using policies that have the greatest likelihood of success, and to monitor implementation to ensure the greatest possible impact. Such funding would constitute a dramatic increase in typical research allocations, but it has the potential to help avoid adoption of unnecessary, costly, and ineffective policies.

It bears emphasizing that needs and theory evaluations alone have the potential to help criminal justice systems avoid expending resources on questionable investments. Consider that a single supermax might cost $1 billion to build and operate over a thirty-year period of time and that four-fifths of states now have at least one.[45] Their widespread adoption has occurred despite questions about the need for them and a theoretical foundation premised on questionable assumptions.[46] Prior to building a supermax, expending, say, $1 million for a needs evaluation would be trivial compared to the resources saved if it turned out that an insufficient need for a supermax existed, that their theoretical foundation was weak, or that cheaper alternatives existed.

Similarly, implementation evaluations are critical – especially because impact evaluations frequently are not possible – and should be integrated into policies in a manner similar to the standards of medical practice. That is, policies should be monitored to ensure that they are applied at appropriate times for appropriate populations and in an appropriate manner.[47] Systems-level monitoring also is needed to identify redundancies, inefficiencies, and possible areas where improvements could be made.[48] Such activities should be ongoing parts of criminal justice systems and policies, not one-time events.

CONDUCT IMPACT EVALUATIONS STRATEGICALLY. Although impact evaluations cannot realistically be conducted on all criminal justice policies, they should be pursued when and where possible, especially for policies that have the greatest likelihood of generating large-scale benefits.[49] As Mark Lipsey and his colleagues have emphasized, "Resources should be directed mainly toward evaluations with the greatest potential for practical and policy significance from expected evaluation results and for which the program circumstances are amenable to productive research."[50]

Efforts should also be made to ensure that researchers evaluate a range of policies, including not only those that target individuals but also those that attempt to improve and affect entire communities, justice system operations, or state crime rates. David Farrington has argued that "a new research agenda of experiments should be developed, designed to advance knowledge about the causes of offending as well as to test the effectiveness of intervention technologies in different neighborhoods and countries."[51] An extension of that argument is to suggest that experiments be targeted at the nuts and bolts of criminal justice system operations as well. These experiments might investigate such questions as which types of law enforcement training generate better street-level decision making by officers, which types of assessment instruments generate better decision making among court personnel, and which types of prison management styles produce greater order and safety.[52]

Although experiments have many advantages, they also suffer from many limitations and they vary greatly in their rigor.[53] They thus are no panacea. In addition, and as James Heckman and Jeffrey Smith have emphasized, much can be learned from well-conducted nonexperimental research.[54] The implication? Because of their costs, experimental designs should be reserved for policies where the most gain can be had, and quasi-experimental designs should be used, where possible, in all other cases.

Finally, it bears emphasizing that outcome, and especially impact, evaluations should be coupled with implementation evaluations to identify the policy features that produce the outcomes.[55] Consider a well-designed experiment of a program that provides many different types of services. Drug courts, for example, consist of such activities as rapid processing of cases, more interactions between offenders and judges, drug treatment, assistance with finding employment and housing and any other needed services, as well as higher levels of supervision.[56] An impact evaluation might show that the court reduces recidivism.[57] However, we would not know what caused the effect. Was it, for example, all of the services or some combination of them? Such questions are critical because offering services that are not helpful ultimately wastes resources. In addition, components of a program that seem to contribute the most to producing some impact could be increased to create even larger impacts. At a minimum, we would want to prioritize quality implementation of these components over others.

CONDUCT BREAK-EVEN COST-EFFICIENCY EVALUATIONS TO ASSESS SENSITIVITY. Cost-efficiency analyses rarely are conducted in criminal justice, and when undertaken they frequently fail to include critical dimensions. For example, a cost-efficiency analysis might focus only on recidivism impacts and fail to include mention of positive impacts along other dimensions or any of a range of unintended negative impacts. Such an analysis would produce interesting results, but they likely would be substantially biased. Ideally, then, cost-efficiency evaluations would be conducted on policies that have any potential for incurring substantial costs and they would measure and monetize all policy impacts.[58]

That said, given their costs, such analyses generally will have to be pursued, as with impact evaluations, on a selective basis. For policies of any substantial cost, however, break-even analyses should be undertaken at the outset – ideally, prior to implementation – to identify precisely how much impact is required for the benefits to at least equal the costs. In many instances, this exercise may reveal that the needed impact well exceeds what can be realistically expected.[59] For example, a preliminary cost-efficiency evaluation of a supermax prison might highlight that an unrealistically large reduction in systemwide prison order and violence would have to be achieved before the benefits would equal the costs.[60]

Institutionalize Evaluation Research into Criminal Justice System Operations

A variant on the earlier recommendation is to require that criminal justice systems institutionalize evaluation research as a core activity.[61] At present, research units within criminal justice systems typically are staffed by few people and have enormous responsibility for producing descriptive reports about different dimensions of system operations. They generally do not have the time, ability, or resources to evaluate many of the major policies, programs, or practices within their particular agency. A clear alternative exists. Specifically, agencies could be charged with expanding their research divisions and making evaluation research, especially empirically based monitoring of core activities and services, a priority.

This point, echoed throughout this book, merits emphasis: many criminal justice systems do not measure relevant dimensions of performance or outcomes.[62] In turn, they cannot provide ongoing monitoring of such dimensions. As a result, they also cannot support scholarly investigations into the causes of such outcomes as specific police actions, court decisions, or inmate behavior. The lack of institutionalized monitoring constitutes a particular problem in contexts where high-quality, efficient, and effective operations cannot be safely assumed or where reasonable concerns about the possibility of abuses and danger exist. That would certainly seem to characterize many law enforcement agencies and prison systems, which typically manage dangerous people and rely on staff who operate under considerable stress.

As but one prominent example of the lack of performance monitoring in criminal justice, consider prison systems nationally. Most cannot tell us much about their compliance with standards; how they treat their inmates; or the amount, level, or quality of services and programs that inmates receive.[63] Inattention to monitoring these dimensions does not stem from a lack of guidance. Such dimensions of performance have long been identified by researchers. For example, in 1981, Martha Burt discussed a range of performance dimensions of prisons, including security (e.g., escape rates), living and safety conditions (e.g., victimization, prison atmosphere, overcrowding, sanitation), inmate physical and mental health; program and services impacts (e.g., improvements in basic skills, education, vocational training), and postrelease success (e.g., recidivism, employment).[64] Similarly, and as detailed in Chapter 6, Charles Logan has identified eight dimensions that warrant monitoring: security, safety, order, care, inmate activity, justice, conditions, and management. Both authors provided explicit lists of specific measures that could be used to operationalize each dimension as well as methodologies for generating the data necessary for measurement.[65]

More recently, the American Correctional Association has promoted performance-based standards, which serve to extend the association's long-standing focus on accrediting only those correctional systems that meet a range of standards related to such dimensions as staff training, food service, rules and discipline, and administrative and fiscal controls. The performance-based standards, in conjunction with the accreditation standards are, as Gerald Gaes and his colleagues have emphasized, "very important to the development of prison performance measurement ... and may pave the way for an eventual national system of prison performance."[66] They have, however, yet to be institutionalized on a widespread basis. In addition, accreditation, while providing an important marker of system performance, does not itself require regularly collecting data on or monitoring many of the dimensions of performance detailed by Burt, Logan, and Gaes, or of factors researchers have identified as contributing to violence and order.[67]

The institutionalization of evaluation research as a core activity of criminal justice agency functions would go a long way toward offsetting these problems.[68] At the same time, it would facilitate the development of more appropriate measures of performance. As things stand, the available data frequently do not include relevant information for assessing agency performance. In such contexts, researchers fall back on using the data that exist, even if that means relying on measures that really do not provide an accurate reflection of performance. Unfortunately, the best evaluation methodologies and the best statistical techniques gain us nothing if they involve data of questionable reliability, validity, or relevance.

The institutionalization of research as a core activity could also facilitate efforts to implement the evaluation hierarchy. For example, if prison systems monitored true levels of assaults and violence, they would be better able to show empirically why supermax prisons are needed (or not), whether changes in these levels are attributable to a few "bad apple" inmates or to different management strategies across prison facilities, and whether levels of violence decline after using supermax housing.[69] Clearly, funding limitations limit what local and state criminal justice systems can undertake.[70] Even so, considerable advances could be made with even nominal increases in research funding.

A final observation – each part of the criminal justice system (e.g., law enforcement, the courts, prisons, probation, and parole) operates according to goals and activities specific to their responsibilities. Ultimately, of course, one common goal is to reduce crime and recidivism. These outcomes, however, hardly exhaust the different mandates of each part of the system. Prisons, for example, emphasize the safety of inmates and staff, the humane treatment of inmates, victim rights, and meaningful work opportunities as distinct and important goals.[71] In addition, police departments and the courts have a variety of additional emphases (e.g., prompt and courteous responses to citizen calls, timely processing of cases, delivery of "just" decisions).[72] For these reasons, evaluation research ideally should be institutionalized in a way that leads to the targeting of different components of the criminal justice system to ensure that all relevant dimensions of performance are examined.

Create Independent Criminal Justice Research Agencies

One strategy for increasing the amount and quality of evaluation research and for creating stronger links between researcher and policy-maker and practitioner communities is for states to establish criminal justice policy councils that serve both a research and policy deliberation function. Such councils should be autonomous, to the extent possible, and charged with conducting research and bringing together scholars, practitioners, and policy makers together to discuss crime problems, proposed or existing solutions, and the research that should be undertaken. Although full autonomy is likely impossible, examples of such organizational arrangements exist (e.g., the U.S. Government Accountability Office and the now-disbanded Texas Criminal Justice Policy Council). The virtue of such organizational arrangements lies in the fact that they would have as their explicit focus the development of applied research and that they might, if well run, be less vulnerable to partisan politics dictating the scope or content of the research.[73]

A related approach is to develop, as Alfred Blumstein has advocated, "forums that will be more closely allied with the policy process, such as sentencing commissions or presidential commissions."[74] These types of entities, which such national organizations as the American Society of Criminology or the Academy of Criminal Justice Sciences might spearhead, have the potential to ensure that research informs the development, implementation, and evaluation of policy. Still another option, one advocated by Francis Cullen, is the development of institutes or centers, possibly within universities, "devoted to the dissemination of research knowledge in an accessible form."[75]

Another possibility, promoted by Lawrence Sherman, involves creating "Centers for Crime Prevention" in the largest cities or metropolitan areas in every state.[76] In Sherman's view, "[E]ach center would be a resource for evidence about the local crime and justice issues, as well as a link to national and international knowledge."[77] Centers would be responsible for merging data from different agencies, describing the types of problems in their areas and the scope of each, and developing and testing new ideas for addressing them. Not least, they would work with other centers, as well as universities and federal agencies, to undertake coordinated, multisite studies aimed at developing knowledge about effective crime prevention and criminal justice strategies.

Some critics express concern that such arrangements might give the federal government undue influence, and, in particular, create mechanisms through which partisan politics may bias research and in turn practice.[78] Here, again, such criticisms have merit. It bears emphasizing, however, that political influences are not necessarily harmful, that they permeate many aspects of research, whether federally funded or not, and that procedures can be introduced to try to temper political misuse of such centers or other arrangements for increasing applied criminal justice research.

Consider, as but one example, the recommendation made by Blumstein and Petersilia that a separate federal agency be created that is charged with spearheading criminal justice research for the country and coordinating research activities at centers throughout the United States.[79] This agency would be committed to scientific integrity, which would be enforced in part through oversight from the National Academy of Sciences and the National Science Foundation. In addition, the director would ideally be separated from the political process by, among other things, serving five-year fixed terms. Such steps would not fully insulate an agency from political influence, but it would, again, help temper misuse. At the same time, it would underscore, if only symbolically, the importance of research as a means by which to foster accountability and the development of evidence-based policies and practices.

Develop a Bank of Knowledge about Effective and Ineffective Policies

A final recommendation is that a centralized repository, or bank, of information about effective and ineffective programs be developed. Given the magnitude of the effort required, such an undertaking would require federal funds or the coordinated efforts of several foundations. The repository would, if it is to be useful, be updated regularly to provide the most current information about: effective policies; the problems that they are best suited to address; racial, ethnic, gender, and cultural differences in effectiveness; the conditions necessary for the policies to be effective; how best to implement them; how best to measure and monitor implementation and outcomes; and the type and level of benefits to expect.

At present, a wealth of reviews on effective policies exists. However, many of them repeat much of what is covered in other texts, with some special angle or perspective to be sure, but nonetheless covering much the same terrain.[80] Many of the best reviews, such as those conducted by Sherman and his colleagues in 1997, have not been regularly updated.[81] Others, such as the work of the Crime and Justice Group of the Campbell Collaboration (www.campbellcollaboration.org), have resulted in comprehensive reviews of many topics but rest on the voluntary contributions of researchers and have not generated reviews of many aspects of crime prevention and the criminal justice system.[82] Separately, the National Institute of Corrections (www.ncic.org) provides publications that summarize research on a variety of issues and provide guidance on effective practice. For example, the agency has collaborated with the Crime and Justice Institute to produce an integrated model of evidence-based practice and of how to implement the model in criminal justice systems across different components of these systems (e.g., pretrial, probation, parole) and at varying jurisdictional levels (e.g., local, county, state).[83] In addition to these efforts, meta-analytic techniques, which involve a systematic, quantitative assessment of prior research, are increasingly common and have provided important insights into the types and characteristics of programs that are effective.[84]

Despite these efforts, there remain numerous gaps in what is covered, much redundancy of information, and many instances where the compiled information is too difficult to obtain or decipher. In the meantime, thousands of evaluations occur annually without the findings or insights registering in meta-analyses or reviews. In addition, numerous studies highlight that the causes of and possible solutions to reducing specific types of crimes can and do vary. That should not be surprising. In medicine, numerous distinct diseases exist, and we hardly expect that they should all be caused by the same factors and treated in the same way. Much the same holds true for a system, such as criminal justice, that manages a diverse range of offenses, including violent crime (e.g., homicide, sexual violence, firearm violence, robbery, domestic violence, child abuse), property crime (e.g., burglary, auto theft, financial crimes, identity theft), transactional crime (e.g., organized crime, environmental crime, money laundering, tax evasion), transnational crime (e.g., human trafficking, terrorism, cybercrime), and crimes against morality (e.g., drugs, hate crimes, prostitution, gambling).[85]

Juxtaposed against this situation is one in which policy makers and practitioners want clear statements about what works. A centralized repository of information about criminal justice policies, easily accessible to as wide an audience as possible and therefore through many different media, would go a long way to addressing this problem.[86] It would need, however, to rely on experienced researchers and the scholarly community and to include policy makers and practitioners to ensure that the material can be understood readily and interpreted correctly.[87]

This repository should provide information about as wide a spectrum of policies as possible. Of course, a central emphasis would be on policies aimed at reducing recidivism. Any such emphasis, however, should go well beyond "punishment" versus "rehabilitation" classifications. Sufficient evidence appears to exist now to assert that, under ideal and sometimes even under less-than-ideal conditions, rehabilitation can reduce recidivism and that increased punishment can also do so but less consistently and with smaller impacts.[88] The critical questions are, Which specific approaches achieve the greatest returns? and, on a related front, Under what conditions to specific sanctions and programs achieve reductions in recidivism? The latter question recognizes the fact that policy impacts may depend greatly on a range of factors, such as the targeting of appropriate clientele, complete and high-quality implementation, and the like.

The repository also should document the range of impacts associated with various policies. Although significant advances have been made in recidivism research, few studies exist that systematically document the impacts of various criminal justice policies on a range of outcomes, including justice.[89] For example, an evaluation of a drug court might focus on recidivism, and yet neglect to examine potential impacts on drug use and offending, housing or homelessness, employment, family functioning, and other critical dimensions of success in society. Similarly, few reentry programs have been evaluated in such a way as to document their impacts on these types of dimensions. It thus remains largely an open question as to which types of policies produce the best improvements across a range of outcomes, much less which ones do so for the least cost. Even so, exceptions exist, and a critical role of a centralized repository would be to highlight that multiple outcomes frequently are relevant to providing a balanced and appropriate assessment of a particular policy.

It bears emphasizing that the creation of a bank of evaluation research on criminal justice policies would help to highlight the quality of our state of knowledge. As it stands, many scholars feel that the situation is dire.

Chris Eskridge has eloquently articulated this view, arguing that criminology and criminal justice now stands approximately where medicine did in the eighteenth century. The field lacks solid "diagnostic instruments," "consistent treatment modalities," and well-tested, effective offense- and offender-specific treatments; it thus has allowed society to respond to crime "using crude, homespun, untested remedies" rather than effective, evidence-based policies.[90] Many other scholars, however, suggest that a considerable body of evidence exists in support of many particular policies as well as general principles of effective practice.[91] The truth likely consists of a mix of both perspectives, but it would be preferable to specify more precisely where the state of knowledge is solid and where it is not.

Finally, the bank should also include updated information on public opinion polls and how the public nationally and at the state and local levels view crime and various efforts to address it. Policy makers frequently reference the public will, yet they frequently have no data to back their claims or use data that skew or distort public views.[92] Here, again, a comprehensive and updated compilation of research on public opinion would not only highlight what is known but also underscore the complexity of public opinion and areas where significant gaps exist.

Ultimately, an effective criminal justice system must ensure that all efforts are systematically integrated and coordinated with one another to increase system accountability, effectiveness, and efficiency.[93] To this end, a one-stop source of information on best practices, models, and principles – presented in a manner accessible to policy makers, practitioners, and the public[94] – is critical.[95] Politics inevitably will govern the selection of policies, but such influences need not necessarily be harmful, especially in a democracy.[96] And to be clear, evaluation research is no substitute for a deliberate and careful policy-making process.[97] It can, however, contribute to more tempered policy discussions and informed decisions about the wisdom of different criminal justice policies.[98]

Discussion Questions

What do you believe are the primary problems in criminal justice policy today?

How can evaluation research improve criminal justice policies?

How would you increase the use of evaluation research in the development, implementation, monitoring, and assessment of criminal justice policy?

How would you organize the development and funding of criminal justice policy so that it was more effective and efficient?

What specific steps for increasing the amount and quality of criminal justice evaluation research do you think would produce the largest improvements in research and in policy?

Some people argue that criminal justice policy frequently is motivated purely by political considerations, while others argue that political influences on policy is a good thing. What do you think? What role should politics play in criminal justice policy? What limits should there be on its influence?

Notes

1. Introduction

1. Listwan et al. (2008).
2. See Figure 2.4; see also Mears (2008a) and Sabol et al. (2009).
3. King (2009:1).
4. Law itself is a category that encompasses many sources that the federal government and state and local governments use to define crime and how to respond it. As Marion and Oliver (2006:24–27) have noted, the different sources include criminal law, common law, constitutional law, natural law, statutory law, substantive and procedural law, case law, and administrative law.
5. Flanagan and Longmire (1996); Sherman et al. (1997); Cullen, Fisher, and Applegate (2000); Sherman et al. (2002); Lipsey et al. (2005); Roberts and Hough (2005b); Listwan et al. (2008).
6. Petersilia (1991); Blumstein and Petersilia (1995); Blumstein (1997); Clear (2001); Knepper (2007).
7. See Zahn (1999:8); see also Farrington (2000), Chilton (2001), Huff (2002), Sherman (2003a), Laub (2004), Cullen (2005), LaFree (2007), and Tonry (2008).
8. The society is typically characterized as having a more theoretical focus, while the academy is characterized as having more of a policy focus. The distinction cannot be readily discerned from the proceedings of society and academy conferences or the content in the two organization's flagship journals (*Criminology* and *Justice Quarterly*, respectively). Not surprisingly, many criminologists are members of both organizations (Sorensen et al., 2006).
9. See, for example, Maxfield and Babbie (2005).
10. See, for example, Chambers et al. (1992), Patton (2002), Rossi et al. (2004), Wholey et al. (2004), Chen (2005), McDavid and Hawthorn (2006), Daponte (2008), Grinnell and Unrau (2008), Bardach (2009), and Holden and Zimmerman (2009).
11. See, for example, Welsh and Harris (2008), Bardach (2009).
12. A few texts address evaluation considerations that apply to a select set of criminal justice policies. In these instances, a more narrow spectrum of evaluation approaches is emphasized and only a few policies are discussed (e.g., Tilley 2002). Mays and

Ruddell (2008) have examined a range of criminal justice policies and practices, but not through an evaluation framework. One important contribution to the criminal justice policy literature is Klein and Teilmann's (1980) edited volume, which provides an introduction to a wide range of evaluation topics – methods and statistical approaches, sources of data, how theory and policy can influence one another, challenges of field research, benefits of evaluation – and a select set of specific issues (e.g., deterrence, female criminality, diversion). However, it predates many of the most prominent criminal justice policies that have emerged in the three decades since it was published and is not grounded in a guiding or integrated evaluation framework. Even so, the work still holds much relevance for criminal justice evaluation, especially for readers interested in more in-depth discussion of specific topics (e.g., data sources, evaluating legislation).

13. See also Sherman et al. (1997), Farabee et al. (2005), Lipsey et al. (2005), Mears (2007b), and Listwan et al. (2008).
14. Klein and Teilmann (1980); Mears (2008a).
15. Knepper (2007).

2.   Irrational Criminal Justice Policy

1. Mears, Wang et al. (2008).
2. Mosher et al. (2002); Lynch and Addington (2007).
3. For detailed information on the survey, see Mosher et al. (2002), Lynch and Addington (2007), Rand and Catalano (2007), and Rand (2009).
4. Fox and Zawitz (2007).
5. The violent and property victimization rates are the adjusted rates, which take into account a redesign of the NCVS in 1992 (see Rand and Catalano 2007:2).
6. Petersilia (2003); Travis (2005); Travis and Visher (2005).
7. Sabol et al. (2009:3).
8. Petersilia (2005); Mears, Wang et al. (2008).
9. Lynch and Sabol (2001); Mears et al. (2003); Travis and Visher (2005).
10. Hughes (2006:3).
11. Lipsey et al. (2005:vii). See also Sherman et al. (1997).
12. This discussion draws on and extends arguments presented in Mears (2007b). A large literature on research and policy linkages, or the lack thereof, exists. A small sampling includes Petersilia (1991); Blumstein (1997); Cullen and Gendreau (2000); Garland (2001); Stolz (2002); Sherman (2003a, 2004); Gaes et al. (2004); Rossi et al. (2004); Wholey et al. (2004); Eskridge (2005); Farabee (2005); Travis (2005); Mears (2007b); Oliver and Marion (2008); Weiss et al. (2008); Welsh and Harris (2008); and Stohr and Collins (2009).
13. See, for example, Garland (2001); Gottschalk (2006); Useem and Piehl (2008).
14. Stolz (2002); Marion and Oliver (2006); Oliver and Marion (2008); Simon (2007). Some scholars have argued against this type of argument, suggesting that the prison increase in the 1990s was a "pragmatic effort to deal with an escalating crime rate"

and not "an effort to achieve an otherwise extraneous political agenda" (Useem and Piehl, 2008:169).

15. See, generally, Useem and Piehl (2008).
16. Oliver and Marion (2008:398–399).
17. Garland (2001:101–102); see also Beckett (1997); Blumstein (1998); Tonry (2004); Simon (2007); Useem and Piehl (2008).
18. Miller (1973).
19. Skogan (1995:60).
20. Braden (1996).
21. Garland (2001); Tonry (2004).
22. Oliver and Marion (2008:408).
23. Flanagan and Longmire (1996); Garland (2001); Knepper (2007).
24. Mears, Hay, et al. (2007).
25. Beckett (1997); Garland (2001); Stolz (2002); Marion and Oliver (2006); Knepper (2007).
26. See, however, Lipsey and Cullen (2007).
27. Sherman et al. (1997); Cullen and Gendreau (2000); Sherman et al. (2002); Lipsey et al. (2005); Farrington and Welsh (2007); Lipsey and Cullen (2007); Van Voorhis et al. (2007).
28. Blumstein (1997); Tonry (2004); Knepper (2007).
29. Bernard (1992).
30. Sabol et al. (2009).
31. Langan and Levin (2002).
32. Cullen and Gendreau (2000).
33. Roberts (1992:117).
34. Roberts (1992); Roberts and Stalans (1998); Cullen, Fisher, and Applegate (2000); Roberts and Hough (2005a).
35. Cullen, Fisher, and Applegate (2000:19).
36. Dawson (1988); Mears (2007b).
37. See, for example, King's (2009) discussion of sentencing reforms and the emphasis by states on new policies rather than addressing problems with previous ones.
38. Petersilia (2003); Travis (2005).
39. Roberts (1992); Flanagan and Longmire (1996); Roberts and Stalans (1998); Cullen et al. (1998); Cullen, Fisher, and Applegate (2000); Moon et al. (2000); Roberts et al. (2003); Roberts and Hough (2005a–b); Nagin et al. (2006); Mears, Hay et al. (2007).
40. Roberts and Hough (2005b:295–296).
41. Cullen et al. (1998); Cullen, Fisher, and Applegate (2000).
42. Roberts and Hough (2005b:298; emphasis in original).
43. Roberts and Hough (2005b:290).
44. Roberts and Hough (2005b:291). See also Cullen, Fisher, and Applegate (2000).
45. Roberts and Hough (2005b:292).
46. Cullen et al. (2000:3).
47. Blumstein (1997:359).

48. See, especially, Cullen, Fisher, and Applegate (2000:57–60).
49. Roberts and Hough (2005b:293).
50. See, generally, Stolz (2002).
51. Roberts (1992:157–158); see also Cullen, Fisher, and Applegate (2000), Roberts and Hough (2005b).
52. Roberts (1992:158), discussing a study by Immarigeon (1986).
53. Wright et al. (1987); Flanagan and Longmire (1996).
54. Elliott (1997); Mears (2007b).
55. Blumstein and Beck (1999); Mears et al. (2003); Sevigny and Caulkins (2004); Blumstein and Piquero (2007); Gottschalk (2008).
56. Gottfredson et al. (2003); National Institute of Justice (2006).
57. White and Gorman (2000); Kleiman (2004).
58. Mears et al. (2003).
59. Petersilia (2005).
60. Lurigio (2000); Mears et al. (2003); Lipsey and Cullen (2007); Pelissier et al. (2007).
61. Lipsey and Cullen (2007).
62. See, however, Bhati et al. (2008).
63. Petersilia (1991); Blumstein and Petersilia (1995); Blumstein (1997); Cullen and Gendreau (2000); Sherman (2004); Eskridge (2005); Lipsey et al. (2005); Lipsey and Cullen (2007); Mears (2007b).
64. Many of the Academy of Criminal Justice Sciences and American Society of Criminology presidential addresses discuss the reasons for why research and criminal justice policy are not better linked. Other works discuss the issue, from varying perspectives, in considerable depth. A small, but by no means exhaustive, sampling includes the following: Klein and Teilmann (1980); Petersilia (1991); Blumstein and Petersilia (1995); Beckett (1997); Elliott (1997); Blumstein (1997); Cullen and Gendreau (2000); Sherman et al. (2002); Forst (2004); Gaes et al. (2004); Sherman (2004); Eskridge (2005); Farabee (2005); Lipsey et al. (2005); Marion and Oliver (2006); Farrington and Welsh (2007); Mears (2007b); and Welsh and Harris (2008).
65. Petersilia (1991); Blumstein (1997).
66. Rossi (1980); Petersilia (1991); Sjoberg and Vaughan (1993); Cullen and Gendreau (2000); Cullen (2005).
67. Petersilia (1991:1).
68. Petersilia (1991:2). See also Sjoberg and Vaughn (1993), Clear (2001).
69. Petersilia (1991); Eskridge (2005).
70. Petersilia (1991:3–4).
71. Petersilia (1991:6).
72. Blumstein and Petersilia (1995:472).
73. Krouse et al. (2008:19).
74. Petersilia (1991:6).
75. Tonry (2009:5); see also Blumstein (2008).
76. Sherman et al. (1997); Lipsey et al. (2005); Mears (2007b).
77. Lipsey (1998); Weisburd, Lum, and Petrosino (2001); Weisburd, Lum, and Yang (2003).

78. Heckman and Smith (1995); Bardach (2004); Mears (2007b).
79. Weisburd, Lum, and Petrosino (2001); Weisburd, Lum, and Yang (2003).
80. Lipsey (1998).
81. Cullen and Gendreau (2000:124); see also Chilton (2001).
82. Cullen and Gendreau (2000:124).
83. See also Cullen, Fisher, and Applegate (2000).
84. Petersilia (1991:5); see also Blumstein (1997), Cullen (2005).

3. A Solution for Improving Criminal Justice Policy: Evaluation Research

1. This discussion draws on Rossi et al.'s (2004:8–16) description of the emergence of evaluation research as a field.
2. Rossi et al. (2004:9).
3. Scholars sometimes use *research* and *evaluation research* to mean different things. For example, the authors of one article on evidence-based policy noted: "We often use the word *research* to refer to all types of systematic empirical inquiry, including evaluation. We use *evaluation* to refer specifically to research that examines the processes and outcomes of social interventions" (Weiss et al. 2008:44; emphasis in original). I take a somewhat different view of the matter. As can be seen by reviewing the hierarchy, evaluation involves more than a focus on processes and outcomes. It also involves a focus on questions about the need for a policy; the theory, design, or conceptualization of the policy; and its cost-efficiency. It is, however, true that many research studies are not expressly designed as evaluations. Regardless, the distinction between *research* and *evaluation research* is not, in my view, especially helpful. For that reason, the terms are used interchangeably in this book.
4. Rossi et al. (2004:16). Rossi et al. (2004) use the phrase "program evaluation" rather than "policy evaluation" in their definition. In keeping with this book's broad-based focus on a range of laws, programs, practices, rules, protocols, and the like, I have substituted the phrase "policy evaluation" for "program evaluation." The latter is more likely, in my view, to connote a specific facility where particular activities (e.g., drug treatment, counseling) occur as opposed to the range of efforts aimed at improving society.
5. A small sampling of more recent texts includes Chambers et al. (1992); Patton (2002); Rossi et al. (2004); Wholey et al. (2004); Chen (2005); McDavid and Hawthorn (2006); Daponte (2008); and Grinnell and Unrau (2008). Professional associations, such as the American Evaluation Association, exist that supply additional information about evaluation research – see, for example, the report *Guiding Principles for Evaluators* (American Evaluation Association 2004).
6. Rossi et al. (2004); Grinnell and Unrau (2008).
7. Boyd et al. (2008).
8. Rossi et al. (2004:80).
9. McDavid and Hawthorn (2006:21); see also Rossi et al. (2004:34).
10. McDavid and Hawthorn (2006:21); see also Rossi et al. (2004:36).
11. U.S. General Accounting Office (1998).

12. Rossi et al. (2004:208, 224).

13. Lawrence and Mears (2004).

14. Gaes et al. (2004); Hatry et al. (2004); Kopczynski and Pritchard (2004); Rossi et al. (2004); Hatry (2006); McDavid and Hawthorn (2006); Bovens et al. (2008).

15. Welsh and Harris (2008:8).

16. Sherman et al. (1997:v); see also Forst (2004), Eskridge (2005), Farabee (2005), Lipsey et al. (2005), Mears (2007b, 2008a).

17. Lipsey et al. (2005:vii). See also Stolz (2002); Forst (2004); Welsh and Harris (2008); Mears (2007b); Mears and Butts (2008).

18. Hatry et al. (2004); Rossi et al. (2004); Welsh and Harris (2008); McDavid and Hawthorn (2006); Bovens et al. (2008).

19. Rossi et al. (2004:200). Auditing has similarities with evaluation research but also differs in some respects (see, generally, Chelimsky 1985). In the present context, it suffices to say that audits serve an implementation evaluation function by examining whether policies (including programs, laws, practices, etc.) are undertaken in the way they are supposed to be. In more general terms, "auditing is . . . an examination of the match or discrepancy between a criterion (or standard or yardstick) and a condition (or the matter being audited)" (Chelimsky 1985:488). The basis for determining whether a correspondence between what should and what does happen can involve the same activities that evaluation researchers undertake, including the collection of various types of data (e.g., interviews, surveys, documents and reports that describe agency goals and operations) and various types of analyses.

20. Grinnell and Unrau (2008:509–510); Knepper (2007:9); Weiss et al. (2008:29–30).

21. Hatry (2006).

22. Rossi et al. (2004); Hatry (2006).

23. Hatry (2006).

24. Hatry (2006).

25. Mears and Bacon (2009).

26. Stolz (2002:82–94); Marion and Oliver (2006:17–23, 2009:117–120); see also Knepper (2007:139–154).

27. Cullen and Gendreau (2000:158).

28. The example is not hypothetical (see Davis et al. 2003).

29. Rossi et al. (2004:21–22).

30. King (2009).

4. Needs Evaluations

1. Haugtvedt et al. (2008).

2. Action bias arises when physicians emphasize "action rather than inaction" and so pursue any diagnosis and treatment (Groopman 2007:169). The motivations may include wanting to feel that they have at least tried to intervene or to avoid confronting the fact that they do not know the correct diagnosis or treatment.

3. Petersilia (1991); Sjoberg and Vaughn (1993).

4. Rossi et al. (2004:102).
5. Piquero et al. (2007).
6. Akers and Sellers (2009).
7. Liska (1992); Blumstein (1997, 1998); Blumstein and Wallman (2006); Akers and Sellers (2009).
8. McGarrell (1991); Blumstein (1998); Sabol (1999); Butts and Adams (2001); Greenberg and West (2001); Mears (2002a, 2006b); Blumstein and Wallman (2006); Gottschalk (2006, 2008).
9. Blau and Abramovitz (2007).
10. Mears and Watson (2006).
11. Mears (2008a).
12. Mears (2008a).
13. Rossi et al. (2004:130).
14. A small sampling includes Chambers et al. (1992); Patton (2002); Rossi et al. (2004); Wholey et al. (2004); Chen (2005); Maxfield and Babbie (2005); McDavid and Hawthorn (2006); Daponte (2008); Grinnell and Unrau (2008); and Bardach (2009).
15. See, generally, Bardach (2009).
16. Alpert and Piquero (2000); Mays and Ruddell (2008); Sampson (2009).
17. See Collier (2006) regarding domains of police performance.
18. According to Blumstein et al. (2005:375), this assessment is supported by "data on average time served relative to recorded crimes, convictions, and average sentence lengths. The United States was the most punitive for nearly all the crime types, especially when punitiveness is defined narrowly as expected time served per conviction."
19. The precise figure is 2,304,115 (Sabol et al. 2009:8).
20. A small sampling of the reentry literature includes Lynch and Sabol (2001); Petersilia (2003); Travis (2005); Travis and Visher (2005); Blumstein and Wallman (2006); Gottschalk (2006); Western (2006); Walker et al. (2007); Mears, Wang, et al. (2008); and Spelman (2008).
21. Baird and Rosenbaum (1988); von Hirsch and Ashworth (1992); Friedman (1993); Morris and Rothman (1995); Zimring and Hawkins (1995); Tonry and Farrington (2005); Gottschalk (2006).
22. See Raphael and Stoll (2009) for a detailed discussion of state-level variation in incarceration rates.
23. Spelman (2006:97).
24. In reality, medical treatment practices can vary considerably regardless of the amount or distribution of a specific disease (Downie and Macnaughton 2000; Sherman 2003a; Gawande 2007; Groopman 2007). Even so, the logic of the example nonetheless still applies.
25. Greenberg and West (2001) did find, consistent with other research, evidence that states with higher levels of crime tend to have higher incarceration rates. Specifically, they found that states with higher violent crime rates at one time period had higher incarceration rates at a later time period. Such a finding indicates that crime rates and incarceration rates are associated. However, a change analysis provides a more compelling test of whether the two are causally linked. Here, recall that the authors

tested the idea that *increased* crime would result in *increased* incarceration and showed that the two were unrelated (table 3, model A, p. 636), suggesting in turn that no causal relationship between the two exists. Why are the cross-sectional findings less convincing? Several factors come into play, but the main concern stems from the fact that an identified relationship may be temporally far removed from the original cause of it. Assume, for example, that fifty years ago, states with more crime created more capacity for prisons but that thereafter their investment in prisons corresponded identically to that of states with little crime. Cross-sectional analyses of the later years would consistently reveal a relationship between incarceration rates and crime rates, even though no causal relationship any longer exists, as Greenberg and West (2001:617) have emphasized. Spelman (2008) recently provided a different assessment, and found that in general it can be concluded that increases in crime contribute to prison population growth.

26. Gottschalk (2006:25); see also Greenberg and West (2001), Jacobs and Carmichael (2001), Mears (2002a, 2006b), Frampton et al. (2008), Spelman (2008).

27. Spelman (2006:124).

28. Spelman (2009); cf. Raphael (2009).

29. Spelman (2006:123); emphasis added.

30. See especially Useem and Piehl (2008) and Spelman (2009); cf. Raphael (2009) and Raphael and Stoll (2009).

31. Greenberg and West (2001). Gottschalk (2006:18–40) alone has highlighted a range of factors that have been argued to contribute to mass incarceration: increased crime; tougher sentencing laws; a more punitive public; the prison-industrial complex (i.e., the idea that economic benefits induce states and localities, as well as businesses that benefit from prison construction, to push for greater investment in prisons); the illegal drug trade; a law-and-order emphasis promulgated by conservatives; an increasing mistrust among the public in the ability of government to function effectively in providing the most basic of services, including protection from crime, and a consequent need to see visible signs of governmental purpose and competence; and interest groups, such as the National Rifle Association, promoting punitive policies. Liska et al. (1999) have argued that criminal justice population flows depend on mental health system institutional capacity and practices. Other scholars have pointed to these and other such factors (e.g., McGarrell 1991; Friedman 1993; Zimring and Hawkins 1995; Jacobs and Carmichael 2001; Beckett and Sasson 2004; Elsner 2004; Mears 2006b; Blumstein 2008; Spelman 2008; Raphael 2009; Raphael and Stoll 2009).

32. Baird and Rosenbaum (1988); Rossi and Berk (1997); von Hirsch (1998).

33. Rossi and Berk (1997); Cullen, Fisher, and Applegate (2000); Cullen and Gendreau (2000).

34. Roberts and Stalans (1998); Roberts et al. (2003); Roberts and Hough (2005a–b).

35. Greenfeld (1995:1).

36. Beck and Greenfeld (1995:2).

37. Beck and Greenfeld (1995:4). Some states did not report data, and so not all states were represented in the study.

38. For discussion of an "equilibrium model of prison populations," see Spelman (2009:41).
39. Donohue and Wolfers (2006).
40. See, generally, Akers and Sellers (2009) and Raphael and Stoll (2009).
41. Many states have undertaken a range of reform efforts aimed at reducing correctional system growth. However, according to King's (2009:3) national study, these reforms have not addressed a central cause of this growth, and, in particular, the fact that there are "more people facing prison for a broader range of offenses and staying there longer than at any point in history. And many of the policy decisions that resulted in this growth – mandatory minimum sentencing, 'truth-in-sentencing,' extremely long sentences, and life without parole – remain statutory law."
42. Spelman (2009:65).
43. Zimring and Hawkins (1995) provide a detailed discussion of the challenges associated in creating defensible estimates for incapacitation, a discussion that illustrates more broadly the complexities that emerge when trying to estimate reasonable estimates of deterrent and rehabilitative effects of incarceration.
44. Petersilia (2003); Travis (2005); Gottschalk (2006); Western (2006); Pager (2007); Walker et al. (2007); Vieraitis et al. (2008).
45. See, for example, DeFina and Hannon (2009).
46. See, generally, Sabol (1999), Butts and Adams (2001), Mears (2002a), Spelman (2006), Berk (2008), and Martinez (2008). Spelman (2006) has highlighted some of the limitations of the different approaches to forecasting as relates to estimates of impacts. "Bottom-up" simulation studies "demand an enormous amount of data, some of which is of questionable validity" and they "only measure the effects of incapacitation, not deterrence and rehabilitation" (p. 98). "Top-down" studies provide better estimates of the overall impact of crime rates but allow for "innumerable competing explanations of the [prison] system's behavior at any given time" (p. 98). The limitations affect not only estimates of incarceration impacts but also, by extension, the "need" for incarceration. Berk (2008) has provided a review of modern criminal justice forecasting methods and their strengths and limitations.
47. Pratt (2000); Wright (2003, 2008); Quinn et al. (2004); Miethe et al. (2006); McCulloch and Kelly (2007); Zimring et al. (2007); Mears, Mancini, et al. (2008); Velázquez (2008).
48. Council of State Governments (2006).
49. Logan (2003); Tewksbury (2005).
50. Sims and Reynolds (2007).
51. Sample and Bray (2003); La Fond (2005); Goodnough and Davey (2007); Levenson and D'Amora (2007); Maahs and Liederbach (2007); Wright (2008).
52. Wright (2003:97).
53. Velázquez (2008).
54. Velázquez (2008:4).
55. Sample and Bray (2003:62).
56. Sample and Bray (2003:62).
57. Velázquez (2008:2).

58. Roberts et al. (2003:129).
59. Catalano (2006); Rand and Catalano (2007); Rand (2008, 2009).
60. Velázquez (2008:iii).
61. Langan et al. (2003:1).
62. Langan et al. (2003:2); see also Sample and Bray (2003), Zimring et al. (2007).
63. Bartosh et al. (2003); Beech et al. (2003); Hanson et al. (2003); Harris et al. (2003); Doren (2004, 2006); Hanson and Morton-Bourgon (2004); Kemshall and McIvor (2004); Gentry et al. (2005); Hanson (2006); Marshall et al. (2006); Langton et al. (2007).
64. Hart et al. (2007:60).
65. Levenson and D'Amora (2007); Velázquez (2008); Wright (2008).
66. Sample and Bray (2003); Wright (2003); Kemshall and McIvor (2004); La Fond (2005).
67. Levenson and D'Amora (2007:178); Velázquez (2008:4).
68. Levenson and D'Amora (2007); Velázquez (2008).
69. Levenson and D'Amora (2007:186) have noted that "most sex offenders, rather than being predatory, victimize in places in which they are approved to be." From this perspective, the occurrence of sex offending does not logically lead to the idea that a need exists for restricting where sex offenders live. For other incorrect assumptions about sex offenders and sex offender registries, see Barnes et al. (2009).
70. Velázquez (2008:7).
71. Barnes et al. (2009); Zgoba et al. (2009).
72. Levenson and D'Amora (2007:173); see also Velázquez (2008).
73. Levenson and D'Amora (2007:172); see also Velázquez (2008).
74. Levenson and D'Amora (2007:184); see also Velázquez (2008).
75. Levenson and D'Amora (2007:189); see also Velázquez (2008).
76. Levenson and D'Amora (2007:188); see also Wright (2008:17).
77. O'Brien (1995).
78. Use of force would seem to be a critical area of research, yet few reliable estimates exist of the prevalence of it or of when force is used appropriately (Hickman et al. 2008).
79. After examining prior work and presenting his national assessment, Spelman (2006: 125) recently concluded: "Some states could very well benefit from further prison expansion today; others may have expanded too much as it is. Although I don't go there, somebody needs to, and soon." In fact, there is little evidence that states systematically have conducted needs evaluations of the kind recommended here or by Spelman (2006). To the contrary, evidence seems to point to the idea that incarceration policies are driven more by political considerations and by forecast estimates based on weak methodological research designs (Zimring and Hawkins 1995; Sabol 1999; Garland 2001; Langan 2005; Gottschalk 2006; Martinez 2008).
80. Perrone and Pratt (2003); Gaes et al. (2004); Bales et al. (2005); Price and Riccucci (2005); Morris (2007); Gaes (2008); Mears (2008a); Rynne et al. (2008).
81. Kurki and Morris (2001); Mears (2008b).
82. King (1999).
83. Mears (1998b); von Hirsch and Ashworth (1992); Blumstein and Piquero (2007).

84. Tonry (2006); Hartley (2008); Kramer (2009).
85. Garland (2001); Tonry (2006); Frampton et al. (2008).
86. von Hirsch (1998:659); see also Zimring and Hawkins (1995), Rossi and Berk (1997), Roberts and Hough (2005a–b).
87. White and Gorman (2000).
88. Nadelmann (2004).
89. Mears (2003b); Mears and Visher (2005); Hines (2009).
90. Mears (2003b); Hines (2009).
91. Feld (2004).
92. Fagan and Zimring (2000); Mears (2003a); Kupchik (2006).
93. Blomberg and Waldo (2002:341).

5. Theory Evaluations

1. Rossi et al. (2004:54).
2. Rossi et al. (2004:55).
3. Within the natural and social sciences, the very concept of a *theory* can engender considerable debate, with some scientists advocating one approach to theory and others advocating different approaches (Mears and Stafford 2002). Regardless, they all attempt to explain how the world operates. A vast literature on social theory exists. A small sampling includes Merton (1968, 1973); Gibbs (1985); Marini and Singer (1988); Berger and Zelditch (1993); Blalock (1994); and Tindall (2000).
4. Rossi et al. (2004:139).
5. Rossi et al. (2004:80). Many texts exist that describe theory or causal logic evaluations (e.g., McLaughlin and Jordan 2004; McDavid and Hawthorn 2006).
6. Rossi et al. (2004:153).
7. Rossi et al. (2004:135).
8. The example is a real one that was relayed to me by Professor Robert O. Dawson.
9. Rossi et al. (2004:139).
10. A small sampling includes Rossi et al. (2004); Wholey et al. (2004); Chen (2005); McDavid and Hawthorn (2006); Daponte (2008); and Grinnell and Unrau (2008).
11. Rossi et al. (2004:140). Some evaluators distinguish between implementation theory and policy theory (e.g., Weiss 1997). Implementation theory describes how a policy's various parts relate to one another and should lead to a desired outcome. Policy theory describes how the various parts (e.g., specific services, activities, or decisions) create changes in targeted areas or populations (e.g., changes in attitudes or beliefs). The efforts frequently overlap with one another and, in the end, are united by the goal of clearly articulating, in as much detail as possible, the nuts and bolts of a policy and how it should or can lead to change.
12. Drawn from Harrell et al. (1996); see also United Way of America (1996); McLaughlin and Jordan (2004); Rossi et al. (2004); and Hatry (2006).
13. Hatry (2006:15).
14. Hatry (2006:19).
15. Rossi et al. (2004:210–212).

16. Bardach (2009).
17. Merrall and Bird (2009).
18. This figure draws on examples provided by Harrell et al. (1996) and the United Way of America (1996).
19. For detailed descriptions of ACTION and studies of it, see Mears, Scott, and Bhati (2007a–c).
20. Mears, Scott, and Bhati (2007a–c).
21. Butts and Roman (2004:237–261).
22. Goldkamp (2003); Gottfredson et al. (2003); National Institute of Justice (2006).
23. Agnew (2005); Lilly et al. (2007); Akers and Sellers (2009).
24. See, for example, Agnew (2005:128–132).
25. Tittle (1995); Agnew (2005).
26. Weisburd and Braga (2006).
27. O'Donnell et al. (2008:136).
28. Literature from the policy arena, as well as from the social, medical, and natural sciences, attests to this fact. A small sampling of works that discuss or illustrate dose effects includes Tallarida (2000); Bowers et al. (2004); Rossi et al. (2004); Imbens (2000); Weisburd and Braga (2006); Fauci et al. (2008); and DeBeck et al. (2009).
29. Weiss (1997).
30. Rossi et al. (2004:146).
31. The example is not hypothetical – see Mears, Roman et al. (2006); Roman et al. (2007); see also O'Connor and Duncan (2008).
32. Rossi et al. (2004:148).
33. See, generally, Chambers et al. (1992), Harrell et al. (1996), Rossi et al. (2004), Wholey et al. (2004), Chen (2005), McDavid and Hawthorn (2006), and Daponte (2008).
34. Rossi et al. (2004:153).
35. Rossi et al. (2004:153).
36. Rossi et al. (2004:157–159, paraphrased and revised to reflect a criminal justice focus).
37. Rossi et al. (2004:159).
38. Levenson and Cotter (2005).
39. Rossi et al. (2004:162).
40. Chambers et al. (1992:159).
41. Mears (2007a).
42. Rossi et al. (2004); McDavid and Hawthorn (2006); Bardach (2009).
43. Wholey (2004).
44. Rossi et al. (2004:136).
45. Butts and Roman (2004); Wilson et al. (2006).
46. Barnes et al. (2009); Zgoba et al. (2009).
47. This discussion draws on Mears and Reisig (2006) and Mears (2008b).
48. Mears and Watson (2006); Sundt, Castellano, and Briggs (2008).
49. Wells et al. (2002).
50. Kurki and Morris (2001:385).
51. National Institute of Corrections (1997); King (1999).

52. Mears (2006a:40).
53. Miller (1995); King (1999); Haney (2003); Collins (2004); Sullivan (2006).
54. Different goals have been associated with supermax housing, but, at least among prison wardens, order clearly constitutes a central one (Mears and Castro 2006).
55. Feeley and Simon (1992); Pizarro et al. (2006); Simon (2007).
56. Pizarro and Stenius (2004:258).
57. Mears and Reisig (2006).
58. See, generally, Akers and Sellers (2009) and Raphael and Stoll (2009).
59. See, for example, Adams (1992), Sparks et al. (1996), Bottoms (1999).
60. Lynch and Sabol (2001); Travis (2005).
61. Pizarro and Stenius (2004:259).
62. Haney (2003); Ward and Werlich (2003).
63. Rhodes (2004:55).
64. Adams (1992); McCorkle et al. (1995); Reisig (1998); Bottoms (1999); King (1999); Austin and Irwin (2001); Kurki and Morris (2001); Irwin (2005); Mears and Reisig (2006).
65. Sparks et al. (1996:313).
66. Sykes (1958).
67. Useem and Kimball (1991); Irwin (2005).
68. DiIulio (1987).
69. Mears and Watson (2006).
70. Haney (2003); King (2005); Lovell et al. (2007).
71. Ward and Werlich (2003).
72. Crouch and Marquart (1989).
73. Boin (2001).
74. Mears and Watson (2006).
75. Mears and Watson (2006); Lovell et al. (2007); Mears (2008b); Mears and Bales (2009).
76. Mears and Castro (2006).
77. Briggs et al. (2003).
78. Mears (2008a).
79. Adams (1992); Bottoms (1999).
80. Gendreau and Keyes (2001:127).
81. Mears and Castro (2006).
82. This discussion draws on Mears, Roman et al. (2006) and Mears (2007a).
83. Johnson et al. (1997); McGarrell et al. (1999); O'Connor and Pallone (2002); Henriques and Lehren (2006); Sumter (2006); U.S. Government Accountability Office (2006); O'Connor and Duncan (2008).
84. Burnside et al. (2005); Farabee (2005); Mears, Roman et al. (2006); Mears (2007a); O'Connor and Duncan (2008).
85. Sumter (2006:525); see also Johnson et al. (1997); Clear and Sumter (2002); Burnside et al. (2005); Camp et al. (2006).
86. O'Connor (2004, 2005); Mears, Roman et al. (2006); Sumter (2006); Mears (2007a); O'Connor and Duncan (2008).
87. McGarrell et al. (1999); Hodge and Pittman (2003); Stern (2006).

88. U.S. Department of Justice (1993); McGarrell et al. (1999); Branch (2002); Corrections Compendium (2003); Burnside et al. (2005); Mears, Roman et al. (2006); Mears (2007a); O'Connor and Duncan (2008).
89. Sundt, Dammer, and Cullen (2002:72).
90. Smith and Sosin (2001:653).
91. U.S. Government Accountability Office (2006:45–46).
92. Mears, Roman et al. (2006).
93. Johnson and Larson (2003).
94. Clear et al. (2000); Maruna (2001); Jensen and Gibbons (2002); O'Connor (2005).
95. Johnson et al. (2000); Clear and Sumter (2002); Burnside et al. (2005); Camp et al. (2006); Mears, Roman et al. (2006); O'Connor and Duncan (2008).
96. O'Connor and Perreyclear (2002).
97. Johnson et al. (2000); Regnerus (2003); Mears, Roman et al. (2006).
98. Regnerus (2003); Smith (2003).
99. Akers and Sellers (2009).
100. Mears, Roman et al. (2006).
101. See, for example, Lipsey (1999, 2009), Cullen and Gendreau (2000), Lipsey and Cullen (2007), and Howell (2009).
102. Martinson (1974).
103. Barlow (1995).
104. Gottfredson and Hirschi (1990).
105. Mears and Watson (2006).
106. Nagin (1998); Lilly et al. 2007; Akers and Sellers (2009).
107. See, for example, Levin et al. (2000) and Boyd et al. (2008).
108. Lynch and Sabol (2004:268); Spelman (2006).
109. Lynch and Sabol (2004); Roberts and Hough (2005a–b); Spelman (2006); Clear (2007).
110. Cullen, Fisher, and Applegate (2000); Mears, Mancini et al. (2008).
111. Roberts and Stalans (1998); Roberts et al. (2003); Roberts and Hough (2005a–b).
112. Roberts and Stalans (1998); Roberts et al. (2003); Roberts and Hough (2005a–b).
113. Wright (2003:101).
114. Levenson and D'Amora (2007:188).
115. Petrosino et al. (2003); Farabee (2005); Akers and Sellers (2009).
116. Kleiman (2004:436–437).
117. Kleiman (2004:437).
118. White and Gorman (2000).
119. Pizarro and Stenius (2004:258).
120. Lipsey (1999, 2009); Cullen and Gendreau (2000); Welsh and Farrington (2006); Lipsey and Cullen (2007); Mears (2008a); Drake et al. (2009); Howell (2009); Lipsey (2009).
121. Eskridge (2005); Farabee (2005); Mears (2007b).
122. Marx (1995).
123. White and Gorman (2000).

124. Hodgins (1993); Mears (2001a, 2004a).
125. Farrington (2002).
126. Mears (2001b).
127. Mears (2001b),
128. Butts and Roman (2004).
129. Lipsey (1998).
130. Cullen and Gendreau (2000); Welsh and Farrington (2006); Lipsey and Cullen (2007); Howell (2009); Lipsey (2009).

6.   Implementation Evaluations

1. See, generally, Chambers et al. (1992); Harrell et al. (1996); Rossi et al. (2004); Wholey et al. (2004); Chen (2005); McDavid and Hawthorn (2006); and Daponte (2008).
2. Rossi et al. (2004:170).
3. Rossi et al. (2004:171); see also Hatry (2006).
4. The full set of delivery and operational questions can be found in Rossi et al. (2004:171–172); the questions reported here are paraphrased from the original or modified. Rossi et al. do not actually distinguish the "delivery" from the "operational" questions. However, the set of questions clearly falls into these two distinct categories. Additional examples of implementation evaluation questions can be found in many other sources (e.g., Love 2004:68–69).
5. Gaes et al. (2004); Mears (2008a).
6. Burt (1981).
7. Logan (1993).
8. A full list of potentially useful indicators for each of the domains and subdomains is provided in Logan (1993:42–57).
9. Logan (1993:21).
10. Hatry (2006).
11. Love (2004:67).
12. Many sources provide detailed descriptions of different classifications and descriptions of implementation evaluations and the kinds of questions they examine. See, for example, the following texts: Chambers et al. (1992); Patton (2002); Rossi et al. (2004); Wholey et al. (2004); Chen (2005); McDavid and Hawthorn (2006); Daponte (2008); Grinnell and Unrau (2008); and Bardach (2009).
13. Poister (2004:99); see also Hatry (2006).
14. Hatry (2006:xiii).
15. Forst (2004:113).
16. Bardach (2009); Stohr and Collins (2009).
17. Gottfredson et al. (2003).
18. See, for example, Hickert et al. (2009).
19. Beck and Greenfeld (1995:4). Some states did not report data, and so not all states were represented in the study.
20. Rossi et al. (2004:75); see, generally, Hatry (2006) and Bardach (2009).

21. See, generally, Chambers et al. (1992); Harrell et al. (1996); Rossi et al. (2004); Wholey et al. (2004); Chen (2005); Hatry (2006); McDavid and Hawthorn (2006); and Daponte (2008).
22. Poister (2004:121).
23. See Kurki and Morris (2001); Haney (2003); Rhodes (2004).
24. Haney (2003); Collins (2004); Mears and Watson (2006).
25. Many texts exist that provide examples of types of implementation and performance statistics and how to present them (e.g., Love 2004; Poister 2004; Chen 2005; Hatry 2006).
26. The purposes to which implementation evaluations can be put sometimes are used to distinguish one implementation evaluation from another even though the underlying activities may be similar. For example, the main feature distinguishing so-called formative evaluations from performance-monitoring efforts consists of the former's emphasis on providing feedback that will be used to improve the design and operations of a policy versus the latter's emphasis on providing a foundation for judging agency performance and for identifying, on a regular basis, ways to improve agency efficiency.
27. Rossi et al. (2004:34–36).
28. Rossi et al. (2004:36).
29. Rossi et al. (2004:191–195).
30. Love (2004); Lipsey et al. (2005); Durlak and DuPre (2008); Lipsey (2009).
31. Rossi et al. (2004:179).
32. Mears (1998a–b, 2000).
33. Riveland (1999); Mears (2008b).
34. Butts and Travis (2002:2).
35. DiIulio (1995); Fox (1996).
36. Mears (2002b).
37. U.S. General Accounting Office (1995).
38. Mears (1998a).
39. Griffin et al. (1998); Snyder and Sickmund (2006); Griffin (2008).
40. Other classifications of transfer laws exist (e.g., Howell 2009:283–284).
41. Sanborn (1994).
42. Feld (2000:117–118); see also Sanborn (1994).
43. Mears (2003a); Howell (2009).
44. Griffin (2008:6).
45. Humes (1996:322).
46. Humes (1996:203).
47. Humes (1996:131).
48. Humes (1996:130); see also Mears (1998a–b).
49. Sanborn (1994); Mears (1998a, 2003a); Feld (1999); Kupchik (2006); Howell (2009).
50. Mears and Field (2000).
51. Howell (2009:305).
52. Howell (2009:305).
53. Sanborn (1994).

54. Butts and Mears (2001); Howell (2009).
55. Snyder et al. (2000).
56. Sanborn (1993); Mears (2000, 2003a).
57. Howell (2009:305).
58. Bishop and Frazier (2000).
59. Howell (2009:294); see, generally, Grisso (2004).
60. Hahn et al. (2007); Howell (2009). See also Johnson et al. (2009) – their study showed that an increase in recidivism can result from transferred youths leapfrogging over a series of graduated sanctions and thus not receiving interventions and treatments that were associated with lower levels of recidivism.
61. Worden (2000:222).
62. Davis et al. (2003:263–264).
63. Tjaden and Thoennes (2000:iii).
64. Mears (2003b); Hines (2009).
65. Mears (2003b).
66. Sherman and Berk (1984).
67. Maxwell et al. (2002); Bridges et al. (2008); Hines (2009); Iyengar (2009).
68. Hines (2009:125); see also Maxwell et al. (2002).
69. Hines (2009:125).
70. Hines (2009:125).
71. Humphries (2002:91).
72. Humphries (2002:91).
73. Hines (2009:125; emphasis in original).
74. Humphries (2002:92).
75. Davis et al. (2008:634).
76. Buzawa and Buzawa (2008:673).
77. Davis et al. (2008:634).
78. Buzawa and Buzawa (2008:672).
79. Garner (2005:569).
80. Belknap and Potter (2005); Dixon (2008); Iyengar (2009).
81. See, in particular, Iyengar (2009:93).
82. Garner and Maxwell (2009:46).
83. Davis et al. (2003:266).
84. See Crowell and Burgess (1996) and Chalk and King (1998) for a discussion of similar issues with a wide panoply of domestic violence laws, programs, and services.
85. Visher et al. (2008:ii).
86. Visher et al. (2008:ii and passim).
87. Feld (2009).
88. Sample and Bray (2003); Wright (2003).
89. Mears and Bacon (2009).
90. Grisso (2004); Mears (2004a–b).
91. Mears and Kelly (2002).
92. See, generally, Greene (2007).
93. Leo (2008:3).
94. Tillyer et al. (2008); Piquero (2009).

95. Linn (2009).
96. Forst (2004:103).
97. Greene (2007:750).
98. Forst (2004); Mears (2008a); Mears and Butts (2008); Mears and Bacon (2009).
99. Smith (2005).
100. Smith (2005); Gross (2008).
101. Smith (2005:189).
102. Smith (2005:189).
103. See also Forst (2004); Gross (2008).
104. A small sample of sources that discuss criminal justice policy implementation failures includes Klein and Teilmann (1980); Casper and Brereton (1984); Elliott (1997); Maguire (2004); and Mears (2007b).
105. Feld (1999).
106. U.S. General Accounting Office (2003); Lipsey et al. (2005).
107. Davis et al. (2003).
108. Buzawa and Buzawa (2008:676).
109. Lipsey (1999).
110. Dawson (1988).
111. Farabee (2005:38).
112. Perry (2003).

7. Outcome Evaluations and Impact Evaluations

1. Apparently, toothbrushing alone (i.e., without toothpaste) can greatly reduce periodontal disease, although toothpaste can enhance this effect (see, for example, Löe 2000).
2. Spelman (2009).
3. This account, described first in Malcolm (1958), comes from Mears and Stafford (2002:10).
4. See, generally, Farabee (2005); see also Bales and Mears (2008).
5. See, generally, Hatry (2006).
6. Mears and Butts (2008).
7. Curtis et al. (2004); Tolman et al. (2008).
8. Rossi et al. (2004:204).
9. Rossi et al. (2004:205); see also Poister (2004:99–100) and, more generally, Wholey et al. (2004) and Hatry (2006).
10. Hatry (2006:19). On this issue, Rossi et al. (2004:205) disagree. They treat all service delivery, even the quality of it, as outputs. That approach runs counter to much performance monitoring and evaluation research. In addition, in a criminal justice context, it means that the importance of many critical aspects of law enforcement, court, and correctional system operations and efforts might go unappreciated. Justice clearly constitutes a critical outcome, for example, and is part and parcel to what it would mean to have an effective police force or court system, regardless of impacts on crime.

11. Adapted from Hatry (2006:19).
12. Rossi et al. (2004:213).
13. See, for example, Rossi and Berk (1997).
14. Rossi et al. (2004:210–212).
15. See, for example, Langan and Levin (2002) and O'Donnell et al. (2008).
16. This discussion draws on Rossi et al. (2004:217–222). For discussions of other relevant properties for assessing measures, see standard research methods texts (e.g., Maxfield and Babbie 2005; Viswanathan 2005).
17. Hatry (2006).
18. Cummings (2006:7).
19. Although not discussed here, a large literature on causality exists (see, for example, Pearl 2000; Woodward 2003).
20. Mears, Roman et al. (2006).
21. Mears and Bales (2009); see also Lovell et al. (2007).
22. For discussions of this type of analysis, see Yaffee (2000) and Berk (2008).
23. Connell et al. (2008); this literature is discussed in more detail in the next chapter.
24. Connell et al. (2008).
25. Grinc (1994); Connell et al. (2008); Innes et al. (2009).
26. Campbell and Stanley (1966); Klein and Teilmann (1980); Shadish et al. (2002); Kaplan (2004); Rossi et al. (2004); Wholey et al. (2004); McDavid and Hawthorn (2006).
27. Rossi et al. (2004:237).
28. For an introduction to the issue of sample sizes and the question of how many are enough, see Kraemer (1987) and other social science research texts.
29. Weisburd, Lum, and Petrosino (2001:53).
30. Rossi et al. (2004:241).
31. "Statistical significance testing . . . can be used to guide a judgment about whether a specific difference is likely to have occurred simply by chance or more likely represents the effect of the intervention" (Rossi et al. 2004:240).
32. See, for example, Donohue and Wolfers (2006) and Zimmerman (2009).
33. Bishop and Frazier (2000); Butts and Mears (2001); Mears (2003a); Kupchik (2006); Hahn et al. (2007); Johnson et al. (2009).
34. For an overview of these techniques, see Rossi et al. (2004:274–297). For discussion of specific types of techniques, see any standard multivariate regression statistical text, reviews (e.g., Winship and Morgan 1999), or evaluation readers (e.g., Klein and Teilmann 1980; Wholey et al. 2004). Many sources exist that provide in-depth discussions of specific statistical methodologies. See Yaffee (2000), for example, for a systematic introduction to time-series analysis, and Caliendo and Kopeinig (2008) for an introduction to propensity score matching.
35. Rossi et al. (2004:289).
36. Rossi et al. (2004:238); see also Cummings (2006:7).
37. Rossi et al. (2004:236).
38. Johnson and Larson (2003).
39. See, generally, Mears, Roman et al. (2006).

40. Rossi et al. (2004:314–317).
41. Mears, Roman et al. (2006).
42. Farrington (2003:52).
43. These, along with selection bias, are the "classic" threats typically presented in text-books. A brief description of each follows: *history* (events occur that cause the out-come), *maturation* (subjects change in the natural course of development and not because of the intervention), *testing* (improvements in pre- versus posttests are due not to the intervention but to subjects' familiarity with the content of the test), *instrumentation* (changes in how key variables are measured may create the appear-ance of program effects), *statistical regression* (assignment of subjects to an interven-tion based on their extreme scores, which can result in their scores tending to regress to the mean at a posttest), *selection* (subjects selected for treatment may systematically differ from the control group in ways related to the outcomes of interest), *mortality* (some subjects most likely to fail or succeed, relative to some outcome, may drop out more so than others), *ambiguous temporal sequence* (it may not be clear whether the key causal variable preceded or followed the outcomes), and *selection-based interac-tions* (selection effect threat may interact with other types of threats) (McDavid and Hawthorn 2006:98–100). For further discussions, see Farrington (2003) and stan-dard texts on impact evaluations (e.g., Campbell and Stanley 1966; Shadish et al. 2002).
44. Farrington (2003:54).
45. Rossi et al. (2004:213).
46. Mears and Bhati (2006).
47. Gaes and Camp (2009).
48. Lipsey (2006).
49. Blomberg (1980).
50. Heckman and Smith (1995); Sherman (2003a); Rossi et al. (2004).
51. Rossi et al. (2004:261).
52. See, for example, Goldkamp (2008).
53. Heckman and Smith (1995:99).
54. Hines (2009:125).
55. Goldkamp (2008:112).
56. Mrazek and Haggerty (1994:372); Rossi et al. (2004:260).
57. Curtis et al. (2004).
58. Humes (1996:202).
59. Heckman and Smith (1995:105).
60. Sherman (2003a:15).
61. Rossi et al. (2004:252).
62. Feynman and Leighton (1989).
63. Rossi et al. (2004:312–313); see also Lipsey (1998) and Merrall and Bird (2009).
64. Rossi et al. (2004:309).
65. Stevens (1992:172). It typically is easier to avoid type I errors (i.e., achieving statistical significance when no true policy effect exists) (Rossi et al. (2004:309).
66. Weisburd, Lum, and Yang (2003).

67. Rossi et al. (2004:314).
68. Rossi et al. (2004:314); see also Weisburd, Lum, and Yang (2003).
69. Merrall and Bird (2009).
70. Rossi et al. (2004:315).
71. Rossi et al. (2004:322).
72. Robinson and Shapland (2008).
73. Heckman and Smith (1995:108).
74. Mears and Watson (2006).
75. Mears and Bales (2009).
76. Weisburd, Lum, and Petrosino (2001:64).
77. Rossi et al. (2004:324).
78. Sherman (2003a:15).
79. Institute of Medicine (2001).
80. Sherman (2003a:7); Millenson (1997).
81. Rossi et al. (2004:227–231).
82. Rossi et al. (2004:204).
83. Huddleston et al. (2008:2).
84. Butts and Roman (2004:2).
85. Butts and Roman (2004:3).
86. Butts and Roman (2004).
87. Butts and Roman (2004:238).
88. Huddleston et al. (2008).
89. DeMatteo et al. (2009).
90. Huddleston et al. (2008:2).
91. Merrall and Bird (2009).
92. Wilson et al. (2006).
93. Roman and DeStefano (2004); Wilson et al. (2006); cf. Huddleston et al. (2008).
94. Wilson et al. (2006:479).
95. Wilson et al. (2006:480).
96. Wilson et al. (2006:480).
97. Kleiman (2003).
98. Cook and Ludwig (2009:71).
99. Hahn et al. (2003:12).
100. Kleck and Kates (2001); Wellford et al. (2005); Cook and Ludwig (2009).
101. Cook and Ludwig (2009:73).
102. Kleck and Kates (2001).
103. Hahn et al. (2003:11).
104. Hahn et al. (2003:14).
105. Wellford et al. (2005).
106. Hahn et al. (2003:18).
107. Piquero (2005:785).
108. Cook and Ludwig (2009:77).
109. Mays and Ruddell (2008:94).

110. Worrall (2008:326–327).
111. Cook and Ludwig (2009:92).
112. Kleck and Kates (2001:332).
113. Cook and Ludwig (2009:91); see also Kleck and Kates (2001:332).
114. Piquero (2005:779).
115. A small sample of reviews of or commentaries on the issue includes Sherman et al. (1997); Sherman et al. (2002); Sherman (2003a, 2004); Berk (2005); Eskridge (2005); Farabee (2005); Lipsey et al. (2005); and Mears (2007b).
116. Sherman et al. (1997).
117. See Farrington's (2003:57) discussion.
118. Farrington and Welsh (2005:29).
119. Huizinga and Henry (2008:225, 243–244).
120. Nagin (1998); Sabol (1999); Western (2006); Blumstein and Piquero (2007); Akers and Sellers (2009).
121. See, for example, Blumstein (1998) and Nagin (1998).
122. Pager (2007:145).
123. Clear (2007).
124. Petersilia et al. (2008:2); see, generally, Cullen and Gendreau (2000); Travis (2005); Travis and Visher (2005).

8. Cost-Efficiency Evaluations

1. In reality, a consumer might be concerned about several qualitatively different outcomes (e.g., reliable transportation, comfort, prestige). In that case, the calculus becomes more complicated and, as the discussion in this chapter highlights, would require a cost-benefit analysis rather than a cost-effectiveness analysis.
2. Many people, especially those in poverty, do not obtain dental treatment for themselves or their children (Hoffman and Paradise 2008).
3. Collier (2006:166).
4. Cohen (2005:7); see also Roman and Farrell (2002).
5. Cohen (2005); Bushway and Reuter (2008).
6. Miller et al. (1996).
7. Tonry (2009:16).
8. Cohen (2005).
9. Cohen (2005).
10. Cohen (2005:94).
11. Weimer and Friedman (1979).
12. For discussions of cost-benefit analysis, see Kee (2004), Rossi et al. (2004), McDavid and Hawthorn (2006), and Bardach (2009). For discussions of cost-benefit analysis in criminal justice, see Dhiri and Brand (1999), Cohen (2000, 2005), Cook and Ludwig (2000); Welsh and Farrington (2000), Nagin (2001), Roman and Harrell (2001), Aos (2002), Roman and Farrell (2002), Aos et al. (2006), Bushway and Reuter (2008), Marsh et al. (2008), and Drake et al. (2009). See Cohen and

Piquero (2009) concerning estimates of the monetary value of saving high-risk youth and the methodology for arriving at the estimates.

13. Cohen (2000); Cook and Ludwig (2000).
14. Cohen (2000:277).
15. This example and the discussion of it draws on Lawrence and Mears (2004).
16. See, for example, Cohen (2000, 2005) and Cook and Ludwig (2000).
17. Kee (2004:509).
18. Kee (2004:509).
19. Kee (2004:510).
20. Welsh and Farrington (2000:351).
21. See, for example, Aos et al. (2006:37).
22. Cohen (2000:278–279).
23. Kee (2004:511).
24. Dhiri and Brand (1999:18).
25. Dhiri and Brand (1999:18).
26. Rossi et al. (2004:356).
27. For example, Cohen (2000) has emphasized the importance of distinguishing external costs and social costs. "An external cost is a cost imposed by one person onto another.... Social costs are costs that reduce the aggregate well-being of society" (p. 272). A stolen car can be viewed as entailing an external cost (the victim lost the use of his or her car) but not a social cost (in aggregate, the victim's loss is offset by the offender's gain). However, economists disagree about the issue, with some arguing that stolen cars create social costs by forcing consumers to purchase security equipment and to take a variety of measures to avoid victimization (p. 272). The issue underscores the conceptual dimensions that factor prominently into cost-benefit analysis.
28. Cohen (2000:278).
29. Hatry (2006).
30. Lawrence and Mears (2004:14).
31. Cohen (2000:290).
32. See, especially, Cohen (2000, 2005).
33. Cohen (2000:288–289).
34. Cook and Ludwig (2000); Bushway and Reuter (2008).
35. Aos (2002); Cohen and Piquero (2009).
36. Marsh et al. (2009:153).
37. Cohen (2000); Aos (2002); Aos et al. (2006).
38. Welsh and Farrington (2000).
39. Aos (2002:12).
40. Kee (2004:537).
41. U.S. Office of Management and Budget (1992).
42. Aos et al. (2006:14).
43. Rossi et al. (2004:359).
44. Kee (2004:528); Lawrence and Mears (2004:4).
45. Lawrence and Mears (2004).

46. McDavid and Hawthorn (2006:243).
47. Gaes et al. (2004).
48. Bardach (2009:111–125).
49. Rossi et al. (2004:336).
50. Mears and Bhati (2006).
51. Cohen (2005); Tonry (2008).
52. Cohen (2000:276).
53. Kee (2004:539).
54. McDavid and Hawthorn (2006:249–250).
55. Marsh et al. (2008:128).
56. See, however, Hatry (2006:22).
57. The community policing literature is vast. Some sources include Rosenbaum et al. (1998); Alpert and Piquero (2000); Greene (2000); Skogan (2003, 2006); Skogan and Frydl (2004); Cordner and Biebel (2005); Worrall and Kovandzic (2007); Connell et al. (2008); Williamson (2008); and Innes et al. (2009).
58. Alpert and Piquero (2000).
59. Schafer (2001:25–26) has provided a systematic comparison of traditional policing and community policing.
60. Alpert and Piquero (2000); Schafer (2001); Cordner and Biebel (2005); Collier (2006); Connell et al. (2008); Innes et al. (2009).
61. Horowitz and Zedlewski (2006).
62. See, for example, Greene (2000), Worrall and Kovandzic (2007), Connell et al. (2008), and Innes et al. (2009).
63. See, for example, Connell et al. (2008).
64. Cordner and Biebel (2005:157–158).
65. Cordner and Biebel (2005:157).
66. Cordner and Biebel (2005); Weisburd et al. (2008).
67. Worrall and Kovandzic (2007:159).
68. See Cohen (2005).
69. Sabol et al. (2009:39).
70. Sabol et al. (2009:39).
71. Many accounts of the prison privatization debate exist – see, for example, Harding (1997); Reisig and Pratt (2000); Perrone and Pratt (2003); Tabarrok (2003); Gaes et al. (2004); Bales et al. (2005); Thomas (2005); Gaes (2008); and Mays and Ruddell (2008).
72. Gaes (2008).
73. Gaes et al. (2004); Gaes (2008).
74. See, generally, Gaes et al. (2004) and Gaes (2008); see also Office of Program and Policy Analysis and Government Accountability (2008).
75. Gaes et al. (2004); Gaes (2008).
76. Mears (2008a).
77. Gaes (2008:35).
78. Gaes et al. (2004).

79. Cohen (2000, 2005); Welsh and Farrington (2000); Gaes et al. (2004); Swaray et al. (2005); Horowitz and Zedlewski (2006); Mears (2007b); Bushway and Reuter (2008); Marsh et al. (2008).

80. Welsh and Farrington (2000:307).

81. See, however, Pager (2007).

82. Freeman (2008:408).

83. Mears and Bacon (2009).

84. Cullen and Gendreau (2000); Gaes and Camp (2009); Lipsey (2009).

85. Cohen (2000, 2005); Welsh and Farrington (2000); Aos et al. (2006); Bushway and Reuter (2008); Marsh et al. (2008, 2009); Cohen and Piquero (2009); Raphael and Stoll (2009).

86. Aos et al. (2006:11).

87. Aos et al. (2006:11).

88. Aos et al. (2006:9).

89. Aos et al. (2006:9).

90. Greenberg (1990); Donohue (2009); Marsh et al. (2009); Spelman (2009).

91. Cohen and Piquero (2009:25).

92. Lipsey (2009).

93. Roman and Butts (2005).

94. Bushway and Reuter (2008).

9. Conclusion

1. Eskridge (2005:305).

2. Forst (2004); Mears and Bacon (2009).

3. Klein and Teilmann (1980); Blumstein and Petersilia (1995); Sherman et al. (1997); Cullen and Gendreau (2000); Sherman et al. (2002); Tilley (2002); Gaes et al. (2004); Eskridge (2005); Lipsey et al. (2005); Welsh and Farrington (2006); Lipsey and Cullen (2007); Mears (2008a); Mears and Butts (2008); Worrall (2008); Lipsey (2009).

4. Mears and Bacon (2009).

5. Welsh and Harris (2008).

6. Rossi (1980:897).

7. Petersilia (1991); Mears (2007b).

8. Petersilia (1991:12–13).

9. Two examples merit mention. First, Peter Reuter, a professor at the University of Maryland, offers a course on policy analysis that includes an emphasis on many dimensions, not simply research methods, involved in such analysis (Reuter 2006). In the past, for instance, the course has included an emphasis on how to develop and present advice to policy makers concerning critical policy-related questions and how to be creative in drawing on different sources of information to inform the advice that is given. Second, Harvard's John F. Kennedy School of Government

offers courses on policy analysis that emphasize an introduction to a range of similar considerations. One course, Seminar on Criminal Justice Policy and Management, focuses specifically on crime policy.

10. Rossi (1980); Petersilia (1991); Sjoberg and Vaughn (1993).
11. Piquero et al. (2007); Mears, Wang et al. (2008).
12. Sparks et al. (1996); Mears and Reisig (2006).
13. Petersilia (1991); Cullen (2005).
14. Wellford (1997:7).
15. See, generally, Sorensen et al. (2006), Steiner et al. (2006), Kleck et al. (2007), and Jennings et al. (2008).
16. Cullen and Gendreau (2000).
17. Rossi (1980:902–903).
18. As Rossi (1980:903) has noted: "We [in academia] should not lift our eyebrows when our better graduate students take non-academic research positions, conveying the notion that by doing so they have left the company of the elect."
19. Petersilia (1991:14).
20. Petersilia (1991:12–13); see also Clear (2001).
21. Chilton (2001); Oliver and Marion (2008).
22. Blumstein (1997); Cullen and Gendreau (2000).
23. Travis (2005); Travis and Visher (2005); Mears, Wang et al. (2008).
24. Blumstein and Petersilia (1995); Farabee (2005).
25. Chambers et al. (1992); Rossi et al. (2004); Chen (2005); Bardach (2009).
26. Rossi (1980:894).
27. Rossi (1980:894).
28. Rossi (1980:895).
29. Rossi (1980:895).
30. Pratt and Cullen (2005); Akers and Seller (2009).
31. Merton (1968, 1973); Sjoberg and Vaughn (1993).
32. The literature on risk prediction is vast. A sampling of some reviews and illustrative articles include: Cullen and Gendreau (2000); Benda et al. (2001); Krysik and LeCroy (2002); Campbell et al. (2007); Onifade et al. (2008); Schwalbe (2008).
33. Rossi (1980); Petersilia (1991); Blumstein and Petersilia (1995); Wellford (1997); Cullen and Gendreau (2000); Clear (2001); Sherman (2004); Cullen (2005); Lipsey et al. (2005).
34. Farabee (2005:67–68).
35. Petersilia (1991); Blumstein (1997); American Evaluation Association (2004); Weiss et al. (2008).
36. Weiss et al. (2008).
37. Rossi (1980); Petersilia (1991); Clear (2001); Sherman (2004).
38. Clear (2001:725).
39. Petersilia (1991:12).
40. Mears (2007b).
41. Cullen and Gendreau (2000); Sherman (2004).
42. Listwan et al. (2008:444–446).
43. This discussion draws on and extends arguments in Mears (2007b).

44. Mears (2008a).
45. Mears and Watson (2006).
46. Mears and Reisig (2006).
47. Welsh and Harris (2008:263).
48. Logan (1993); Mears (2008a); Mears and Bacon (2009).
49. Farrington (2003); Sherman (2003b); Tonry (2004); Farabee (2005).
50. Lipsey et al. (2005:2).
51. Farrington (2000:17); see also Farrington and Welsh (2005).
52. See, generally, Sparks et al. (1996), Mears and Kelly (1999), Forst (2004), Mears and Bacon (2009).
53. Mrazek and Haggerty (1994); Sherman et al. (2002); Farrington (2003); Sherman (2003b); Rossi et al. (2004); Lipsey et al. (2005); Tilley (2009).
54. Heckman and Smith (1995).
55. See, for example, Mears and Kelly (2002); see, generally, Rossi et al. (2004).
56. Butts and Roman (2004).
57. Gottfredson et al. (2003).
58. Welsh and Farrington (2000:352).
59. Lawrence and Mears (2004).
60. Lawrence and Mears (2004).
61. This discussion draws on Mears (2008a).
62. Gaes et al. (2004).
63. Logan (1993); Gaes et al. (2004); Mears (2008a).
64. Burt (1981).
65. Logan (1993).
66. Gaes et al. (2004:38).
67. Burt (1981); Logan (1993); Sparks et al. (1996); Bottoms (1999); Gendreau and Keyes (2001); Gaes et al. (2004).
68. See, for example, Sherman (2004:169).
69. Mears (2008a).
70. Sherman (2004:170).
71. Gaes et al. (2004:9).
72. Forst (2004).
73. Basu et al. (1999).
74. Blumstein (1997:360).
75. Cullen (2005:28).
76. Sherman (2004:171).
77. Sherman (2004:171).
78. See, for example, Chilton (2001).
79. Blumstein and Petersilia (1995:485).
80. A small sampling of scholarship in this area includes Sherman et al. (1997); Lipsey (1999, 2009); Cullen and Gendreau (2000); Butts and Mears (2001); Mihalic et al. (2001); MacKenzie (2006); Perry et al. (2006); Welsh and Farrington (2006); Drake et al. (2009); Howell (2009); and Lipsey (2009). See also the work from the Campbell Collaboration (http://www.campbellcollaboration.org).
81. Sherman et al. (1997).

82. The mission of the Campbell Collaboration, as stated on its web site, is "[to help] people make well-informed decisions by preparing, maintaining and disseminating systematic reviews in education, crime and justice, and social welfare"; the collaboration's efforts are "based on voluntary cooperation among researchers of a variety of backgrounds" (http://www.campbellcollaboration.org/about_us/index.php).

83. Crime and Justice Institute (2004).

84. See, for example, Curtis et al. (2004); Lipsey and Cullen (2007); Lipsey (2009); Welsh and Farrington (2009).

85. The list of crimes comes from Tonry's (2009) edited volume on crime and policy. Notably, genocide was not included but clearly would belong in any list of crimes for which effective policies are needed (Maier-Katkin et al. 2009).

86. Cullen (2005:27).

87. Petersilia (1991); Blumstein and Petersilia (1995); Cullen and Gendreau (2000).

88. Lipsey and Cullen (2007:314–315); Lipsey (2009).

89. Wellford (1997); Forst (2004); Gaes et al. (2004).

90. Eskridge (2005:303).

91. See, for example, Petersilia (1991), Crime and Justice Institute (2004), Cullen (2005), Farrington and Welsh (2006), Van Voorhis et al. (2007), Drake et al. (2009), Howell (2009), Lipsey (2009).

92. Roberts (1992); Skolnick (1995); Cullen and Gendreau (2000); Roberts et al. (2003); Roberts and Hough (2005b).

93. Marion and Oliver (2006); Welsh and Harris (2008).

94. Cullen and Gendreau (2000:160).

95. For a different view of the matter, see Walter et al. (2005) and Weiss et al. (2008) and their concerns about the limits of "imposed use" – that is, situations in which "government agencies . . . impose the use of evaluation evidence on local policymakers and practitioners" (Weiss et al. 2008:30). For example, in some cases, "applicants for federal program funds [must] show that the program they wish to run has been scientifically evaluated and found effective" (p. 30). She and her colleagues found that considerable ambiguity exists about which programs are deemed effective and that experts use varying criteria for their assessments (p. 43).

96. Garland (2001).

97. Stolz (2002); Robinson (2003); Eskridge (2005); Marion and Oliver (2006); Welsh and Harris (2008).

98. Skolnick (1995); Blumstein (1997); Laub (2004); Tonry (2004).

References

Adams, Kenneth. 1992. "Adjusting to Prison Life." *Crime and Justice* 16:275–359.

Agnew, Robert. 2005. *Why Do Criminals Offend? A General Theory of Crime and Delinquency*. Los Angeles: Roxbury.

Akers, Ronald L., and Christine S. Sellers. 2009. *Criminological Theories: Introduction, Evaluation, and Application*. 5th edition. New York: Oxford University Press.

Alpert, Geoffrey P., and Alex R. Piquero, eds. 2000. *Community Policing*. 2nd edition. Prospect Heights, IL: Waveland Press.

American Evaluation Association. 2004. *Guiding Principles for Evaluators*. Fairhaven, MA: American Evaluation Association.

Aos, Steve. 2002. *Cost-Benefit Analysis for Juvenile Justice Programs*. Washington, DC: Justice Research and Statistics Association.

Aos, Steve, Marna Miller, and Elizabeth Drake. 2006. *Evidence-Based Public Policy Options to Reduce Future Prison Construction, Criminal Justice Costs, and Crime Rates*. Olympia, WA: State Institute for Public Policy.

Austin, James, and John Irwin. 2001. *It's About Time: America's Imprisonment Binge*. Belmont, CA: Wadsworth.

Baird, Robert M., and Stuart E. Rosenbaum, eds. 1988. *Philosophy of Punishment*. Buffalo, NY: Prometheus Books.

Bales, William D., Laura E. Bedard, Susan T. Quinn, David T. Ensley, and Glen P. Holley. 2005. "Recidivism of Public and Private State Prison Inmates in Florida." *Criminology and Public Policy* 4:57–82.

Bales, William D., and Daniel P. Mears. 2008. "Inmate Social Ties and the Transition to Society: Does Visitation Reduce Recidivism?" *Journal of Research in Crime and Delinquency* 45:287–321.

Bardach, Eugene. 2009. *A Practical Guide for Policy Analysis: The Eightfold Path to More Effective Problem Solving*. 3rd edition. New York: CQ Press.

———. 2004. "Presidential Address – The Extrapolation Problem: How Can We Learn from the Experience of Others?" *Journal of Policy Analysis and Management* 23:205–220.

Barlow, Hugh D., ed. 1995. *Crime and Public Policy: Putting Theory to Work*. Boulder, CO: Westview Press.

289

Barnes, J. C., Tony Dukes, Richard Tewksbury, and Timothy M. De Troye. 2009. "Analyzing the Impact of a Statewide Residence Restriction Law on South Carolina Sex Offenders." *Criminal Justice Policy Review* 20:21–43.

Bartosh, Darci L., Tina Garby, Deborah Lewis, and Steve Gray. 2003. "Differences in the Predictive Validity of Actuarial Risk Assessments in Relation to Sex Offender Type." *International Journal of Offender Therapy and Comparative Criminology* 47:422–438.

Basu, Onker N., Mark W. Dirsmith, and Parveen P. Gupta. 1999. "The Coupling of the Symbolic and the Technical in an Institutionalized Context: The Negotiated Order of the GAO's Audit Reporting Process." *American Sociological Review* 64:506–526.

Beck, Allen J., and Lawrence A. Greenfeld. 1995. *Violent Offenders in State Prison: Sentences and Time Served*. Washington, DC: Bureau of Justice Statistics.

Beckett, Katherine. 1997. *Making Crime Pay: Law and Order in Contemporary American Politics*. New York: Oxford University Press.

Beckett, Katherine, and Theodore Sasson. 2004. *The Politics of Injustice: Crime and Punishment in America*. 2nd edition. Thousand Oaks, CA: Sage.

Beech, Anthony R., Dawn D. Fisher, and David Thornton. 2003. "Risk Assessment of Sex Offenders." *Professional Psychology: Research and Practice* 34:339–352.

Belknap, Joanne, and Hillary Potter. 2005. "The Trials of Measuring the 'Success' of Domestic Violence Policies." *Criminology and Public Policy* 4:559–566.

Benda, Brent B., Robert F. Corwyn, and Nancy J. Toombs. 2001. "Recidivism among Adolescent Serious Offenders: Prediction of Entry into the Correctional System for Adults." *Criminal Justice and Behavior* 28:588–613.

Berger, Joseph, and Morris Zelditch Jr., eds. 1993. *Theoretical Research Programs: Studies in the Growth of Theory*. Stanford, CA: Stanford University Press.

Berk, Richard A. 2008. "Forecasting Methods in Crime and Justice." *Annual Review of Law and Social Science* 4:219–238.

———. 2005. "Knowing When to Fold 'Em: An Essay on Evaluating the Impact of Ceasefire, Compstat, and Exile." *Criminology and Public Policy* 4:451–466.

Bernard, Thomas J. 1992. *The Cycle of Juvenile Justice*. New York: Oxford University Press.

Bhati, Avi, John Roman, and Aaron Chalfin. 2008. *Evidence on the Prospects of Expanding Treatment to Drug-Involved Offenders*. Washington, DC: Urban Institute.

Bishop, Donna M., and Charles E. Frazier. 2000. "Consequences of Transfer." Pp. 227–276 in *The Changing Boundaries of Juvenile Justice: Transfer of Adolescents to the Criminal Court*, edited by Jeffrey Fagan and Franklin E. Zimring. Chicago: University of Chicago Press.

Blalock, Hubert M., Jr. 1994. "Why Have We Failed to Systematize Reality's Complexities?" Pp. 121–136 in *Formal Theory in Sociology*, edited by Jerald Hage. Albany: State University of New York Press.

Blau, Joel, and Mimi Abramovitz. 2007. *The Dynamics of Social Welfare Policy*. New York: Oxford University Press.

Blomberg, Thomas G. 1980. "Widening the Net: An Anomaly in the Evaluation of Diversion Programs." Pp. 572–592 in *Handbook of Criminal Justice Evaluation*, edited by Malcolm W. Klein and Katherine S. Teilmann. Beverly Hills, CA: Sage.

Blomberg, Thomas G., and Gordon P. Waldo. 2002. "Evaluation Research, Policy, and Politics." *Evaluation Review* 26:340–351.

Blumstein, Alfred. 2008. "Federal Support of Local Criminal Justice." *Criminology and Public Policy* 7:351–358.

———. 1998. "U.S. Criminal Justice Conundrum: Rising Prison Populations and Stable Crime Rates." *Crime and Delinquency* 44:127–135.

———. 1997. "Interaction of Criminological Research and Public Policy." *Journal of Quantitative Criminology* 12:349–362.

Blumstein, Alfred, and Allen J. Beck. 1999. "Population Growth in U.S. Prisons, 1980–1996." Pp. 17–61 in *Prisons*, edited by Michael H. Tonry and Joan Petersilia. Chicago: University of Chicago Press.

Blumstein, Alfred, and Joan Petersilia. 1995. "Investing in Criminal Justice Research." Pp. 465–487 in *Crime*, edited by James Q. Wilson and Joan Petersilia. San Francisco: Institute for Contemporary Studies Press.

Blumstein, Alfred, and Alex R. Piquero. 2007. "Restore Rationality to Sentencing Policy." *Criminology and Public Policy* 6:679–687.

Blumstein, Alfred, Michael H. Tonry, and Asheley van Ness. 2005. "Cross-National Measures of Punitiveness." *Crime and Justice* 33:347–376.

Blumstein, Alfred, and Joel Wallman. 2006. *The Crime Drop in America*. 2nd edition. New York: Cambridge University Press.

Boin, Arjen. 2001. "Securing Safety in the Dutch Prison System: Pros and Cons of a Supermax." *Howard Journal* 40:335–346.

Bottoms, Anthony E. 1999. "Interpersonal Violence and Social Order in Prisons." Pp. 205–282 in *Prisons*, edited by Michael H. Tonry and Joan Petersilia. Chicago: University of Chicago Press.

Bovens, Mark, Thomas Schillemans, and Paul T. Hart. 2008. "Does Public Accountability Work? An Assessment Tool." *Public Administration* 86:225–242.

Bowers, Kate J., Shane D. Johnson, and Alex F. G. Hirschfield. 2004. "Closing Off Opportunities for Crime: An Evaluation of Alley-Gating." *European Journal on Criminal Policy and Research* 10:285–308.

Boyd, Rebecca J., Sheila M. Huss, and David L. Myers. 2008. "Antecedents and Consequences of Juvenile Case Processing: Where Are We Now, and Where Do We Go from Here?" *Youth Violence and Juvenile Justice* 6:195–220.

Braden, Maria. 1996. *Women Politicians and the Media*. Lexington: University Press of Kentucky.

Branch, Alvia Y. 2002. *Faith and Action: Implementation of the National Faith-Based Initiative for High-Risk Youth*. Philadelphia: Public/Private Ventures.

Bridges, F. Stephen, Kimberly M. Tatum, and Julie C. Kunselman. 2008. "Domestic Violence Statutes and Rates of Intimate Partner and Family Homicide." *Criminal Justice Policy Review* 19:117–130.

Briggs, Chad S., Jody L. Sundt, and Thomas C. Castellano. 2003. "The Effect of Supermaximum Security Prisons on Aggregate Levels of Institutional Violence." *Criminology* 41:1341–1376.

Burnside, Jonathan, Nancy Loucks, Joanna R. Adler, and Gerry Rose. 2005. *My Brother's Keeper: Faith-Based Units in Prisons*. Portland, OR: Willan.

Burt, Martha R. 1981. *Measuring Prison Results: Ways to Monitor and Evaluate Corrections Performance*. Washington, DC: National Institute of Justice.

Bushway, Shawn, and Peter Reuter. 2008. "Economists' Contribution to the Study of Crime and the Criminal Justice System." *Crime and Justice* 37:389–451.

Butts, Jeffrey A., and William Adams. 2001. *Anticipating Space Needs in Juvenile Detention and Correctional Facilities*. Washington, DC: Office of Juvenile Justice and Delinquency Prevention.

Butts, Jeffrey A., and Daniel P. Mears. 2001. "Reviving Juvenile Justice in a Get-Tough Era." *Youth and Society* 33:169–198.

Butts, Jeffrey A., and John Roman, eds. 2004. *Juvenile Drug Courts and Teen Substance Abuse*. Washington, DC: Urban Institute.

Butts, Jeffrey A., and Jeremy Travis. 2002. *The Rise and Fall of American Youth Violence: 1980 to 2000*. Washington, DC: Urban Institute.

Buzawa, Eve S., and Aaron D. Buzawa. 2008. "Courting Domestic Violence Victims: A Tale of Two Cities." *Criminology and Public Policy* 7:671–685.

Caliendo, Marco, and Sabine Kopeinig. 2008. "Some Practical Guidance for the Implementation of Propensity Score Matching." *Journal of Economic Surveys* 22:31–72.

Camp, Scott D., Jody Klein-Saffran, Okyun Kwon, Dawn M. Daggett, and Victoria Joseph. 2006. "An Exploration into Participation in a Faith-Based Prison Program." *Criminology and Public Policy* 5:529–550.

Campbell, Donald T., and Julian C. Stanley. 1966. *Experimental and Quasi-Experimental Designs for Research*. Chicago: Rand McNally.

Campbell, Mary Ann, Sheila French, and Paul Gendreau. 2007. *Assessing the Utility of Risk Assessment Tools and Personality Measures in the Prediction of Violent Recidivism for Adult Offenders*. St. John, Canada: University of New Brunswick-Saint John, Centre for Criminal Justice Studies.

Casper, Jonathan D., and David Brereton. 1984. "Evaluating Criminal Justice Reforms." *Law and Society Review* 18:121–144.

Catalano, Shannan M. 2006. *Criminal Victimization, 2005*. Washington, DC: Bureau of Justice Statistics.

Chalk, Rosemary, and Patricia A. King, eds. 1998. *Violence in Families: Assessing Prevention and Treatment Programs*. Washington, DC: National Research Council and Institute of Medicine.

Chambers, Donald E., Kenneth R. Wedel, and Mary K. Rodwell. 1992. *Evaluating Social Programs*. Boston: Allyn and Bacon.

Chelimsky, Eleanor. 1985. "Comparing and Contrasting Auditing and Evaluation: Some Notes on Their Relationship." *Evaluation Review* 9:483–503.

Chen, Huey Tsyh. 2005. *Practical Program Evaluation: Assessing and Improving Planning, Implementation, and Effectiveness*. Thousand Oaks, CA: Sage.

Chilton, Roland. 2001. "Viable Policy: The Impact of Federal Funding and the Need for Independent Research Agendas – The American Society of Criminology 2000 Presidential Address." *Criminology* 39:1–8.

Clear, Todd R. 2007. *Imprisoning Communities: How Mass Incarceration Makes Disadvantaged Neighborhoods Worse.* New York: Oxford University Press.

——. 2001. "Has Academic Criminal Justice Come of Age? ACJS Presidential Address." *Justice Quarterly* 18:709–726.

Clear, Todd R., Patricia L. Hardyman, Bruce Stout, Karol Lucken, and Harry R. Dammer. 2000. "The Value of Religion in Prison: An Inmate Perspective." *Journal of Contemporary Criminal Justice* 16:53–74.

Clear, Todd R., and Melvina T. Sumter. 2002. "Prisoners, Prison, and Religion: Religion and Adjustment to Prison." Pp. 127–159 in *Religion, the Community, and the Rehabilitation of Criminal Offenders,* edited by Thomas P. O'Connor and Nathaniel J. Pallone. New York: Haworth Press.

Cohen, Mark A. 2005. *The Costs of Crime and Justice.* New York: Routledge.

——. 2000. "Measuring the Costs and Benefits of Crime and Justice." Pp. 263–315 in *Measurement and Analysis of Crime and Justice,* edited by David Duffee. Washington, DC: National Institute of Justice.

Cohen, Mark A., and Alex R. Piquero. 2009. "New Evidence on the Monetary Value of Saving High-Risk Youth." *Journal of Quantitative Criminology* 25:25–49.

Collier, Paul M. 2006. "In Search of Purpose and Priorities: Police Performance Indicators in England and Wales." *Public Money and Management* 26:165–172.

Collins, William C. 2004. *Supermax Prisons and the Constitution: Liability Concerns in the Extended Control Unit.* Washington, DC: National Institute of Corrections.

Connell, Nadine M., Kristin Miggans, and Jean M. McGloin. 2008. "Can a Community Policing Initiative Reduce Serious Crime?" *Police Quarterly* 11:127–150.

Cook, Philip J., and Jens Ludwig. 2009. "Firearm Violence." Pp. 71–114 in *The Oxford Handbook of Crime and Public Policy,* edited by Michael H. Tonry. New York: Oxford University Press.

——. 2000. *Guns and Violence: The Real Costs.* New York: Oxford University Press.

Cordner, Gary, and Elizabeth P. Biebel. 2005. "Problem-Oriented Policing in Practice." *Criminology and Public Policy* 4:155–180.

Corrections Compendium. 2003. "Faith-Based Programming." *Corrections Compendium* 28(8):8–20.

Council of State Governments. 2006. *CSG Launches Initiative on State Sex Offender Management Policy.* Press Release, May 5. Lexington, KY: Council of State Governments.

Crime and Justice Institute. 2004. *Implementing Evidence-Based Principles in Community Corrections: The Principles of Effective Intervention.* Boston: Crime and Justice Institute.

Crouch, Ben M., and James W. Marquart. 1989. *An Appeal to Justice: Litigated Reform of Texas Prisons.* Austin: University of Texas Press.

Crowell, Nancy A., and Ann W. Burgess, eds. 1996. *Understanding Violence against Women.* Washington, DC: National Academy of Sciences.

Cullen, Francis T. 2005. "The Twelve People Who Saved Rehabilitation: How the Science of Criminology Made a Difference." *Criminology* 43:1–42.

Cullen, Francis T., Bonnie S. Fisher, and Brandon K. Applegate. 2000. "Public Opinion about Punishment and Corrections." *Crime and Justice* 27:1–79.

Cullen, Francis T., and Paul Gendreau. 2000. "Assessing Correctional Rehabilitation: Policy, Practice, and Prospects." Pp. 109–175 in *Policies, Processes, and Decisions of the Criminal Justice System*, edited by Julie Horney. Washington, DC: National Institute of Justice.

Cullen, Francis T., John P. Wright, Shayna Brown, Melissa M. Moon, Michael B. Blankenship, and Brandon K. Applegate. 1998. "Public Support for Early Intervention Programs: Implications for a Progressive Policy Agenda." *Crime and Delinquency* 44:187–204.

Cummings, Rick. 2006. "'What If': The Counterfactual in Program Evaluation." *Evaluation Journal of Australasia* 6:8–15.

Curtis, Nicola M., Kevin R. Ronan, and Charles M. Borduin. 2004. "Multisystemic Treatment: A Meta-Analysis of Outcome Studies." *Journal of Family Psychology* 18:411–419.

Daponte, Beth O. 2008. *Evaluation Essentials: Methods for Conducting Sound Research*. San Francisco: Jossey-Bass.

Davis, Robert C., Barbara E. Smith, and Bruce Taylor. 2003. "Increasing the Proportion of Domestic Violence Arrests That Are Prosecuted: A Natural Experiment in Milwaukee." *Criminology and Public Policy* 2:263–282.

Davis, Robert C., Chris S. O'Sullivan, Donald J. Farole Jr., and Michael Rempel. 2008. "A Comparison of Two Prosecution Policies in Cases of Intimate Partner Violence: Mandatory Case Filing versus Following the Victim's Lead." *Criminology and Public Policy* 7:633–662.

Dawson, Robert O. 1988. "The Third Justice System: The New Juvenile-Criminal System of Determinate Sentencing for the Youthful Violent Offender in Texas." *St. Mary's Law Journal* 19:943–1016.

DeBeck, Kora, Thomas Kerr, Kathy Li, M. J. Milloy, Julio Montaner, and Evan Wood. 2009. "Incarceration and Drug Use Patterns among a Cohort of Injection Drug Users." *Addiction* 104:69–76.

DeFina, Robert, and Lance Hannon. 2009. "The Impact of Mass Incarceration on Poverty." *Crime and Delinquency*. Available online: http://cad.sagepub.com/pap.dtl (accessed December 16, 2009).

DeMatteo, David, Douglas B. Marlowe, David S. Festinger, and Patricia L. Arabia. 2009. "Outcome Trajectories in Drug Court: Do All Participants Have Serious Drug Problems?" *Criminal Justice and Behavior* 36:354–368.

Dhiri, Sanjay, and Sam Brand. 1999. *Analysis of Costs and Benefits: Guidance for Evaluators*. London: Home Office.

DiIulio, John J., Jr. 1995. "Moral Poverty." *Chicago Tribune*, December 15, A31.

———. 1987. *Governing Prisons*. New York: Free Press.

Dixon, Jo. 2008. "Mandatory Domestic Violence Arrest and Prosecution Policies: Recidivism and Social Governance." *Criminology and Public Policy* 7:663–670.

Donohue, John J. 2009. "Assessing the Relative Benefits of Incarceration: Overall Changes and the Benefits on the Margin." Pp. 269–341 in *Do Prisons Make Us Safer? The Benefits and Costs of the Prison Boom*, edited by Steven Raphael and Michael A. Stoll. New York: Russell Sage Foundation.

Donohue, John J., and Justin Wolfers. 2006. "Uses and Abuses of Empirical Evidence in the Death Penalty Debate." *Stanford Law Review* 58:791–846.

Doren, Dennis M. 2006. "Recidivism Risk Assessments: Making Sense of Controversies." Pp. 3–15 in *Sexual Offender Treatment: Controversial Issues*, edited by William L. Marshall, Yolanda M. Fernandez, Liam E. Marshall, and Geris A. Serran. Hoboken, NJ: Wiley.

———. 2004. "Toward a Multidimensional Model for Sexual Recidivism Risk." *Journal of Interpersonal Violence* 19:835–856.

Downie, Robin S., and Jane Macnaughton. 2000. *Clinical Judgment: Evidence in Practice*. New York: Oxford University Press.

Drake, Elizabeth K., Steve Aos, and Marna G. Miller. 2009. "Evidence-Based Public Policy Options to Reduce Crime and Criminal Justice Costs: Implications in Washington State." *Violence and Victims* 4:170–196.

Durlak, Joseph A., and Emily P. DuPre. 2008. "Implementation Matters: A Review of Research on the Influence of Implementation on Program Outcomes and the Factors Affecting Implementation." *American Journal of Community Psychology* 41:327–350.

Elliott, Delbert S. 1997. "Implementing and Evaluating Crime Prevention and Control Programs and Policies." *Crime, Law, and Social Change* 28:287–310.

Elsner, Alan. 2004. *Gates of Injustice: The Crisis in America's Prisons*. Upper Saddle River, NJ: Pearson.

Eskridge, Chris W. 2005. "The State of the Field of Criminology." *Journal of Contemporary Criminal Justice* 21:296–308.

Fagan, Jeffrey, and Franklin E. Zimring, eds. 2000. *The Changing Borders of Juvenile Justice: Waiver of Juveniles to the Criminal Court*. Chicago: University of Chicago Press.

Farabee, David. 2005. *Rethinking Rehabilitation: Why Can't We Reform Our Criminals?* Washington, DC: AEI Press.

Farrington, David P. 2003. "Methodological Quality Standards for Evaluation Research." *Annals of the American Academy of Political and Social Science* 587:49–68.

———. 2002. "Families and Crime." Pp. 129–148 in *Crime: Public Policies for Crime Control*, edited by James Q. Wilson and Joan Petersilia. Oakland, CA: Institute for Contemporary Studies Press.

———. 2000. "Explaining and Preventing Crime: The Globalization of Knowledge – The American Society of Criminology 1999 Presidential Address." *Criminology* 38:1–24.

Farrington, David P., and Brandon C. Welsh. 2007. *Saving Children from a Life of Crime: Early Risk Factors and Effective Interventions*. New York: Oxford University Press.

———. 2005. "Randomized Experiments in Criminology: What Have We Learned in the Last Two Decades?" *Journal of Experimental Criminology* 1:9–38.

Fauci, Anthony S., Eugene Braunwald, Dennis L. Kasper, Stephen L. Hauser, Dan L. Longo, J. Larry Jameson, and Joseph Loscalzo. 2008. *Harrison's Principles of Internal Medicine*. 17th edition. New York: McGraw-Hill.

Feeley, Malcolm M., and Jonathan Simon. 1992. "The New Penology: Notes on the Emerging Strategy of Corrections and Its Implication." *Criminology* 30:449–474.

Feld, Barry C. 2009. *Cases and Materials on Juvenile Justice Administration*. 3rd edition. St. Paul, MN: West.

———. 2004. "Juvenile Transfer." *Criminology and Public Policy* 3:599–604.

_____. 2000. "Legislative Exclusion of Offenses." Pp. 83–144 in *The Changing Borders of Juvenile Justice: Waiver of Juveniles to the Criminal Court*, edited by Jeffrey Fagan and Franklin E. Zimring. Chicago: University of Chicago Press.

_____. 1999. *Bad Kids: Race and the Transformation of the Juvenile Court*. New York: Oxford University Press.

Feynman, Richard P., and Ralph Leighton. 1989. *What Do You Care What Other People Think? Further Adventures of a Curious Character*. New York: Bantam.

Flanagan, Timothy J., and Dennis R. Longmire, eds. 1996. *Americans View Crime and Justice: A National Public Opinion Survey*. Thousand Oaks, CA: Sage.

Forst, Brian. 2004. *Errors of Justice: Nature, Sources, and Remedies*. New York: Cambridge University Press.

Fox, James A. 1996. *Trends in Juvenile Violence: A Report to the United States Attorney General on Current and Future Rates of Juvenile Offending*. Washington, DC: Bureau of Justice Statistics.

Fox, James A., and Marianne W. Zawitz. 2007. *Homicide Trends in the United States*. Washington, DC: Bureau of Justice Statistics. Available online: http://www.ojp.usdoj.gov/bjs/homicide/homtrnd.htm (accessed December 16, 2009).

Frampton, Mary L., Ian H. López, and Jonathan Simon, eds. 2008. *After the War on Crime: Race, Democracy, and a New Reconstruction*. New York: New York University Press.

Freeman, Richard. 2008. "Incarceration, Criminal Background Checks, and Employment in a Low(er) Crime Society." *Criminology and Public Policy* 7:405–412.

Friedman, Lawrence M. 1993. *Crime and Punishment in American History*. New York: Basic Books.

Gaes, Gerald G. 2008. "Cost, Performance Studies Look at Prison Privatization." *National Institute of Justice Journal* 259:32–36.

Gaes, Gerald G., and Scott D. Camp. 2009. "Unintended Consequences: Experimental Evidence for the Criminogenic Effect of Prison Security Level Placement on Post-Release Recidivism." *Journal of Experimental Criminology* 5:139–162.

Gaes, Gerald G., Scott D. Camp, Julianne B. Nelson, and William G. Saylor. 2004. *Measuring Prison Performance: Government Privatization and Accountability*. New York: AtlaMira Press.

Garland, David. 2001. *The Culture of Control: Crime and Social Order in Contemporary Society*. Chicago: University of Chicago Press.

Garner, Joel. 2005. "What Does 'the Prosecution' of Domestic Violence Mean?" *Criminology and Public Policy* 4:567–574.

Garner, Joel H., and Christopher D. Maxwell. 2009. "Prosecution and Conviction Rates for Intimate Partner Violence." *Criminal Justice Review* 34:44–79.

Gawande, Atul. 2007. *Better: A Surgeon's Notes on Performance*. New York: Metropolitan Books.

Gendreau, Paul, and David Keyes. 2001. "Making Prisons Safer and More Humane Environments." *Canadian Journal of Criminology* 43:123–130.

_____. 1998. *Performance Measurement and Evaluation: Definitions and Relationships*. Washington, DC: U.S. General Accounting Office.

Gentry, Amanda L., Catherine N. Dulmus, and Matthew T. Theriot. 2005. "Comparing Sex Offender Classification Using the Static-99 and LSI-R Assessment Instruments." *Research on Social Work Practice* 15:557–563.

Gibbs, Jack P. 1985. "The Methodology of Theory Construction in Criminology." Pp. 23–50 in *Theoretical Methods in Criminology*, edited by Robert F. Meier. Beverly Hills, CA: Sage.

Goldkamp, John S. 2008. "Missing the Target and Missing the Point: 'Successful' Random Assignment but Misleading Results." *Journal of Experimental Criminology* 4:83–115.

———. 2003. "The Impact of Drug Courts." *Criminology and Public Policy* 2:197–206.

Goodnough, Abby, and Monica Davey. 2007. "For Sex Offenders, Dispute on Therapy's Benefits." *New York Times*, A1, March 6.

Gottfredson, Denise C., Stacy S. Najaka, and Brook Kearley. 2003. "Effectiveness of Drug Treatment Courts: Evidence from a Randomized Trial." *Criminology and Public Policy* 2:171–196.

Gottfredson, Michael R., and Travis Hirschi. 1990. *A General Theory of Crime*. Stanford, CA: Stanford University Press.

Gottschalk, Marie. 2008. "Hiding in Plain Sight: American Politics and the Carceral State." *Annual Review of Political Science* 11:235–260.

———. 2006. *The Prison and the Gallows: The Politics of Mass Incarceration in America*. New York: Cambridge University Press.

Greenberg, David F. 1990. "The Cost-Benefit Analysis of Imprisonment." *Social Justice* 17:49–75.

Greenberg, David F., and Valerie West. 2001. "State Prison Populations and Their Growth, 1971–1991." *Criminology* 39:615–653.

Greene, Jack R. 2007. "Making Police Oversight Independent and Transparent." *Criminology and Public Policy* 6:747–754.

———. 2000. "Community Policing in America: Changing the Nature, Structure, and Function of the Police." Pp. 299–370 in *Policies, Processes, and Decisions of the Criminal Justice System*, edited by Julie Horney. Washington, DC: National Institute of Justice.

Greenfeld, Lawrence A. 1995. *Prison Sentences and Time Served for Violence*. Washington, DC: Bureau of Justice Statistics.

Griffin, Patrick. 2008. *Different from Adults: An Updated Analysis of Juvenile Transfer and Blended Sentencing Laws, with Recommendations for Reform*. Pittsburgh, PA: National Center for Juvenile Justice.

Griffin, Patrick, Patricia Torbet, and Linda Szymanski. 1998. *Trying Juveniles as Adults in Criminal Court: An Analysis of State Transfer Provisions*. Washington, DC: Office of Juvenile Justice and Delinquency Prevention.

Grinc, Randolph M. 1994. "'Angels in Marble': Problems in Stimulating Community Involvement in Community Policing." *Crime and Delinquency* 40:437–468.

Grinnell, Richard M., Jr., and Yvonne A. Unrau. 2008. *Social Work Research and Evaluation: Foundations of Evidence-Based Practice*. 8th edition. New York: Oxford University Press.

Grisso, Thomas. 2004. *Double Jeopardy: Adolescent Offenders with Mental Disorders.* Chicago: University of Chicago Press.

Groopman, Jerome. 2007. *How Doctors Think.* Boston: Houghton Mifflin.

Gross, Samuel R. 2008. "Convicting the Innocent." *Annual Review of Law and Social Science* 4:173–192.

Hahn, Robert A., Oleg O. Bilukha, Alex Crosby, Mindy T. Fullilove, Akiva Liberman, Eve K. Moscicki, Susan Snyder, Farris Tuma, and Peter Briss. 2003. *Evaluating the Effectiveness of Strategies for Preventing Violence: Firearms Laws.* Atlanta, GA: Centers for Disease Control.

Hahn, Robert A., Angela McGowan, Akiva Liberman, Alex Crosby, Mindy Fullilove, Robert Johnson, Eve Moscicki, LeShawndra Price, Susan Snyder, Farris Tuma, Jessica Lowy, Peter Briss, Stella Cory, and Glenda Stone. 2007. *Effects on Violence of Laws and Policies Facilitating the Transfer of Youth from the Juvenile to the Adult Justice System.* Atlanta: Centers for Disease Control.

Haney, Craig. 2003. "Mental Health Issues in Long-Term Solitary and 'Supermax' Confinement." *Crime and Delinquency* 49:124–156.

Hanson, R. Karl. 2006. "Stability and Change: Risk Factors for Sexual Offenders." Pp. 17–31 in *Sexual Offender Treatment: Controversial Issues*, edited by William L. Marshall, Yolanda M. Fernandez, Liam E. Marshall, and Geris A. Serran. Hoboken, NJ: Wiley.

Hanson, R. Karl, and Kelly Morton-Bourgon. 2004. *Predictors of Sexual Recidivism: An Updated Meta-Analysis.* User Report 2004–02. Ottawa: Public Safety and Emergency Preparedness Canada.

Hanson, R. Karl, Kelly E. Morton, and Andrew J. R. Harris. 2003. "Sexual Offender Recidivism Risk: What We Know and What We Need to Know." *Annals of the New York Academy of Sciences* 989:154–166.

Harding, Richard W. 1997. *Private Prisons and Public Accountability.* New Brunswick, NJ: Transaction.

Harrell, Adele, Martha Burt, Harry Hatry, Shelli Rossman, Jeffrey Roth, and William Sabol. 1996. *Evaluation Strategies for Human Services Programs: A Guide for Policymakers and Providers.* Washington, DC: Urban Institute.

Harris, Grant T., Marnie E. Rice, Vernon L. Quinsey, Martin L. Lalumiere, Douglas Boer, and Carol Lang. 2003. "A Multisite Comparison of Actuarial Risk Instruments for Sex Offenders." *Psychological Assessment* 15:413–425.

Hart, Stephen D., Christine Michie, and David J. Cooke. 2007. "Precision of Actuarial Risk Assessment Instruments: Evaluating the 'Margins of Error' of Group v. Individual Predictions of Violence." *British Journal of Psychiatry* 49:60–65.

Hartley, Richard D. 2008. "Sentencing Reforms and the War on Drugs: An Analysis of Sentence Outcomes for Narcotics Offenders Adjudicated in U.S. District Courts on the Southwest Border." *Journal of Contemporary Criminal Justice* 24:437–461.

Hatry, Harry P. 2006. *Performance Measurement: Getting Results.* 2nd edition. Washington, DC: Urban Institute.

Hatry, Harry P., Joseph S. Wholey, and Kathryn E. Newcomer. 2004. "Other Issues and Trends in Evaluation." Pp. 670–684 in *Handbook of Practical Program Evaluation*, 2nd edition, edited by Joseph S. Wholey, Harry P. Hatry, and Kathryn E. Newcomer. San Francisco: Jossey-Bass.

Haugtvedt, Curtis P., Paul M. Herr, and Frank R. Kardes, eds. 2008. *Handbook of Consumer Psychology*. New York: Psychology Press.

Heckman, James J., and Jeffrey A. Smith. 1995. "Assessing the Case for Social Experiments." *Journal of Economic Perspectives* 9:85–110.

Henriques, Diana B., and Andrew Lehren. 2006. "Religion for Captive Audience, with Taxpayers Footing the Bill." *New York Times*, December 10, A1, 32–33.

Hickert, Audrey O., Scott W. Boyle, and Derrik R. Tollefson. 2009. "Factors that Predict Drug Court Completion and Drop Out: Findings from an Evaluation of Salt Lake County's Adult Felony Drug Court." *Journal of Social Service Research* 35:149–162.

Hickman, Matthew J., Alex R. Piquero, and Joel H. Garner. 2008. "Toward a National Estimate of Police Use of Nonlethal Force." *Criminology and Public Policy* 7:563–604.

Hines, Denise A. 2009. "Domestic Violence." Pp. 115–139 in *The Oxford Handbook of Crime and Public Policy*, edited by Michael H. Tonry. New York: Oxford University Press.

Hodge, David R., and Jason Pittman. 2003. "Faith-Based Drug and Alcohol Treatment Providers: An Exploratory Study of Texan Providers." *Journal of Social Service Research* 30:19–40.

Hodgins, Sheilagh, ed. 1993. *Mental Disorder and Crime*. Newbury Park, CA: Sage.

Hoffman, Catherine, and Julia Paradise. 2008. "Health Insurance and Access to Health Care in the United States." *Annals of the New York Academy of Sciences* 1136:149–160.

Holden, Debra J., and Marc A. Zimmerman. 2009. *A Practical Guide to Program Evaluation Planning: Theory and Case Examples*. Thousand Oaks, CA: Sage.

Horowitz, Jake, and Edwin Zedlewski. 2006. "Applying Cost-Benefit Analysis to Policing Evaluations." *Justice Research and Policy* 8:51–66.

Howell, James C. 2009. *Preventing and Reducing Juvenile Delinquency: A Comprehensive Framework*. 2nd edition. Thousand Oaks, CA: Sage.

Huddleston, C. West, Douglas B. Marlowe, and Rachel Casebolt. 2008. *Painting the Current Picture: A National Report Card on Drug Courts and Other Problem-Solving Court Programs in the United States*. Alexandria, VA: National Drug Court Institute.

Huff, C. Ronald. 2002. "Wrongful Conviction and Public Policy: The American Society of Criminology 2001 Presidential Address." *Criminology* 40:1–18.

Hughes, Kristen A. 2006. *Justice Expenditure and Employment in the United States, 2001*. Washington, DC: Bureau of Justice Statistics.

Huizinga, David, and Kimberly L. Henry. 2008. "The Effect of Arrest and Justice System Sanctions on Subsequent Behavior: Findings from Longitudinal and Other Studies." Pp. 220–254 in *The Long View of Crime: A Synthesis of Longitudinal Research*, edited by Akiva M. Liberman. New York: Springer.

Humes, Edward. 1996. *No Matter How Loud I Shout: A Year in the Life of Juvenile Court*. New York: Simon and Schuster.

Humphries, Drew. 2002. "No Easy Answers: Public Policy, Criminal Justice, and Domestic Violence." *Criminology and Public Policy* 2:91–96.

Imbens, Guido. 2000. "The Role of Propensity Score in Estimating Dose-Response Functions." *Biometrica* 87:706–710.

Immarigeon, Russ. 1986. "Surveys Reveal Broad Support for Alternative Sentencing." *Journal of the National Prison Project* 9:1–4.

Innes, Martin, Laurence Abbott, Trudy Lowe, and Colin Roberts. 2009. "Seeing Like a Citizen: Field Experiments in 'Community Intelligence-led Policing.'" *Police Practice and Research* 10:99–114.

Institute of Medicine. 2001. *Crossing the Quality Chasm: A New Health System for the 21st Century*. Committee on Quality of Health Care in America. Washington, DC: National Academy Press.

Irwin, John. 2005. *The Warehouse Prison: Disposal of the New Dangerous Class*. Los Angeles: Roxbury.

Iyengar, Radha. 2009. "Does the Certainty of Arrest Reduce Domestic Violence? Evidence from Mandatory and Recommended Arrest Laws." *Journal of Public Economics* 93:85–98.

Jacobs, David, and Jason T. Carmichael. 2001. "The Politics of Punishment across Time and Space: A Pooled Time-Series Analysis of Imprisonment Rates." *Social Forces* 80: 61–91.

Jennings, Wesley G., Chris L. Gibson, Jeffrey T. Ward, and Kevin M. Beaver. 2008. "'Which Group Are You In?': A Preliminary Investigation of Group-Based Publication Trajectories of Criminology and Criminal Justice Scholars." *Journal of Criminal Justice Education* 19:227–250.

Jensen, Kenneth D., and Stephen G. Gibbons. 2002. "Shame and Religion as Factors in the Rehabilitation of Serious Offenders." *Journal of Offender Rehabilitation* 35:215–230.

Johnson, Byron R., Spencer De Li, David B. Larson, and Michael McCullough. 2000. "A Systematic Review of the Religiosity and Delinquency Literature." *Journal of Contemporary Criminal Justice* 16:32–52.

Johnson, Byron R., and David B. Larson. 2003. *The InnerChange Freedom Initiative: A Preliminary Evaluation of a Faith-Based Prison Program*. Philadelphia: Center for Research on Religion and Urban Civil Society.

Johnson, Byron R., David B. Larson, and Timothy C. Pitts. 1997. "Religious Programs, Institutional Adjustment, and Recidivism among Former Inmates in Prison Fellowship Programs." *Justice Quarterly* 14:145–166.

Johnson, Kristin, Lonn Lanza-Kaduce, and Jennifer Woolard. 2009. "Disregarding Graduated Treatment: Why Transfer Aggravates Recidivism." *Crime and Delinquency*. Available online: http://cad.sagepub.com/pap.dtl (accessed December 16, 2009).

Kaplan, David. 2004. *The Sage Handbook of Quantitative Methodology for the Social Sciences*. Thousand Oaks, CA: Sage.

Kee, James E. 2004. "Cost-Effectiveness and Cost-Benefit Analysis." Pp. 506–541 in *Handbook of Practical Program Evaluation*, 2nd edition, edited by Joseph S. Wholey, Harry P. Hatry, and Kathryn E. Newcomer. San Francisco: Jossey-Bass.

Kemshall, Hazel, and Gill McIvor, eds. 2004. *Managing Sex Offender Risk*. Philadelphia: Jessica Kingsley Publishers.

King, Roy D. 2005. "Effects of Supermax Custody." Pp. 118–145 in *The Effects of Imprisonment*, edited by Alison Liebling and Shadd Maruna. Portland, OR: Willan Publishing.

_____. 1999. "The Rise and Rise of Supermax: An American Solution in Search of a Problem?" *Punishment and Society* 1:163–186.

King, Ryan S. 2009. *The State of Sentencing 2008: Developments in Policy and Practice.* Washington, DC: Sentencing Project.

Kleck, Gary, and Don B. Kates. 2001. *Armed: New Perspectives on Gun Control.* New York: Prometheus.

Kleck, Gary, Shun-Yung K. Wang, and Jongyeon Tark. 2007. "Article Productivity among the Faculty of Criminology and Criminal Justice Doctoral Programs, 2000–2005." *Journal of Criminal Justice Education* 18:385–405.

Kleiman, Mark A. R. 2004. "Toward (More Nearly) Optimal Sentencing for Drug Offenders." *Criminology and Public Policy* 3:435–440.

———. 2003. "Drug Courts Can Work: Would Something Else Work Better?" *Criminology and Public Policy* 2:167–170.

Klein, Malcolm W., and Katherine S. Teilmann, eds. 1980. *Handbook of Criminal Justice Evaluation.* Beverly Hills, CA: Sage.

Knepper, Paul. 2007. *Criminology and Social Policy.* Thousand Oaks, CA: Sage.

Kopczynski, Mary E., and Kathleen Pritchard. 2004. "The Use of Evaluation by Nonprofit Organizations." Pp. 649–669 in *Handbook of Practical Program Evaluation*, 2nd edition, edited by Joseph S. Wholey, Harry P. Hatry, and Kathryn E. Newcomer. San Francisco: Jossey-Bass.

Kraemer, Helena C. 1987. *How Many Subjects? Statistical Power Analysis in Research.* Thousand Oaks, CA: Sage.

Kramer, John H. 2009. "Mandatory Sentencing Guidelines: The Framing of Justice." *Criminology and Public Policy* 8:313–321.

Krouse, William J., Celinda Franco, and Nathan James. 2008. *Department of Justice (DOJ) Appropriations for FY2008 and FY2009.* Washington, DC: Congressional Research Service.

Krysik, Judy, and Craig W. LeCroy. 2002. "The Empirical Validation of an Instrument to Predict Risk of Recidivism among Juvenile Offenders." *Research on Social Work Practice* 12:71–81.

Kupchik, Aaron. 2006. *Judging Juveniles: Prosecuting Adolescents in Adult and Juvenile Courts.* New York: New York University Press.

Kurki, Leena, and Norval Morris. 2001. "Supermax Prisons." *Crime and Justice* 28:385–424.

La Fond, John Q. 2005. *Preventing Sexual Violence: How Society Should Cope with Sex Offenders.* Washington, DC: American Psychological Association.

LaFree, Gary. 2007. "Expanding Criminology's Domain: The American Society of Criminology 2006 Presidential Address." *Criminology* 45:1–31.

Langan, Patrick A. 2005. "Crime and Punishment in the United States, 1981–1999." *Crime and Justice* 33:123–159.

Langan, Patrick A., and David J. Levin. 2002. *Recidivism of Prisoners Released in 1994.* Washington, DC: Bureau of Justice Statistics.

Langan, Patrick A., Erica L. Schmitt, and Matthew R. Durose. 2003. *Recidivism of Sex Offenders Released from Prison in 1994.* Washington, DC: Bureau of Justice Statistics.

Langton, Calvin M., Howard E. Barbaree, Michael C. Seto, Edward J. Peacock, Leigh Harkins, and Kevin T. Hansen. 2007. "Actuarial Assessment of Risk for Reoffense among Adult Sex Offenders: Evaluating the Predictive Accuracy of the Static-2002 and Five Other Instruments." *Criminal Justice and Behavior* 34:37–59.

Laub, John H. 2004. "The Life Course of Criminology in the United States: The American Society of Criminology 2003 Presidential Address." *Criminology* 42:1–26.

Lawrence, Sarah, and Daniel P. Mears. 2004. *Benefit-Cost Analysis of Supermax Prisons: Critical Steps and Considerations*. Washington, DC: Urban Institute.

Leo, Richard A. 2008. *Police Interrogation and American Justice*. Cambridge, MA: Harvard University Press.

Levenson, Jill S., and Leo P. Cotter. 2005. "The Impact of Sex Offender Residence Restrictions: 1,000 Feet from Danger or One Step from Absurd?" *International Journal of Offender Therapy and Comparative Criminology* 49:168–178.

Levenson, Jill S., and David A. D'Amora. 2007. "Social Policies Designed to Prevent Sexual Violence: The Emperor's New Clothes?" *Criminal Justice Policy Review* 18:168–199.

Levin, David J., Patrick A. Langan, and Jodi M. Brown. 2000. *State Court Sentencing of Convicted Felons, 1996*. Washington, DC: Bureau of Justice Statistics.

Liberman, Akiva M., ed. 2008. *The Long View of Crime: A Synthesis of Longitudinal Research*. New York: Springer.

Lilly, J. Robert, Francis T. Cullen, and Richard A. Ball. 2007. *Criminological Theory: Context and Consequences*. 4th edition. Thousand Oaks, CA: Sage.

Linn, Edith. 2009. *Arrest Decisions: What Works for the Officer?* New York: Peter Lang Publishing.

Lipsey, Mark W. 2009. "The Primary Factors That Characterize Effective Interventions with Juvenile Offenders: A Meta-Analytic Review." *Victims and Offenders* 4:124–147.

———. 2006. "The Effects of Community-Based Group Treatment for Delinquency." Pp. 162–184 in *Deviant Peer Influences in Programs for Youth: Problems and Solutions*, edited by Kenneth A. Dodge, Thomas J. Dishion, and Jennifer E. Lansford. New York: Guilford Press.

———. 1999. "Can Rehabilitative Programs Reduce the Recidivism of Juvenile Offenders? An Inquiry into the Effectiveness of Practical Programs." *Virginia Journal of Social Policy and Law* 6:611–641.

———. 1998. "Design Sensitivity: Statistical Power for Applied Experimental Research." Pp. 39–68 in *Handbook of Applied Social Research Methods*, edited by Leonard Bickman and Debra J. Rog. Thousand Oaks, CA: Sage.

Lipsey, Mark W., John L. Adams, Denise C. Gottfredson, John V. Pepper, David Weisburd, eds. 2005. *Improving Evaluation of Anticrime Programs*. Washington, DC: National Academies Press.

Lipsey, Mark W., and Francis T. Cullen. 2007. "The Effectiveness of Correctional Rehabilitation: A Review of Systematic Reviews." *Annual Review of Law and Social Science* 3:297–320.

Liska, Allen E. 1992. *Social Threat and Social Control*. Albany: State University of New York Press.

Liska, Allen E., Fred E. Markowitz, Rachel Bridges-Whaley, and Paul E. Bellair. 1999. "Modeling the Relationships between the Criminal Justice and Mental Health Systems." *American Journal of Sociology* 104:1742–1773.

Listwan, Shelley J., Cheryl L. Jonson, Francis T. Cullen, and Edward J. Latessa. 2008. "Cracks in the Penal Harm Movement: Evidence from the Field." *Criminology and Public Policy* 7:423–466.

Loë, Harald. 2000. "Oral Hygiene in the Prevention of Caries and Periodontal Disease." *International Dental Journal* 50:129–139.

Logan, Charles. 1993. "Criminal Justice Performance Measures for Prisons." Pp. 15–59 in *Performance Measures for the Criminal Justice System*. Washington DC: Bureau of Justice Statistics.

Logan, Wayne A. 2003. "Sex Offender Registration and Community Notification: Emerging Legal and Research Issues." *Annals of the New York Academy of Sciences* 989:337–351.

Love, Arnold. 2004. "Implementation Evaluation." Pp. 63–97 in *Handbook of Practical Program Evaluation*, 2nd edition, edited by Joseph S. Wholey, Harry P. Hatry, and Kathryn E. Newcomer. San Francisco: Jossey-Bass.

Lovell, David, L. Clark Johnson, and Kevin C. Cain. 2007. "Recidivism of Supermax Prisoners in Washington State." *Crime and Delinquency* 53:633–656.

Lurigio, Arthur J. 2000. "Drug Treatment Availability and Effectiveness." *Criminal Justice and Behavior* 27:495–528.

Lynch, James P., and Lynn A. Addington, eds. 2007. *Understanding Crime Statistics: Revisiting the Divergence of the NCVS and UCR*. New York: Cambridge University Press.

Lynch, James P., and William J. Sabol. 2004. "Assessing the Effects of Mass Incarceration on Informal Social Control in Communities." *Criminology and Public Policy* 3:267–294.

———. 2001. *Prisoner Reentry in Perspective*. Washington, DC: Urban Institute.

Maahs, Jeff, and John Liederbach. 2007. "Surfing for Porn: Obscenity and the Internet." Pp. 251–624 in *Current Legal Issues in Criminal Justice*, edited by Craig Hemmens. Los Angeles: Roxbury.

MacKenzie, Doris L. 2006. *What Works in Corrections: Reducing the Criminal Activities of Offenders and Delinquents*. New York: Cambridge University Press.

Maguire, Mike. 2004. "The Crime Reduction Programme in England and Wales: Reflections on the Vision and the Reality." *Criminal Justice* 4:213–237.

Maier-Katkin, Daniel, Daniel P. Mears, and Thomas J. Bernard. 2009. "Towards a Criminology of Crimes against Humanity." *Theoretical Criminology* 13:227–255.

Malcolm, Norman. 1958. *Ludwig Wittgenstein: A Memoir*. New York: Oxford University Press.

Marini, Margaret M., and Burton Singer. 1988. "Causality in the Social Sciences." Pp. 347–409 in *Sociological Methodology*, edited by Clifford C. Clogg. Washington, DC: American Sociological Association.

Marion, Nancy E., and Willard M. Oliver. 2009. "Congress, Crime, and Budgetary Responsiveness: A Study in Symbolic Politics." *Criminal Justice Policy Review* 20:115–135.

————. 2006. *The Public Policy of Crime and Criminal Justice*. Upper Saddle River, NJ: Prentice Hall.

Marsh, Kevin, Aaron Chalfin, and John K. Roman. 2008. "What Does Cost-Benefit Analysis Add to Decision Making? Evidence from the Criminal Justice Literature." *Journal of Experimental Criminology* 4:117–135.

Marsh, Kevin, Chris Fox, and Carol Hedderman. 2009. "Do You Get What You Pay For? Assessing the Use of Prison from an Economic Perspective." *Howard Journal of Criminal Justice* 48:144–157.

Marshall, William L., Yolanda M. Fernandez, Liam E. Marshall, and Geris A. Serran, eds. 2006. *Sexual Offender Treatment: Controversial Issues*. Hoboken, NJ: Wiley.

Martinez, Pablo E. 2008. "Projecting Prison Populations Starting with Projected Admissions." *Prison Journal* 88:493–516.

Martinson, Robert. 1974. "What Works? Questions and Answers about Prison Reform." *Public Interest* 35:22–54.

Maruna, Shadd. 2001. *Making Good: How Ex-Convicts Reform and Rebuild Their Lives*. Washington, DC: American Psychological Association.

Marx, Gary T. 1995. "The Engineering of Social Control: The Search for the Silver Bullet." Pp. 225–246 in *Crime and Inequality*, edited by John Hagan and Ruth Peterson. Palo Alto, CA: Stanford University Press.

Maxfield, Michael G., and Earl Babbie. 2005. *Research Methods for Criminal Justice and Criminology*. 4th edition. Belmont, CA: Thomson Wadsworth.

Maxwell, Christopher D., Joel H. Garner, and Jeffrey A. Fagan. 2002. "The Preventative Effects of Arrest on Intimate Partner Violence: Research, Policy, and Theory." *Criminology and Public Policy* 2:51–80.

Mays, G. Larry, and Rick Ruddell. 2008. *Making Sense of Criminal Justice Policies and Practices*. New York: Oxford University Press.

McCorkle, Richard C., Terance D. Miethe, and Kriss A. Drass. 1995. "The Roots of Prison Violence: A Test of the Deprivation, Management, and Not-So-Total Institution Models." *Crime and Delinquency* 41:317–331.

McCulloch, Trish, and Lynn Kelly. 2007. "Working with Sex Offenders in Context: Which Way Forward?" *Probation Journal* 54:7–21.

McDavid, James C., and Laura R. L. Hawthorn. 2006. *Program Evaluation and Performance Measurement: An Introduction to Practice*. Thousand Oaks, CA: Sage.

McGarrell, Edmund F. 1991. "Differential Effects of Juvenile Justice Reform on Incarceration Rates of States." *Crime and Delinquency* 37:262–280.

McGarrell, Edmund F., Greg Brinker, and Diana Etindi. 1999. *The Role of Faith-Based Organizations in Crime Prevention and Justice*. Washington, DC: Hudson Institute.

McLaughlin, John A., and Gretchen B. Jordan. 2004. "Using Logic Models." Pp. 7–32 in *Handbook of Practical Program Evaluation*, 2nd edition, edited by Joseph S. Wholey, Harry P. Hatry, and Kathryn E. Newcomer. San Francisco: Jossey-Bass.

Mears, Daniel P. 2008a. "Accountability, Efficiency, and Effectiveness in Corrections: Shining a Light on the Black Box of Prison Systems." *Criminology and Public Policy* 7:143–152.

―――. 2008b. "An Assessment of Supermax Prisons Using an Evaluation Research Framework." *Prison Journal* 88:43–68.

―――. 2007a. "Faith-Based Reentry Programs: Cause for Concern or Showing Promise?" *Corrections Today* 69(2):30–33.

―――. 2007b. "Towards Rational and Evidence-Based Crime Policy." *Journal of Criminal Justice* 35:667–682.

―――. 2006a. *Evaluating the Effectiveness of Supermax Prisons*. Washington, DC: Urban Institute.

―――. 2006b. "Exploring State-Level Variation in Juvenile Incarceration Rates: Symbolic Threats and Competing Explanations." *Prison Journal* 86:470–490.

―――. 2004a. "Mental Health Needs and Services in the Criminal Justice System." *Houston Journal of Health Law and Policy* 4:255–284.

―――. 2004b. "Identifying Adolescent Substance Abuse." Pp. 185–220 in *Juvenile Drug Courts and Teen Substance Abuse*, edited by Jeffrey A. Butts and John Roman. Washington, DC: Urban Institute Press.

―――. 2003a. "A Critique of Waiver Research: Critical Next Steps in Assessing the Impacts of Laws for Transferring Juveniles to the Criminal Justice System." *Youth Violence and Juvenile Justice* 1:156–172.

―――. 2003b. "Research and Interventions to Reduce Domestic Violence Revictimization." *Trauma, Violence, and Abuse* 4:127–147.

―――. 2002a. *The Role of Statistical Models in Planning Juvenile Corrections Capacity*. Washington, DC: Urban Institute.

―――. 2002b. "Sentencing Guidelines and the Transformation of Juvenile Justice in the Twenty-First Century." *Journal of Contemporary Criminal Justice* 18:6–19.

―――. 2001a. "Critical Challenges in Addressing the Mental Health Needs of Juvenile Offenders." *Justice Policy Journal* 1:41–61.

―――. 2001b. "The Immigration-Crime Nexus: Toward an Analytic Framework for Assessing and Guiding Theory, Research, and Policy." *Sociological Perspectives* 44:1–19.

―――. 2000. "Assessing the Effectiveness of Juvenile Justice Reforms: A Closer Look at the Criteria and the Impacts on Diverse Stakeholders." *Law and Policy* 22:175–202.

―――. 1998a. "Evaluation Issues Confronting Juvenile Justice Sentencing Reforms: A Case Study of Texas." *Crime and Delinquency* 44:443–463.

―――. 1998b. "The Sociology of Sentencing: Reconceptualizing Decision-Making Processes and Outcomes." *Law and Society Review* 32:667–724.

Mears, Daniel P., and Sarah Bacon. 2009. "Improving Criminal Justice through Better Decision Making: Lessons from the Medical System." *Journal of Criminal Justice* 37:142–154.

Mears, Daniel P., and William D. Bales. 2009. "Supermax Incarceration and Recidivism." *Criminology* 47:801–836.

Mears, Daniel P., and Avinash S. Bhati. 2006. "No Community Is an Island: The Effects of Resource Deprivation on Urban Violence in Spatially and Socially Proximate Communities." *Criminology* 44:509–548.

Mears, Daniel P., and Jeffrey A. Butts. 2008. "Using Performance Monitoring to Improve the Accountability, Operations, and Effectiveness of Juvenile Justice." *Criminal Justice Policy Review* 19:264–284.

Mears, Daniel P., and Jennifer L. Castro. 2006. "Wardens' Views on the Wisdom of Supermax Prisons." *Crime and Delinquency* 52:398–431.

Mears, Daniel P., and Samuel H. Field. 2000. "Theorizing Sanctioning in a Criminalized Juvenile Court." *Criminology* 38:983–1020.

Mears, Daniel P., Carter Hay, Marc Gertz, and Christina Mancini. 2007. "Public Opinion and the Foundation of the Juvenile Court." *Criminology* 45:223–258.

Mears, Daniel P., and William R. Kelly. 2002. "Linking Process and Outcomes in Evaluating a Statewide Drug Treatment Program for Youthful Offenders." *Crime and Delinquency* 48:99–115.

———. 1999. "Assessments and Intake Processes in Juvenile Justice Processing: Emerging Policy Considerations." *Crime and Delinquency* 45:508–552.

Mears, Daniel P., Christina Mancini, Marc Gertz, and Jake Bratton. 2008. "Sex Crimes, Children, and Pornography: Public Views and Public Policy." *Crime and Delinquency* 54:532–559.

Mears, Daniel P., and Michael D. Reisig. 2006. "The Theory and Practice of Supermax Prisons." *Punishment and Society* 8:33–57.

Mears, Daniel P., Caterina G. Roman, Ashley Wolff, and Janeen Buck. 2006. "Faith-Based Efforts to Improve Prisoner Reentry: Assessing the Logic and Evidence." *Journal of Criminal Justice* 34:351–367.

Mears, Daniel P., Michelle L. Scott, and Avinash S. Bhati. 2007a. "A Process and Outcome Evaluation of an Agricultural Crime Prevention Initiative." *Criminal Justice Policy Review* 18:51–80.

———. 2007b. *A Process and Impact Evaluation of the Agricultural Crime, Technology, Information, and Operations Network (ACTION) Program*. Washington, DC: Urban Institute.

———. 2007c. "Opportunity Theory and Agricultural Crime Victimization." *Rural Sociology* 72:151–184.

Mears, Daniel P., and Mark C. Stafford. 2002. "Central Analytical Issues in the Generation of Cumulative Sociological Knowledge." *Sociological Focus* 35:5–24.

Mears, Daniel P., and Christy A. Visher. 2005. "Trends in Understanding and Addressing Domestic Violence." *Journal of Interpersonal Violence* 20:204–211.

Mears, Daniel P., Xia Wang, Carter Hay, and William D. Bales. 2008. "Social Ecology and Recidivism: Implications for Prisoner Reentry." *Criminology* 46:301–340.

Mears, Daniel P., and Jamie Watson. 2006. "Towards a Fair and Balanced Assessment of Supermax Prisons." *Justice Quarterly* 23:232–270.

Mears, Daniel P., Laura Winterfield, John Hunsaker, Gretchen E. Moore, and Ruth M. White. 2003. *Drug Treatment in the Criminal Justice System: The Current State of Knowledge*. Washington, DC: Urban Institute.

Merrall, Elizabeth L. C., and Sheila M. Bird. 2009. "A Statistical Perspective on the Design of Drug-Court Studies." *Evaluation Review* 33:257–280.

Merton, Robert K. 1973. *The Sociology of Science: Theoretical and Empirical Investigations*. Chicago: University of Chicago Press.

———. 1968. *Social Theory and Social Structure*. New York: Free Press.

Miethe, Terance D., Jodi Olson, and Ojmarrh Mitchell. 2006. "Specialization and Persistence in the Arrest Histories of Sex Offenders: A Comparative Analysis of Alternative Measures and Offense Types." *Journal of Research in Crime and Delinquency* 43:204–229.

Mihalic, Sharon, Katherine Irwin, Delbert Elliott, Abigail Fagan, and Diane Hansen. 2001. *Blueprints for Violence Prevention*. Washington, DC: Office of Juvenile Justice and Delinquency Prevention.

Millenson, Michael. 1997. *Demanding Medical Excellence: Doctors and Accountability in the Information Age*. Chicago: University of Chicago Press.

Miller, Nan D. 1995. "International Protection of the Rights of Prisoners: Is Solitary Confinement in the United States a Violation of International Standards?" *California Western International Law Journal* 26:139–172.

Miller, Ted R., Mark A. Cohen, and Brian Wiersema. 1996. *Victim Costs and Consequences: A New Look*. Washington, DC: National Institute of Justice.

Miller, Walter B. 1973. "Ideology and Criminal Justice Policy: Some Current Issues." *Journal of Criminal Law and Criminology* 64:141–162.

Moon, Melissa M., Jody L. Sundt, Francis T. Cullen, and John P. Wright. 2000. "Is Child Saving Dead? Public Support for Juvenile Rehabilitation." *Crime and Delinquency* 46:38–60.

Morris, John C. 2007. "Government and Market Pathologies of Privatization: The Case of Prison Privatization." *Politics and Policy* 35:318–341.

Morris, Norval, and David J. Rothman, eds. 1995. *The Oxford History of the Prison*. New York: Oxford University Press.

Mosher, Clayton J., Terance D. Miethe, and Dretha Mae Phillips. 2002. *The Mismeasure of Crime*. Thousand Oaks, CA: Sage.

Mrazek, Patricia J., and Robert J. Haggerty, eds. 1994. *Reducing Risks for Mental Disorders: Frontiers for Preventive Intervention Research*. Washington, DC: National Academies Press.

Nadelmann, Ethan A. 2004. "Criminologists and Punitive Drug Prohibition: To Serve or to Challenge?" *Criminology and Public Policy* 3:441–450.

Nagin, Daniel S. 2001. "Measuring the Economic Benefits of Developmental Prevention Programs." *Crime and Justice* 28:347–384.

———. 1998. "Criminal Deterrence Research at the Outset of the Twenty-First Century." *Crime and Justice* 23:1–42.

Nagin, Daniel S., Alex R. Piquero, Elizabeth S. Scott, and Laurence Steinberg. 2006. "Public Preferences for Rehabilitation versus Incarceration of Juvenile Offenders: Evidence from a Contingent Valuation Survey." *Criminology and Public Policy* 5:627–652.

National Institute of Corrections. 1997. *Supermax Housing: A Survey of Current Practice*. Washington, DC: National Institute of Corrections.

National Institute of Justice. 2006. *Drug Courts: The Second Decade*. Washington, DC: National Institute of Justice.

O'Brien, Robert M. 1995. "Crime and Victimization Data." Pp. 57–81 in *Criminology*, 2nd edition, edited by Joseph F. Sheley. New York: Wadsworth.

O'Connor, Thomas P. 2005. "What Works, Religion as a Correctional Intervention: Part II." *Journal of Community Corrections* 14(2):4–26.

———. 2004. "What Works, Religion as a Correctional Intervention: Part I." *Journal of Community Corrections* 14(1):11–27.

O'Connor, Thomas P., and Jeff B. Duncan. 2008. "Religion and Prison Programming: The Role, Impact, and Future Direction of Faith in Correctional Systems." *Offender Programs Report* 11:81–96.

O'Connor, Thomas P., and Nathaniel J. Pallone, eds. 2002. *Religion, the Community, and the Rehabilitation of Criminal Offenders.* New York: Haworth Press.

O'Connor, Thomas P., and Michael Perreyclear. 2002. "Prison Religion in Action and Its Influence on Offender Rehabilitation." *Journal of Offender Rehabilitation* 35: 11–33.

O'Donnell, Ian, Eric P. Baumer, and Nicola Hughes. 2008. "Recidivism in the Republic of Ireland." *Criminology and Criminal Justice* 8:123–146.

Office of Program and Policy Analysis and Government Accountability. 2008. *While DMS Has Improved Monitoring, It Needs to Strengthen Private Prison Oversight and Contracts.* Tallahassee: Florida Legislature.

Oliver, Willard M., and Nancy E. Marion. 2008. "Political Party Platforms: Symbolic Politics and Criminal Justice Policy." *Criminal Justice Policy Review* 19:397–413.

Onifade, Eyitayo, William Davidson, Christina Campbell, Garrett Turke, Jill Malinowski, and Kimberly Turner. 2008. "Predicting Recidivism in Probationers with the Youth Level of Service Case Management Inventory (YLS/CMI)." *Criminal Justice and Behavior* 35:474–483.

Pager, Devah. 2007. *Marked: Race, Crime, and Finding Work in an Era of Mass Incarceration.* Chicago: University of Chicago Press.

Patton, Michael Q. 2002. *Qualitative Research and Evaluation Methods.* Thousand Oaks, CA: Sage.

Pearl, Judea. 2000. *Causality: Models, Reasoning, and Inference.* New York: Cambridge University Press.

Pelissier, Bernadette, Nicole Jones, and Timothy Cadigan. 2007. "Drug Treatment Aftercare in the Criminal Justice System: A Systematic Review." *Journal of Substance Abuse Treatment* 32:311–320.

Perrone, Dina, and Travis C. Pratt. 2003. "Comparing the Quality of Confinement and Cost-Effectiveness of Public Versus Private Prisons: What We Know, Why We Do Not Know More, and Where to Go from Here." *Prison Journal* 83:301–322.

Perry, Amanda E., Cynthia McDougall, and David P. Farrington, eds. 2006. *Reducing Crime: The Effectiveness of Criminal Justice Interventions.* Hoboken, NJ: John Wiley.

Perry, Rick. 2003. *Gov. Perry Signs $117 Billion State Budget: Governor Uses Line-Item Veto Power to Eliminate $81 Million in Spending.* Press release, June 22. Austin, TX: Office of the Governor.

Petersilia, Joan. 2005. "From Cell to Society: Who Is Returning Home?" Pp. 15–49 in *Prisoner Reentry and Crime in America*, edited by Jeremy Travis and Christy Visher. New York: Cambridge University Press.

———. 2003. *When Prisoners Come Home: Parole and Prisoner Reentry.* New York: Oxford University Press.

———. 1991. "Policy Relevance and the Future of Criminology." *Criminology* 29:1–16.

Petersilia, Joan, Richard Rosenfeld, Richard J. Bonnie, Robert D. Crutchfield, Mark A. R. Kleiman, John H. Laub, Christy A. Visher, Carole Petrie, Eugenia Grohman, and Linda DePugh. 2008. *Parole, Desistance from Crime, and Community Integration*. Washington, DC: National Academies Press.

Petrosino, Anthony, Carolyn Turpin-Petrosino, and John Buehler. 2003. "Scared Straight and Other Juvenile Awareness Programs for Preventing Juvenile Delinquency: A Systematic Review of Randomized Experimental Evidence." *Annals of the American Academy of Political and Social Science* 589:41–62.

Piquero, Alex R. 2009. "Finding the Right Balance between Data, Research, Findings, and Policy in Racial Profiling." *Criminology and Public Policy* 8:371–379.

———. 2005. "Reliable Information and Rational Policy Decisions: Does Gun Research Fit the Bill?" *Criminology and Public Policy* 4:779–798.

Piquero, Alex R., David P. Farrington, and Alfred Blumstein. 2007. *Key Issues in Criminal Career Research: New Analyses of the Cambridge Study in Delinquent Development*. Cambridge Studies in Criminology. New York: Cambridge University Press.

Pizarro, Jesenia, and Vanja M. K. Stenius. 2004. "Supermax Prisons: Their Rise, Current Practices, and Effect on Inmates." *Prison Journal* 84:248–264.

Pizarro, Jesenia, Vanja M. K. Stenius, and Travis C. Pratt. 2006. "Supermax Prisons: Myths, Realities, and the Politics of Punishment in American Society." *Criminal Justice Policy Review* 17:6–21.

Poister, Theodore H. 2004. "Performance Monitoring." Pp. 98–125 in *Handbook of Practical Program Evaluation*, 2nd edition, edited by Joseph S. Wholey, Harry P. Hatry, and Kathryn E. Newcomer. San Francisco: Jossey-Bass.

Pratt, John. 2000. "Sex Crimes and the New Punitiveness." *Behavioral Sciences and the Law* 18:135–151.

Pratt, Travis C., and Francis T. Cullen. 2005. "Assessing Macro-Level Predictors and Theories of Crime: A Meta-Analysis." *Crime and Justice* 32:373–450.

Price, Byron E., and Norma M. Riccucci. 2005. "Exploring the Determinants of Decisions to Privatize State Prisons." *American Review of Public Administration* 35:223–235.

Quinn, James F., Craig J. Forsyth, and Carla Mullen-Quinn. 2004. "Societal Reaction to Sex Offenders: A Review of the Myths Surrounding Their Crimes and Treatment Amenability." *Deviant Behavior* 25:215–232.

Rand, Michael R. 2009. *Criminal Victimization, 2008*. Washington, DC: Bureau of Justice Statistics.

———. 2008. *Criminal Victimization, 2007*. Washington, DC: Bureau of Justice Statistics.

Rand, Michael R., and Shannan M. Catalano. 2007. *Criminal Victimization, 2006*. Washington, DC: Bureau of Justice Statistics.

Raphael, Steven. 2009. "Explaining the Rise in U.S. Incarceration Rates." *Criminology and Public Policy* 8:87–95.

Raphael, Steven, and Michael A. Stoll, eds. 2009. *Do Prisons Make Us Safer? The Benefits and Costs of the Prison Boom*. New York: Russell Sage Foundation.

Regnerus, Mark D. 2003. "Linked Lives, Faith, and Behavior: Intergenerational Religious Influence on Adolescent Delinquency." *Journal for the Scientific Study of Religion* 42:189–203.

Reisig, Michael D. 1998. "Rates of Disorder in Higher-Custody State Prisons: A Comparative Analysis of Managerial Practices." *Crime and Delinquency* 44:229–244.

Reisig, Michael D., and Travis C. Pratt. 2000. "The Ethics of Correctional Privatization: A Critical Examination of the Delegation of Coercive Authority." *Prison Journal* 80:210–222.

Reuter, Peter. 2006. *Policy Analysis for Crime Control Planning (CCJS 720).* Syllabus. College Park: University of Maryland, School of Public Policy and Department of Criminology and Criminal Justice. Available online: http://www.publicpolicy.umd.edu/faculty/reuter/CCJS%20720%20Syllabus/Syllabus.htm (accessed October 1, 2009).

Rhodes, Lorna A. 2004. *Total Confinement: Madness and Reason in the Maximum Security Prison.* Los Angeles: University of California Press.

Riveland, Chase. 1999. *Supermax Prisons: Overview and General Considerations.* Washington, DC: National Institute of Corrections.

Roberts, Julian V. 1992. "Public Opinion, Crime, and Criminal Justice." *Crime and Justice* 16:99–180.

Roberts, Julian V., and Mike Hough. 2005a. "The State of the Prisons: Exploring Public Knowledge and Opinion." *Howard Journal* 44:286–306.

———. 2005b. *Understanding Public Attitudes to Criminal Justice.* Maidenhead, United Kingdom: Open University Press.

Roberts, Julian V., and Loretta J. Stalans. 1998. "Crime, Criminal Justice, and Public Opinion." Pp. 31–57 in *The Handbook of Crime and Punishment*, edited by Michael H. Tonry. New York: Oxford University Press.

Roberts, Julian V., Loretta J. Stalans, David Indermaur, and Mike Hough. 2003. *Penal Populism and Public Opinion: Lessons from Five Countries.* New York: Oxford University Press.

Robinson, Gwen, and Joanna Shapland. 2008. "Reducing Recidivism: A Task for Restorative Justice?" *British Journal of Criminology* 48:337–358.

Robinson, Matthew B. 2003. "An Obligation to Make a Difference in the Real World? Thoughts on the Proper Role of Criminologists and Critical Criminologists in the 21st Century." *Western Criminology Review* 4:226–238.

Roman, Caterina G., Ashley Wolff, Vanessa Correa, and Janeen Buck. 2007. "Assessing Intermediate Outcomes of a Faith-Based Residential Prisoner Reentry Program." *Research on Social Work Practice* 17:199–215.

Roman, John, and Jeffrey A. Butts. 2005. *The Economics of Juvenile Jurisdiction.* Washington, DC: Urban Institute.

Roman, John, and Christine DeStefano. 2004. "Drug Court Effects and the Quality of Existing Evidence." Pp. 107–135 in *Juvenile Drug Courts and Teen Substance Abuse*, edited by Jeffrey A. Butts and John Roman. Washington, DC: Urban Institute.

Roman, John, and Graham Farrell. 2002. "Cost-Benefit Analysis for Crime Prevention: Opportunity Costs, Routine Savings, and Crime Externalities." *Crime Prevention Studies* 14:53–92.

Roman, John, and Adele Harrell. 2001. "Assessing the Costs and Benefits Accruing to the Public from a Graduated Sanctions Program for Drug-Using Defendants." *Law and Policy* 23:237–268.

Rosenbaum, Dennis P., Arthur J. Lurigio, and Robert C. Davis. 1998. *The Prevention of Crime: Social and Situational Strategies*. Belmont, CA: West/Wadsworth.

Rossi, Peter H. 1980. "The Presidential Address: The Challenge and Opportunities of Applied Social Research." *American Sociological Review* 45:889–904.

Rossi, Peter H., and Richard A. Berk. 1997. *Just Punishments: Federal Guidelines and Public Views Compared*. New York: Aldine de Gruyter.

Rossi, Peter H., Mark W. Lipsey, and Howard E. Freeman. 2004. *Evaluation: A Systematic Approach*. 7th edition. Thousand Oaks, CA: Sage.

Rynne, John, Richard W. Harding, and Richard Wortley. 2008. "Market Testing and Prison Riots: How Public-Sector Commercialization Contributed to a Prison Riot." *Criminology and Public Policy* 7:117–142.

Sabol, William J. 1999. *Prison Population Projection and Forecasting: Managing Capacity*. Washington, DC: Office of Justice Programs.

Sabol, William J., Heather C. West, and Matthew Cooper. 2009. *Prison Inmates, 2008*. Washington, DC: Bureau of Justice Statistics.

Sample, Lisa L., and Timothy M. Bray. 2003. "Are Sex Offenders Dangerous?" *Criminology and Public Policy* 3:59–82.

Sampson, Robert J. 2009. "Racial Stratification and the Durable Tangle of Neighborhood Inequality." *Annals of the American Academy of Political and Social Science* 621:260–280.

Sanborn, Joseph B., Jr. 1994. "Certification to Criminal Court: The Important Policy Questions of How, When, and Why." *Crime and Delinquency* 40:262–281.

———. 1993. "Philosophical, Legal, and Systemic Aspects of Juvenile Court Plea Bargaining." *Crime and Delinquency* 39:509–527.

Schafer, Joseph A. 2001. *Community Policing: The Challenges of Successful Organizational Change*. New York: LFB Scholarly Publishing.

Schwalbe, Craig S. 2008. "A Meta-Analysis of Juvenile Justice Risk Assessment Instruments: Predictive Validity by Gender." *Criminal Justice and Behavior* 35:1367–1381.

Sevigny, Eric L., and Jonathan P. Caulkins. 2004. "Kingpins or Mules: An Analysis of Drug Offenders Incarcerated in Federal and State Prisons." *Criminology and Public Policy* 3:401–434.

Shadish, William R., Thomas D. Cook, and Donald T. Campbell. 2002. *Experimental and Quasi-Experimental Research Designs for Generalized Causal Inference*. Boston: Houghton Mifflin.

Sherman, Lawrence W. 2004. "Research and Policing: The Infrastructure and Political Economy of Federal Funding." *Annals of the American Academy of Political and Social Science* 593:156–178.

———. 2003a. "Misleading Evidence and Evidence-Led Policy: Making Social Science More Experimental." *Annals of the American Academy of Political and Social Science* 589:6–19.

———. 2003b. "Reason for Emotion: Reinventing Justice with Theories, Innovations, and Research – The American Society of Criminology 2002 Presidential Address." *Criminology* 41:1–38.

Sherman, Lawrence W., and Richard A. Berk. 1984. "The Specific Deterrent Effects of Arrest for Domestic Assault." *American Sociological Review* 49:261–271.

Sherman, Lawrence W., David P. Farrington, Brandon C. Welsh, and Doris Layton MacKenzie, eds. 2002. *Evidence-Based Crime Prevention*. London: Routledge.

Sherman, Lawrence W., Denise C. Gottfredson, Doris L. MacKenzie, John Eck, Peter Reuter, and Shawn Bushway, eds. 1997. *Preventing Crime: What Works, What Doesn't, What's Promising*. Washington, DC: Office of Justice Programs.

Simon, Jonathan. 2007. *Governing through Crime: How the War on Crime Transformed American Democracy and Created a Culture of Fear*. New York: Oxford University Press.

Sims, Barbara, and Megan Reynolds. 2007. "Sex Offender Registration, Notification, and Civil Commitment Statutes: Due Process vs. Community Safety." Pp. 195–204 in *Current Legal Issues in Criminal Justice*, edited by Craig Hemmens. Los Angeles: Roxbury.

Sjoberg, Gideon, and Ted R. Vaughan. 1993. "The Bureaucratization of Sociology: Its Impact on Theory and Research." Pp. 54–113 in *A Critique of Contemporary American Sociology*, edited by Ted R. Vaughan, Gideon Sjoberg, and Larry T. Reynolds. Dix Hills, NY: General Hall.

Skogan, Wesley G. 2006. *Police and Community in Chicago: A Tale of Three Cities*. New York: Oxford University Press.

———, ed. 2003. *Community Policing: Can It Work?* Belmont, CA: Wadsworth.

———. 1995. "Crime and the Racial Fears of White Americans." *Annals of the American Academy of Political and Social Science* 539:59–71.

Skogan, Wesley, and Kathleen Frydl, eds. 2004. *Fairness and Effectiveness in Policing: The Evidence*. Washington, DC: National Academies Press.

Skolnick, Jerome H. 1995. "1994 Presidential Address: What Not to Do about Crime." *Criminology* 33:1–15.

Smith, Bruce P. 2005. "Plea Bargaining and the Eclipse of the Jury." *Annual Review of Law and Social Science* 1:131–149.

Smith, Christian. 2003. "Theorizing Religious Effects among American Adolescents." *Journal for the Scientific Study of Religion* 42:17–30.

Smith, Steven R., and Michael R. Sosin. 2001. "The Varieties of Faith-Related Agencies." *Public Administration Review* 61:651–670.

Snyder, Howard N., and Melissa Sickmund. 2006. *Juvenile Offenders and Victims: 2006 National Report*. Washington, DC: Office of Juvenile Justice and Delinquency Prevention.

Snyder, Howard N., Melissa Sickmund, and Eileen Poe-Yamagata. 2000. *Juvenile Transfers to Criminal Court in the 1990s: Lessons Learned from Four Studies*. Washington, DC: Office of Juvenile Justice and Delinquency Prevention.

Sorensen, Jon, Clete Snell, and John J. Rodriguez. 2006. "An Assessment of Criminal Justice and Criminology Journal Prestige." *Journal of Criminal Justice Education* 17:297–322.

Sparks, Richard, Anthony E. Bottoms, and Will Hay. 1996. *Prisons and the Problem of Order*. Oxford: Oxford University Press.

Spelman, William. 2009. "Crime, Cash, and Limited Options: Explaining the Prison Boom." *Criminology and Public Policy* 8:29–77.

_____. 2008. "Specifying the Relationship between Crime and Prisons." *Journal of Quantitative Criminology* 24:149–178.

_____. 2006. "The Limited Importance of Prison Expansion." Pp. 97–129 in *The Crime Drop in America*, edited by Alfred Blumstein and Joel Wallman. New York: Cambridge University Press.

Steiner, Benjamin, and John Schwartz. 2006. "The Scholarly Productivity of Institutions and Their Faculty in Leading Criminology and Criminal Justice Journals." *Journal of Criminal Justice* 34:393–400.

Stern, Gary. 2006. "Faith-Based Confusion." *The (New York) Journal News*, January 8, A1, A8.

Stevens, James. 1992. *Applied Multivariate Statistics for the Social Sciences*. Hillsdale, NJ: Lawrence Erlbaum Associates.

Stohr, Mary K., and Peter A. Collins. 2009. *Criminal Justice Management: Theory and Practice in Justice-Centered Organizations*. New York: Oxford University Press.

Stolz, Barbara A. 2002. *Criminal Justice Policy Making: Federal Roles and Processes*. Westport, CT: Praeger.

Sullivan, Laura. 2006. *Life in Solitary Confinement*. Three-part series, July 26–28. Washington, DC: National Public Radio.

Sumter, Melvina. 2006. "Faith-Based Prison Programs." *Criminology and Public Policy* 5:523–528.

Sundt, Jody L., Thomas C. Castellano, and Chad S. Briggs. 2008. "The Sociopolitical Context of Prison Violence and Its Control: A Case Study of Supermax and Its Effect in Illinois." *Prison Journal* 88:94–122.

Sundt, Jody L., Harry R. Dammer, and Francis T. Cullen. 2002. "The Role of the Prison Chaplain in Rehabilitation." *Journal of Offender Rehabilitation* 35:59–86.

Swaray, Raymond B., Roger Bowles, and Rimawan Pradiptyo. 2005. "The Application of Economic Analysis to Criminal Justice Interventions: A Review of the Literature." *Criminal Justice Policy Review* 16:141–163.

Sykes, Gresham M. 1958. *The Society of Captives*. Princeton, NJ: Princeton University Press.

Tabarrok, Alexander, ed. 2003. *Changing the Guard: Private Prisons and the Control of Crime*. Oakland, CA: Independent Institute.

Tallarida, Ronald J. 2000. *Drug Synergism and Dose-Effect Data Analysis*. Boca Raton, FL: CRC Press.

Tewksbury, Richard. 2005. "Collateral Consequences of Sex Offender Registration." *Journal of Contemporary Criminal Justice* 21:67–81.

Thomas, Charles W. 2005. "Recidivism of Public and Private State Prison Inmates in Florida: Issues and Unanswered Questions." *Criminology and Public Policy* 4: 89–100.

Tilley, Nick. 2009. "Sherman vs. Sherman: Realism vs. Rhetoric." *Criminology and Criminal Justice* 9:135–144.

_____, ed. 2002. *Evaluation for Crime Prevention*. Monsey, NY: Criminal Justice Press.

Tillyer, Rob, Robin S. Engel, and John Wooldredge. 2008. "The Intersection of Racial Profiling Research and the Law." *Journal of Criminal Justice* 36:138–153.

Tindall, David B. 2000. "Some Misconceptions about Scientific Sociological Theory." *Sociological Focus* 33:57–77.

Tittle, Charles R. 1995. *Control Balance: Towards a General Theory of Deviance*. Boulder, CO: Westview Press.

Tjaden, Patricia, and Nancy Thoennes. 2000. *Extent, Nature, and Consequences of Intimate Partner Violence*. Washington, DC: National Institute of Justice and Centers for Disease Control.

Tolman, Ryan T., Charles W. Mueller, Eric L. Daleiden, Roxanna E. Stumpf, and Sarah L. Pestle. 2008. "Outcomes from Multisystemic Therapy in a Statewide System of Care." *Journal of Child and Family Studies* 17:894–908.

Tonry, Michael H., ed. 2009. *The Oxford Handbook of Crime and Public Policy*. New York: Oxford University Press.

———. 2008. "Crime and Human Rights – How Political Paranoia, Protestant Fundamentalism, and Constitutional Obsolescence Combined to Devastate Black America: The American Society of Criminology 2007 Presidential Address." *Criminology* 46:1–34.

———. 2006. "Criminology, Mandatory Minimums, and Public Policy." *Criminology and Public Policy* 5:45–56.

———. 2004. *Thinking about Crime: Sense and Sensibility in American Penal Culture*. New York: Oxford University Press.

Tonry, Michael H., and David P. Farrington, eds. 1995. *Crime and Punishment in Western Countries, 1980–1999*. Chicago: University of Chicago Press.

Travis, Jeremy. 2005. *But They All Come Back: Facing The Challenges of Prisoner Reentry*. Washington, DC: Urban Institute Press.

Travis, Jeremy, and Christy Visher, eds. 2005. *Prisoner Reentry and Crime in America*. New York: Cambridge University Press.

U.S. Department of Justice. 1993. *Survey of Inmates, 1991*. Washington, DC: Bureau of Justice Statistics.

U.S. General Accounting Office. 2003. *Justice Outcome Evaluations: Design and Implementation of Studies Require More Attention*. Washington, DC: U.S. General Accounting Office.

———. 1995. *Juvenile Justice: Juveniles Processed in Criminal Court and Case Dispositions*. Washington, DC: U.S. General Accounting Office.

U.S. Government Accountability Office. 2006. *Faith-Based and Community Initiative*. Washington, DC: U.S. Government Accountability Office.

U.S. Office of Management and Budget. 1992. *Guidelines and Discount Rates for Benefit-Cost Analysis of Federal Programs*. Circular No. A-94. Washington, DC: U.S. Office of Management and Budget.

United Way of America. 1996. *Measuring Program Outcomes: A Practical Approach*. Alexandria, VA: United Way of America.

Useem, Bert, and Peter Kimball. 1991. *States of Siege*. New York: Oxford University Press.

Useem, Bert, and Anne M. Piehl. 2008. *Prison State: The Challenge of Mass Incarceration*. New York: Cambridge University Press.

Van Voorhis, Patricia, Michael C. Braswell, and David Lester. 2007. *Correctional Counseling and Rehabilitation*. 6th edition. Cincinnati, OH: Anderson.

Vieraitis, Lynne M., Tomislav V. Kovandzic, and Thomas B. Marvell. 2008. "The Criminogenic Effects of Imprisonment: Evidence from State Panel Data, 1974–2002." *Criminology and Public Policy* 6:589–622.

Visher, Christy A., Lisa C. Newmark, and Adele V. Harrell. 2008. *The Evaluation of the Judicial Oversight Demonstration: Findings and Lessons on Implementation.* Washington, DC: National Institute of Justice.

Viswanathan, Madhu. 2005. *Measurement Error and Research Design.* Thousand Oaks, CA: Sage.

von Hirsch, Andrew. 1998. "Penal Theories." Pp. 659–682 in *The Handbook of Crime and Punishment*, edited by Michael H. Tonry. New York: Oxford University Press.

von Hirsch, Andrew and Andrew Ashworth, eds. 1992. *Principled Sentencing.* Boston: Northeastern University Press.

Walker, Samuel, Cassia Spohn, and Miriam DeLone. 2007. *The Color of Justice: Race, Ethnicity, and Crime in America.* 4th edition. Belmont, CA: Thomson Wadsworth.

Walter, Isabel, Sandra Nutley, and Huw Davies. 2005. "What Works to Promote Evidence-Based Practice? A Cross-Sector Review." *Evidence and Policy* 1:335–364.

Ward, David A., and Thomas G. Werlich. 2003. "Alcatraz and Marion: Evaluating Supermaximum Custody." *Punishment and Society* 5:53–75.

Weimer, David L., and Lee S. Friedman. 1979. "Efficiency Considerations in Criminal Rehabilitation Research: Costs and Consequences." Pp. 251–272 in *The Rehabilitation of Criminal Offenders: Problems and Prospects*, edited by Lee Sechrest, Susan O. White, and Elizabeth D. Brown. Washington, DC: National Academy of Sciences.

Weisburd, David, and Anthony A. Braga, eds. 2006. *Police Innovation: Contrasting Perspectives.* New York: Cambridge University Press.

Weisburd, David, Cynthia M. Lum, and Anthony Petrosino. 2001. "Does Research Design Affect Study Outcomes in Criminal Justice?" *Annals of the American Academy of Political and Social Science* 578:50–70.

Weisburd, David, Cynthia M. Lum, and Sue-Ming Yang. 2003. "When Can We Conclude That Treatments or Programs 'Don't Work'?" *Annals of the American Academy of Political and Social Science* 587:31–48.

Weisburd, David, Cody W. Telep, Joshua C. Hinkle, and John E. Eck. 2008. *Effects of Problem-Oriented Policing on Crime and Disorder.* Final Report. Washington, DC: National Institute of Justice.

Weiss, Carol H. 1997. "How Can Theory-Based Evaluation Make Greater Headway?" *Evaluation Review* 21:501–524.

Weiss, Carol H., Erin Murphy-Graham, Anthony Petrosino, and Allison G. Gandhi. 2008. "The Fairy Godmother – and Her Warts: Making the Dream of Evidence-Based Policy Come True." *American Journal of Evaluation* 29:29–47.

Wellford, Charles F. 1997. "1996 Presidential Address: Controlling Crime and Achieving Justice." *Criminology* 35:1–11.

Wellford, Charles F., John V. Pepper, and Carol V. Petrie, eds. 2005. *Firearms and Violence: A Critical Review.* Washington, DC: National Academies Press.

Wells, Terry L., W. Wesley Johnson, and Rodney J. Henningsen. 2002. "Attitudes of Prison Wardens toward Administrative Segregation and Supermax Prisons." Pp. 171–180 in

Correctional Perspectives, edited by Leanne F. Alarid and Paul F. Cromwell. Los Angeles: Roxbury.

Welsh, Brandon C., and David P. Farrington. 2009. *Making Public Places Safer: Surveillance and Crime Prevention*. New York: Oxford University Press.

———, eds. 2006. *Preventing Crime: What Works for Children, Offenders, Victims, and Places*. New York: Springer-Verlag.

———. 2000. "Monetary Costs and Benefits of Crime Prevention Programs." *Crime and Justice* 27:305–361.

Welsh, Wayne N., and Philip W. Harris. 2008. *Criminal Justice Policy and Planning*. 3rd edition. Dayton, OH: LexisNexis, Anderson Publishing.

Western, Bruce. 2006. *Punishment and Inequality in America*. New York: Russell Sage Foundation.

White, Helene R., and Dennis M. Gorman. 2000. "Dynamics of the Drug-Crime Relationship." Pp. 151–218 in *The Nature of Crime: Continuity and Change*, edited by Gary LaFree. Washington, DC: National Institute of Justice.

Wholey, Joseph S. 2004. "Evaluability Assessments." Pp. 33–62 in *Handbook of Practical Program Evaluation*, 2nd edition, edited by Joseph S. Wholey, Harry P. Hatry, and Kathryn E. Newcomer. San Francisco: Jossey-Bass.

Wholey, Joseph S., Harry P. Hatry, and Kathryn E. Newcomer, eds. 2004. *Handbook of Practical Program Evaluation*. 2nd edition. San Francisco: Jossey-Bass.

Williamson, Tom. 2008. *The Handbook of Knowledge Based Policing: Current Conceptions and Future Directions*. San Francisco: John Wiley.

Wilson, David B., Ojmarrh Mitchell, and Doris L. MacKenzie. 2006. "A Systematic Review of Drug Court Effects on Recidivism." *Journal of Experimental Criminology* 2:459–487.

Winship, Christopher, and Stephen L. Morgan. 1999. "The Estimation of Causal Effects from Observational Data." *Annual Review of Sociology* 25:659–706.

Woodward, James. 2003. *Making Things Happen: A Theory of Causal Explanation*. New York: Oxford University Press.

Worden, Alissa P. 2000. "The Changing Boundaries of the Criminal Justice System: Redefining the Problem and the Response in Domestic Violence." Pp. 215–266 in *Boundary Changes in Criminal Justice Organizations*, edited by Charles M. Friel. Washington, DC: National Institute of Justice.

Worrall, John L. 2008. "The Effects of Local Law Enforcement Block Grants on Serious Crime." *Criminology and Public Policy* 7:325–350.

Worrall, John L., and Tomislav V. Kovandzic. 2007. "COPS Grants and Crime Revisited." *Criminology* 45:159–190.

Wright, Gerald C., Jr., Robert S. Erikson, and John P. McIver. 1987. "Public Opinion and Policy Liberalism in the American States." *American Journal of Political Science* 31:980–1001.

Wright, Richard G. 2008. "Sex Offender Post-Incarceration Sanctions: Are There Any Limits?" *New England Journal on Criminal and Civil Confinement* 34:17–50.

———. 2003. "Sex Offender Registration and Notification: Public Attention, Political Emphasis, and Fear." *Criminology and Public Policy* 3:97–104.

Velázquez, Tracy. 2008. *The Pursuit of Safety: Sex Offender Policy in the United States*. New York: Vera Institute of Justice.

Yaffee, Robert A. 2000. *Introduction to Time-Series Analysis and Forecasting*. New York: Academic Press.

Zahn, Margaret A. 1999. "Thoughts on the Future of Criminology – The American Society of Criminology 1998 Presidential Address." *Criminology* 37:1–16.

Zgoba, Kristen M., Jill Levenson, and Tracy McKee. 2009. "Examining the Impact of Sex Offender Residency Restrictions on Housing Availability." *Criminal Justice Policy Review* 20:91–110.

Zimmerman, Paul R. 2009. "Statistical Variability and the Deterrent Effect of the Death Penalty." *American Law and Economics Review* 2:1–29.

Zimring, Franklin E., and Gordon Hawkins. 1995. *Incapacitation: Penal Confinement and the Restraint of Crime*. New York: Oxford University Press.

Zimring, Franklin E., Alex R. Piquero, and Wesley G. Jennings. 2007. "Sexual Delinquency in Racine: Does Early Sex Offending Predict Offending in Youth and Youth and Young Adulthood?" *Criminology and Public Policy* 6:507–534.

Index

319